2016-2017

To Patricia C.

for Wint

Sincerely, DeLio

Whitney DeLio

MW00778574

718-784-5587
35-05 30th St
Apt 3c
Astoria, ny 11106

THE GREAT UNKNOWN

Memoir

**A Young Performer's Tragicomic Journey
to an Encounter with God**

Whitney DeLise

Chandelier Classic

Disclaimer
The material in this book comes from my memory of events of my personal experiences (best as I can recall) which happened over 30 years ago. All incidents are portrayed to the best of my recollection, although the names of most people have been changed, as have some identifying details and place names. Some individuals are composites, some characters are deceased. I have tried to recreate events, locales and conversations from my memories of them. In order to maintain their anonymity in most instances I have changed the names of individuals and places, I may have changed some identifying characteristics and details such as physical properties, occupations and places of residence. I tried to relate the substance of those events and conversations as best I could recall. Quotation marks are used in the book for readability, not as an indication that the words appearing in quotes are exact. "Interactions between myself, family members, friends, colleagues, acquaintances, etc. are as true as my memory recollects. I have taken a bit of liberty with dialogue as that is something you don't always remember word-for-word. But the actual connections that instigated the dialogue happened." This book is based upon actual events, persons, and companies. However, numerous of the characters and companies portrayed and the names used herein are fictitious. Any similarity of those fictitious characters, incidents, or companies to the name attributes or actual background of any actual person, living or dead, or to any actual event, or to any existing company, is entirely coincidental, and unintentional.

Cover Photo: John Dorne

Printed in the United States of America
First Printing, 2016
ISBN 978-0-692-69386-5

Chandelier Classic
Chandelier Publishing

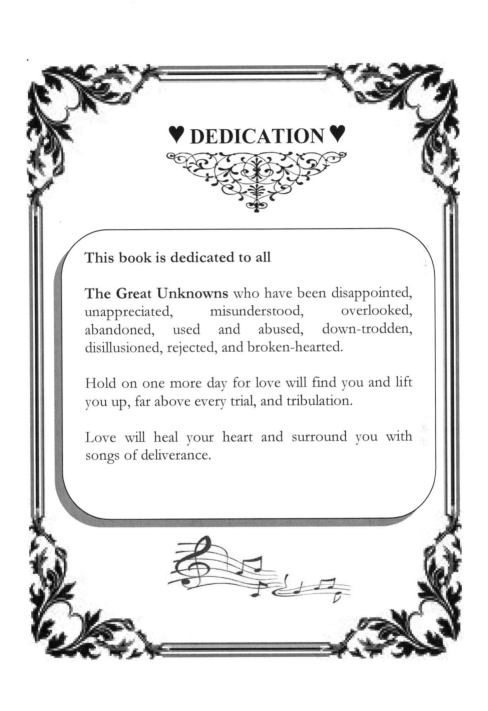

♥ DEDICATION ♥

This book is dedicated to all

The Great Unknowns who have been disappointed, unappreciated, misunderstood, overlooked, abandoned, used and abused, down-trodden, disillusioned, rejected, and broken-hearted.

Hold on one more day for love will find you and lift you up, far above every trial, and tribulation.

Love will heal your heart and surround you with songs of deliverance.

CHAPTER ONE

THE JOB INTERVIEW

IT WAS 1984. Bell Atlantic had broken up, Ronald Reagan was re-elected in a landslide, and Idira Ghandi was assassinated. A man shot 36 people in a McDonald's restaurant, while widespread famine in Ethiopia killed 10,000. Apple released the Macintosh personal computer and Vanessa Williams became the first African American Miss America. Recession continued to be a problem in the U.S. and 70 U.S. banks failed in one year. It hadn't registered in my young agile mind that the failure of 70 U.S. banks contributed to my difficult job search these past months.

I was twenty-four, living with my boyfriend David in Gramercy Park in Manhattan on Twenty Fifth Street near Third Avenue. We had a beautiful, one-bedroom apartment with a serene backyard view of a towering tree, an old stone church with a stain-glass window, and a quiet garden below.

Today, an employment agency had finally sent me on another job interview with a marketing firm to fill the position of Administrative Assistant to the Sales Director. The office was on Park Avenue off Sixtieth Street, with a glorious view of Central Park. I liked the energy of the people in the office. Other companies the agency had sent me to during the previous weeks were conservative law and banking firms with stuffy, quiet office environments that made me feel restless and melancholy. This marketing firm, though, was friendly and buzzing with energy. It was the kind of environment I craved after being out of work for so long and spending a lot of time home alone. The manager offered a generous salary and benefits, so I was keeping my fingers crossed. This was my second interview with this company and both interviews had gone well.

I walked out of the towering, black glass and chrome building onto the cool but sunny spring afternoon. For the first time in a long time, I felt lucky. I was confident the position was already mine and I could relax and just be happy. It would probably be my last days to enjoy a weekday afternoon like this before starting my new job. So rather than taking the subway, I strolled home.

The next morning Carol at the employment agency called me. "Sorry, they chose another candidate," she said.

"That can't be," I told her. "They really liked me. I'm sure they did. Are you sure there's not some mistake? There has to be some mistake," I added.

"Yes, they like you very much, and you were one of the first in the running, but they went with someone else they liked better. But listen, don't give up, we have other orders coming in and other opportunities, so just hang in there."

"Carol, I really wanted that job. Everything seemed so right. Please tell me this isn't so," I pleaded.

"Oooh, I know. I'm so sorry. But listen, I have a financial firm who has an administrative position opening up. I just need to talk with one of the partners tomorrow. He's out of the office today, so be patient. We'll get you a job, I promise," she assured me.

"But I wanted that job! Financial firms are so stuffy and boring. I'm whining now, I know. Okay, okay. Thanks Carol. We'll talk tomorrow?"

"Yes, try to relax, and have a good day," Carol consoled.

I dragged my sluggish body into the kitchen to pour myself some orange juice, and then slumped on the couch in front of the TV set. I thought, "This sucks. A financial firm? She's going to send me to another financial firm where the women wear their collars up to their chins, which are held up by the stick shoved up their ass. Where white-haired men, still wearing their school rings from Harvard, silently walk around looking and feeling important while they talk to each other barely moving their lips. Good grief. Why can't I have what I want! Why?" I pondered.

I exhausted myself all morning with thoughts of, "Why, why, why? Why can't I have that job?" By noon, defeated, I lounged on the couch under the window. As I took another bite of a bologna-cheese sandwich with mayonnaise, the church bells sounded outside my window, as it did every day at this hour. I looked out onto the small stone church admiring the round, multi-colored, stained-glass window adorning its steeple.

Although I had not attended Sunday mass since my Catholic grammar school days, and had lost connection with any type of traditional religious practice since then, the church's presence always gave me a feeling of calm and peaceful comfort.

I particularly enjoyed noticing the way it changed its face each season over its core structure of stability and strength. In the summer, it was festively decorated with vibrant green trees, lush bushes, and clay flower pots filled with bright red geraniums scattered its yard. In the fall, autumn-colored leaves covered the foundation and sprinkled the dry ground. In winter, soft snow laced the bare trees and would blanket the roof and ledges.

Now, in spring, delicate pink blossoms floated gently down from the budding trees onto its window sills, back doorstep, and the damp brown earth below. Hard to imagine why, but the church seemed to be quietly alive with a soft disposition and an aware inner smile. An intense joy welled up in me as I watched the birds glide to and fro from the building ledges to the trees and back again.

Joy is crisp and clear, warm yet cool, colorful, exhilarating, exciting and so overwhelming, that at times it becomes unbearable. The joy of living is sometimes so intense I find it as difficult to bear - as difficult to bear as the moments of utter despair. Yet, how can this be? How can it be that the very experience of joy one longs for, once it catches holds of a person, can be so insufferable?

Perhaps it bubbles up from the depths of my soul and overflows with such great abundance that all I want to do is paint, dance, sing, act, write and share it all with the world, yet there is not enough time, materials, or technique that can even touch the surface in expressing the profound depths and vastness of it all. This always seemed to frustrate, discourage, and even depress me at times. What does one do with all this joy, and how does one do it -- and with who?   Is this the plight of the artist only or of every human being? I don't know.

By late afternoon, for some reason, I began to write. Except for some poetry in High School, I had never written anything before, and the words now flowed out of the pen like a prophetic message.

Read books? It's not enough. I want to live it, feel it, touch it-- experience it. I mean, is it really true that one can sit in a café on the streets of Paris, and a gorgeous Frenchman will smile at you--as you're sipping your Bordeaux-- watching the people go by?--People so different from yourself in language, dress, and ideas. A place that is old and beautiful, with a history as old as the world itself. And he smiles at you, and you smile back. And he approaches you, (gasp!) ... to say, "Hello". And you find out-- he's not French at all! He's from England. Wow! I've never been to England.

First we go to the Tower of Notre Dame, and then we go to dinner, and he tells me about his life back in England. He's a writer. He writes music, and plays guitar for a rock band called 'Fallen Angel'. He comes here to write, reflect, and be inspired. And I tell him about my life. I can tell him anything I want. I'm in Paris.

We do make love though, and again in the morning just as the light from the windows slides around the wall onto this vase of violet colored roses with yellow tints... I've never seen roses like that before, except in old oil paintings. So full, so round, and open, with brown framing the edges of the petals, like antique lace. They sit there in the sun as if they've always been there. Not young budding flowers, but not old. Just in full maturity that would never change. They would stay just as they are, bent over a bit, but never growing older, never withering away.

Oh, but it's so hopeless to hold onto. It goes away as if it never happened. Like a dream. Like you're waking up from a beautiful dream... Tragic--isn't it? But it happened, and we're both never the same again.

Then what do I do? I don't know. Walk around the streets of Paris, I guess. Nothing looks the same. I go back to the café where we first met, and everything looks lonely and empty. The people look like strangers, all of them. Everything looks...foreign.

Then I go to… Venice! Why? Because… Venice is sinking! It's sinking at two and a half centimeters per year. I hear people are moving up to the second floor the water level is so high. In twenty years, Venice won't be there. I have to go to Venice.

I did not know if the writing was any good, but the story was intriguing to me.

On Monday morning, I dressed for my next job interview, choosing a black suit with an A-line skirt, shoulder pads in the jacket, and low black pumps - conservative 1980's look. My hair was tied back in a low ponytail, and I wore glasses instead of contact lenses to appear more serious and professional. I looked in the mirror and thought, "Oh God, who is this?" The truth being, I am a tall, thin, waif-like fashion-model type who usually wore hip hugger jeans, and short tank tops. Now look at me; I looked like a nerdy librarian. But that was the name of the game. The employment agencies wanted me to dress very conservatively if I was to have any chance of getting a corporate job as an Administrative Secretary. I hated the clothes, and I hated having to be someone else, other than who I was, but I needed the job, and I needed the money. I grabbed my shoulder bag and was on my way.

When I found the financial firm, I was surprised to be standing in front of a beautiful four-story brownstone on the Upper East Side in a residential neighborhood on Sixty-Forth Street. This was not your typical office building. I rang the doorbell with the name, 'MWR Inc'. A woman's voice on the intercom instructed me to take the elevator to the third floor as she buzzed me in.

I entered the quiet, spacious lobby with its shiny black and white marble tile floors. A few yards ahead, a blue velvet antique couch supported by wooden claw feet stared at me. It was accompanied by a mahogany coffee table, Architectural Digest Magazines stacked neatly on top. My heart skipped. I was startled by my own reflection in an ostentatiously ornate gold-framed mirror that hung on the floral felt wallpaper to my right. I moved towards the mirror and the gold leaf French provincial table that rested underneath. I took in the scent of a voluminous pink rose that sprung out from the grand bouquet of freshly cut flowers nestled in a towering Lalique vase. I swept my finger across the top of the table and under the silk crochet doily. "It's not even dusty," I thought.

"Should I ascend the white marble spiral staircase to my left or take the old-fashioned cast-iron elevator sitting under it? The voice on the intercom did tell me to take the elevator," I assured myself.

As I squeezed into the elevator, and closed its creaking doors, I felt like an over-sized bird trapped in a tiny cage. "Which film was it where Cary Grant and Audrey Hepburn crashed to the floor in an elevator just like this one?" I tried to remember while pulling down the metal lever to motion the elevator up.

Upon exiting the elevator, I stood in a narrow hallway at the edge of an open door, and peeked my head in, "Hello?"

A man with his back to me, sitting at a desk in front of a large marble fireplace looking at his computer, got up, and turned around to walk towards me. "Welcome, welcome. Come in. My name is Tony Scott," he said as he put out his hand.

I looked up at him and thought I was going to die and go to heaven. Absolute joy filled my eyes, and my brain sizzled. A wave of sheer delight and excitement ran through my entire body. Tony Scott was tall, fit, and the most handsome and distinguished looking man I had ever seen in my life. He was like a young Robert Redford, except he was ten times better looking. He had thick golden blonde hair and laughing blue eyes. He was about thirty-eight years old and mature—yet his warm and inviting smile accentuated his boyish dimples. He was tan and dressed impeccably in a well-fitted designer suite, accented by a ruby handkerchief in his breast pocket, and polished wing-tipped shoes on his feet.

I gingerly accepted his hand and greeted him with giddy surprise and disbelief, "Hi! So pleased to meet you!"

As I entered the casual but elegant front office, my eyes filled with more delight. Directly in front of us were two towering glass French doors leading out to a picturesque patio conveying the Garden of Versailles!.

"Oh, my, look at this! You actually work here? This is incredible." I held my hand to my open mouth. I dropped my hands to my sides, and just stared at all the flowers and plants, statues, and waterfalls. "It's so beautiful," I sighed.

Tony, looking very enchanted by my spontaneous reaction, opened the French doors. "Let's sit outside and talk." His hand motioned me to step in front of him to enter onto the patio.

We sat down together at the dainty floral wrought-iron table with matching chairs. Shortly after, a young woman with milky white skin, her chestnut hair cut into a pixie, appeared carrying a tray filled with delicate fine china. Her long summer skirt moved gently in the breeze, but her stiff-collared shirt, accented by a cameo broach, kept her anchored and from blowing away. She smiled softly as she placed the tray in the middle of the table. "I thought you might like some coffee," she offered.

"Yes, thank you, Susan. Whitney, would you like coffee?" Tony asked.

"Yes, thank you," I replied grinning from ear to ear.

Susan nodded and smiled at me before exiting back into the office. Tony poured my coffee, offering me milk and sugar, as he told me about his job as a Financial Advisor for high profile clients. I watched the way he placed the white linen napkin on his right knee in a matter-of-fact but suave gesture.

He spoke about his partner, Jim, who was out of the office for the day, and told me the woman, Susan, who brought us the coffee, was Jim's secretary. Tony went on to say that he needed his own Administrative Assistant to help him compile monthly and quarterly financial reports to send out to his clients. I gave Tony a brief description of my background and skills, and he appeared authentically receptive. I don't remember the particulars of what we said, but I remember he kept making me laugh. I made him chuckle as well, and all the while I kept thinking I should pinch myself because it all seemed so unreal. He was so extraordinarily handsome, and his smile was intoxicatingly brilliant.

On the spur of the moment, I sprang up, spread out my arms, and twirled around on the slate floor while looking up at the sky, my long skirt flowing in the breeze. "Tony, I would *love* to work here," I lilted. Tony sat back from his chair smiling at me as he watched me whirl around the patio.

"This place is beautiful isn't it? My partner Jim did all this. He loves to dabble in landscaping and gardening. You should see his house up in Westchester. It's even more incredible. Jim is just very talented," Tony added. He looked at his watch and rose from his chair. "I have another appointment, but it was a pleasure meeting with you, and thank you for coming."

My heart stopped. Did I just make a complete fool of myself? Obviously, I did. I don't know what came over me. I had never swirled around like a school girl at a job interview before. "Oh, I'm so embarrassed," I thought. I seized my handbag, shook his hand and thanked him for the interview while tripping towards the front door.

Tony followed after me to show me out, shook my hand and thanked me again. This time, instead of taking the elevator, I ran down the stairs out into the street. I slunk down the subway steps with my head down, and my hand on my forehead thinking, "You foolish idiot--you idiot, you idiot--you blew it!"

When I got home, I looked in the mirror at my mousy librarian clothes, and thought, "You even look like an idiot!"

My boyfriend, David, arrived home from work later on, asking me, "Hey, did you get the job?" I was slumped on the soft leather couch in front of the TV set, hugging a pillow across my chest.

I mumbled, "I don't know."

CHAPTER TWO

GIRLS ON FILM

THE NEXT MORNING, I stumbled from the bedroom into the sun lit living room with its shiny wood floors, feeling groggy, thirsty, and hungry. The light glistened through the empty crystal vase sitting on the glass coffee table nestled in front of the couch. I noticed the table had accumulated a layer of white dust again, even though I had wiped it down yesterday. New York City soot was hard to keep up with.

I ventured into the kitchenette, hoping to find something to eat or drink. I opened the novelty magnet infested refrigerator door to find the usual. In the five years I had known David his refrigerator was always empty except for three ingredients: a bottle of *Absolut* vodka, tonic water, and a lime. Neither of us were drinkers, but David insisted on having these items available in case a guest came over for a nightcap after an evening out.

David was thirty-four, ten years older than me. His gangly body, Beatlesque haircut, dark sunglasses, skinny black jeans, and retro-t-shirts imbued him with the ambience of a 1960's rock star. To me, he was sometimes just a whiny New Yorker. David worked as a freelance Art Director for magazines and ad agencies.

I rested my arm on the refrigerator door, staring into the abyss, waiting for something edible to miraculously appear. I was not a cook, so an empty refrigerator didn't bother me. Like David, I would often grab an egg sandwich and coffee at a deli near my job, eat lunch out, and then in the evening, David would take us both out to dinner. David hated eating at home and always insisted on having dinner in a restaurant or diner. Yet, being out of work for this long made it unpleasant to not have any food in the house, not even orange juice.

If I could cook, or had any incentive to learn, the kitchenette was not an inviting place to whip up a meal. Not only was it tiny, but the counters and cabinets were cluttered with David's toys: plastic Godzilla, Frankenstein, Dracula dolls, Coney Island trinkets, Gumby and Pokey, and various hand puppets.

I closed the refrigerator door, and shuffled a few feet down the hall and knocked on the bathroom door. "Are you out of the shower," I asked.

"I'm shaving," David replied.

"I'm hungry," I whined.

"Go downstairs and get something at the deli. Get me a coffee with milk and sugar, and a bagel," he requested

I stuck the face of a rubber finger puppet in the crack of the bathroom door. "I'm not dressed, I don't have any money, and I have to pee," I said disguising my voice.

I heard a hissing sound from the other side of the door and pulled my hand back out. David had sprayed my finger puppet's face with shaving cream. "Don't make me laugh so hard, I have to pee!" I giggled uncontrollably.

"I'll be out in a minute," he chuckled.

David had a quirky sense of humor and he could always make me laugh. We met in an acting class when I was nineteen. Shortly after, I moved in with him and his dog, Buddy Hackett, a Beagle. He was an art school graduate and, like me, was an aspiring actor who loved comedy. I had a talent for drawing and art as well, but I never went to art school. Instead, I learned how to type 100 wpm and take steno at 135 wpm, because those were skills that could land me a job and speedily move me out of my parent's house in Queens.

David quickly dressed and ran downstairs to get us both breakfast, and I jumped in the shower. While I was enjoying the invigorating pulsation of the hot water pouring down over me, I noticed an enormous bottle labeled with an illustration of a horse on the cluttered bathroom windowsill. David often whined that he was losing his hair. He constantly came home with various bottles of new and expensive hair products and kept experimenting with all sorts of formulas to make sure he kept his thick locks from falling out. After all, he was now thirty-four, well past turning thirty. As I toweled down and got dressed, I wondered why David had bought a bottle of soap for washing horses. Perhaps it was an ad campaign he was working on for a client.

David returned and unwrapped the food at the rustic dining room table. I held the horse formula in front of him. "What's this?" I asked.

David leaned over and pointed to the top of his head, "Do you see a bald spot?"

"No," I replied.

"Come on. You don't see that?" he insisted.

"No. I don't. You have hair. You're not losing your hair. This is for your imaginary bald spot?" I asked.

"It's a new shampoo, *Pony.* They use it for horses to keep their thick manes strong and shiny. It's supposed to work miracles for human hair," David said enthusiastically.

"You washed your hair with horse soap?"

"It's harmless. Try it."

"No thanks," I laughed.

"Fine. I got you a bacon and egg on a roll. Here's today's *New York Times* for the job section," he offered.

"Thanks," I replied.

I appreciated David. He always looked out for me and took care of me like an older brother. His freelance assignments as an Art Director paid well, so it relieved some of my stress when I was seeking a job. He would often make $500 to $3,000 on one design project in just a few days worth of work. The apartment was rent controlled and cost only $500 per month when he moved in, and now four years later, even with yearly rent increases, it was still low for Manhattan at just under $600. Since David was able to accumulate a lot of money easily, he insisted on taking care of the rent and bills, and always paid for dinner.

I had trouble making money because I usually had low paying office jobs that were very oppressive, and they didn't last long. Inevitably, I would get bullied by a manager or a fellow employee and as a result developed a tremendous amount of anxiety and stress until I got laid-off or quit.

My previous job at a consulting firm had lasted for only three weeks. The interviews had gone well, and the manager expressed great relief in finally finding someone like me to fill the position. On my second day, the President and Vice Presidents along with the many other employees appeared to be very happy to have me on board as well. Like always, I put my best foot forward in contributing my experience and enthusiasm at the meeting and on the days that followed within my department. Two VPs in the company took notice of me within the first week of my employment. They commented to my Manager, Marsha, about how impressed they were with my talents, professional demeanor combined with a sincere enthusiasm, and generous and collaborative nature. They told Marsha that they found me nothing less than "inspirational" and a fantastic addition to the firm. I had no knowledge of the praise the VPs were giving Marsha about me, so I had no idea that this was what was making her angry.

One would think that my "Seal of Approval" from the higher ups would make Marsha happy in her choice of hiring me, especially since all the work she delegated to me, behind the scenes, also made her look exceptionally favorable in the eyes of the big wigs at the top, but instead it made her jealous.

I was now a target of bullying. With Marsha, nothing I did was right, even when it was right. I was too skilled at my job for her to find much fault with my work, so she had to grasp at straws to find ways to criticize, harass, and condemn me. I was reprimanded for dropping a rubber band on the floor, and taking a cookie from a plate in the reception area. One could only laugh off the absurdity, but taking it lightly only made Marsha more furious and hostile. Like German Nazis portrayed in old war films, bullies have no sense of humor. So the situation only got worse. Whenever I spoke up at a department meeting I was discredited or told to be quiet or ignored. When I confronted Marsha about her attitude towards me, she would deny that there was any problem on her part, and that I was the one who needed to adjust my attitude and stop being so sensitive.

I could not understand Marsha's behavior. She was an attractive woman with a BA in Business and a Master's in Psychology. She had her own large office with a view, a great salary, benefits, seniority, and respect and appreciation from her bosses. Why was she always so unhappy? The more I tried to express empathy towards Marsha, and appease her criticisms with understanding and gentleness, the more intolerant and abusive she became. While Marsha raved and ranted and made "much ado about nothing", The Rolling Stones songs rumbled through my brain -- "I Can't Get No Satisfaction" having "Sympathy for the Devil".

Within only a few days, I was then the target of office mobbing. Employees sitting in my immediate surroundings gave me the cold shoulder, and would only collaborate, chat, and laugh with each other. Any work related questions I had, they would ignore. They would pretend I didn't even exist. If they did acknowledge me, it would be to throw negative comments across the room to each other regarding my physique, dress, or hairstyle. I ignored their stupid childish behavior, but I then found important documents and files missing from my desk.

I made an appointment with one of the VPs directly above Marsha to seek some advice about my situation, but his face became red with anger which took me aback. He did not offer much consolation, except to tell me that Marsha had not expressed any complaints about me to him, and I should just carry on in learning about the company's products and process in order to increase my confidence and sense of security in my job.

There was very little or no knowledge of "office bullying" and the effects of bullying in those days, nor was there a language to express or explain the tactics used by bullies needed in order to defend oneself. It just wasn't in the VP's realm of experience to comprehend how serious and debilitating bullying was nor how to eliminate it, let alone acknowledge it.

If a person complained about being abused at work, an outsider would chalk it up to the person's inability to handle a difficult boss or co-worker, and they were considered thin-skinned, weak, ineffective, and lacking social skills. So I just dealt with the humiliation, feelings of ineffectiveness, and shame on my own, thinking that there was something wrong with me. At the same time, I also felt that there was nothing wrong with me because I had done nothing at all to bring the experience upon myself. I was always an efficient and responsible employee. I did an excellent job and had a cheerful, positive attitude. I'm a collaborative and enthusiastic person by nature. It confused me how there was always someone in the office who not only hated me for reasons I could not understand, but also had the power to make my life miserable, and find a way to get me eliminated.

After speaking with the VP, I now felt even more vulnerable and alone in my situation, and although I decided to take his advice and to continue to focus on my work and keep a positive attitude, things only got worse. I was given an unreasonable work load, and more criticism. When I defended my position, I was accused of insubordination. I then became become quiet, withdrawn, and hyper-vigilant. Since I was not participating enough in their antagonisms, they started bantering and fighting viciously among each other and getting their panties in a bunch over the most trivial and insignificant things. For a brief moment, I became the observer of the chaos and insanity swirling around me. Although I was relieved that the hatred was now directed away from me and instead towards each other, I could not help but wonder "the what, how, and why" of it all.

Unfortunately, they were not going to leave me out of their miseries for long. One female co-worker, who sat a few desks away from me, was now following me into the bathroom to interrogate me as to why I brought my purse into the restroom all the time. By her third inquiry, I had to refrain myself from shoving a Tampax up her nose. When she insinuated that I was only coming into the bathroom to snort cocaine, I wanted to jam her head first into the toilet bowl and flush. Instead, I smiled and laughed away her insinuations as I exited.

Every day I came into work, I found more and more things missing from my desk, putting me in an anxious and hurried state to re-meet deadlines in order to avoid any more confrontations with Marsha. I was also denied information and resources to complete some of my assignments effectively and on time. By this time I was now waking up in the morning feeling hopeless and depressed, and dreading another day at work.

I went to the personnel office to complain about the way I was being treated, but it all fell on deaf ears. The company was more afraid of a law suit than creating a safe work environment. Instead, they defended Marsha's claim of my insubordination.

My co-workers must have been confronted in some way by the VP because rumors were spreading that I was sleeping with him, a man who was married with an eight month old son. Perhaps this is why he went out of his way to avoid me when he saw me walking down the hall. They probably had led him to believe that I may have started the rumor. At this point, I would have put nothing past their devious minds and hearts. So I quit.

I was the one who not only had to cope with the abuse and post traumatic stress due to this psychological violence, but also the repercussions of lost income, health insurance, employment gaps in my resume that appeared unreasonable and suspicious to future prospective employers, and haunting memories of my past employers character assassinations along with the legitimate fear of untrustworthy job references. I carried the weight of the world on my shoulders and was often left feeling lost, confused, and lonely. Being inexperienced, naïve, and young, it never occurred to me at the time that I was dealing with a pathological narcissist who was really a jealous, selfish, frightened, insecure, and miserable person who thought they could experience empowerment and joy in their life by taking it away from someone else. I also had no knowledge or understanding at the time that there are actually psychopaths living and working among us in everyday social situations who had the façade of dressing, talking and acting like everyone else, but who have absolutely no ability to empathize with another human being. I had a separate compartment in my brain to identify those types of people: Dracula, Freddie Krueger, Hitler, Charles Manson, The Boston Strangler – not your every day manager who enthusiastically hires a person only to employ a systematic laser focused campaign to destroy their life simply because they could and because it gave them a sense of power.

Psychologically, it is like thinking one landed a job in a news room like the Mary Tyler Moore Show,- you anticipate that a manager might turn out to be tough, some co-workers might be a bit quirky, but nothing sinister is going to happen. Then you suddenly find yourself lost in a Saturday Night

Life skit where Mr. Rogers is being played by comedian Eddie Murphy who lives in a run down, dirty tenement in a crime ridden ghetto; "It's a beautiful day in the neighborhood. Can you say "Bastard" boys and girls?" Only the satire is not funny because it is really happening, and that's where much of the denial comes from – this cannot be really happening. It's too absurd - which was also why it was almost impossible to get a family member or friends to grasp what I was going through let alone myself.   Even David chalked it up to office politics and my inability to adapt which only made me more confused, full of self doubt, and then resentful towards David. David would then rebuke my resentment by accusing me of being negative. This would only put me more on the defensive, and spiral me into deeper feelings of anger and resentment, so I found it best to shut up and not talk about it if I were to find any chance of recovering from the trauma.

The Post Traumatic Stress would always evaporate shortly after I left the job and spent time with David and our friends. In a few weeks time, I bounced back to normal with a positive and up-beat attitude. But in the back of my mind, my inability to support myself frightened me.

David admitted that he could never work under anyone because he found office politics to be more stressful and debilitating than the actual job. He was fortunate to have a skill that paid well and was in demand at the time.   He was rarely at a loss for finding freelance assignments as a consultant in graphic design. Although David made a good living, he spent money recklessly. I hated listening to him complain about his lack of funds because he refused to cut corners.

We ate out every night, went to a nightclub or movie about four times a week, and took cabs everywhere. We also traveled to the Caribbean, even though we could not really afford to do so. We loved to travel, so to me, it was money well spent. David and I always had a good time together, and I must admit that our extravagant leisure activities helped me to remember I am a person of worth who deserves to be treated well and enjoy life. It was very therapeutic in alleviating much of the trauma I had experienced from workplace bullying.

Besides, I did not feel comfortable telling David how to manage his money, and he did not want to hear it. His argument was that I should learn how to make as much as him, before I tell people what to do with theirs. I had no idea how to make as much as he did, nor as fast as he did. Nor did I have the skills he insisted I should have to thrive in a toxic work environment. "Perhaps he had a point," I thought.

David munched enthusiastically on his cream cheese and lox bagel. "How did the movie end last night?" he asked.

"I'm not telling you," I teased.

"Come on, what happened," he asked again.

"I'm not telling you. I don't like zoning out in front of the TV. You always make me watch some stupid program with you, and then you end up falling asleep," I complained.

"I didn't fall asleep till the end," he argued.

"You fell asleep in the middle. You were snoring," I insisted.

"Well, what happened? Did they find out who the killer was?" He laughed.

"What do you think?" I asked.

"It was the ex-husband."

"No, it wasn't," I teased.

"Who was it?" he begged.

"I'm not telling you. Watch it again on your own if you want to know."

"It had to be the ex-husband," he insisted.

"Yes, it was the ex-husband," I agreed.

"I knew it!" he gloated.

"How's your back?"

"Better. I have another appointment with the chiropractor this afternoon," he flatly replied.

David's lower back always gave out. I would often find him lying on the futon in agony, perhaps from a slipped disk or pinched nerve. He frequented a chiropractor, which helped temporarily.

"Do you have any more interviews set up this week?" David asked as he slugged down his coffee.

"No," I mumbled.

"Maybe you'll find something in today's paper."

"Maybe," I agreed as I continued to peruse Wednesday's sparse edition.

David rubbed the back of my head, "Don't worry about it, you'll find a job." I flipped through the newspaper thinking about the previous day's interview with Tony Scott.

I was grateful to have David in my life. If he had not been in my life I could have been homeless. I realized that coming from the emotionally toxic environment in Queens as a teenager, all the abusive office jobs, and gaps in employment, David was a nurturing surrogate parent and protective big brother. I loved David, but I sometimes wondered if I was "in love" with him. If I had been able to move out of my parent's house and support myself by having a permanent job where people were kind and respected me, maybe I would have gotten my own apartment and dated men my own age. Maybe I would have not ended up with David at all. If I did end up with David, it would have been out of choice rather than necessity. Who would I be, and where would I be if I were empowered in my own life? Would I be with him? After I met Tony Scott that question became more prominent.

David pulled out a stack of pamphlets from his portfolio, "Look, I got some more brochures from the travel agency yesterday for our trip to Europe next summer!"

As I looked over the colorful brochures of France and Italy, I thought to myself, "This will be my first trip to Europe. David is so excited about taking me. Perhaps it's best that I don't get that job at MWR with Tony Scott. David wants to give me the world, and well, Tony is way out of my league anyway. He probably dates those sophisticated ladies from the Upper East Side who wear smart dresses, high heels, and pearls around their neck.

If I had to go to work and see Tony every day, it would be great, but then I would probably get very confused if it was more than just a crush. I'm being so ridiculous. It was a job interview for Christ sake. He needs a secretary, and I need a job.

David startled me out of my thoughts, "Tom is going to meet us at the coffee shop tonight so we can figure out which hotels to book ahead of time in the major cities like Paris, Venice, and Rome. Isn't this exciting?" he asked.

Tom was David's best friend from Brooklyn. He was an intelligent, reserved person with a thin frame, gaunt face, and a dry bed of hair and a sense of humor to match. For many years he worked as a freelance writer. Tom often lamented over his struggle to find enough assignments, and collect payment because his publishers, for months on end, would assure him *the check is in the mail*. As a result of always being broke, he often appeared disillusioned with his inability to find true love, and grasp the American Dream of financial independence. Since we all spent so much time together, I did my best to try and snap Tom out of his negative, and cynical view of life, or just ignore him when he got cranky. Due to his minimalist lifestyle and uncertain financial situation, Tom considered himself frugal, but some people might construe him as cheap, which probably accounts for why he rarely had a girlfriend, and always ended up tagging along with David and me. It was no surprise that he would be coming to Europe with us.

David and I swiveled into the big, comfy booth opposite Tom who was already there waiting for us at our regular hangout, the local Eudora Coffee Shop. David and I ordered our usual medium rare deluxe burger platters and cokes with lemon. As the waitress left, Tom looked at me sarcastically. "Why are you ordering the deluxe burger platter again? Are you going to finish it this time?"

"Maybe I will, maybe I won't," I replied.

"You never finish it. You leave most of it on your plate," he smirked.

"What do you care? Are you paying for it?" I asked.

"No. Are *you* paying for it? He's paying for it." Tom pointed to David.

"What's that's supposed to mean?" I asked.

"He always pays for it. He pays your half of the rent, too," Tom snipped.

I looked at David. David just put his hands up in the air and said, "Order what you want. It makes no difference to me."

"I'm getting the *deluxe* bacon cheese burger platter and a *large* coke with lemon. After that I'm going to order a cappuccino and a big slice of lemon meringue pie," I chimed. I looked at Tom over my menu, "You can have my leftovers." I stuck my tongue out at Tom.

"I don't want your leftovers," Tom smirked. "I'm just going to have my usual blueberry muffin and Earl Grey tea."

Tom always talked down to me to insinuate that I did not deserve anything in life. He criticized me for allowing David to pay the rent and the checks when we ate out. David happily insisted on it, and David was my boyfriend, not Tom, so I could not understand why he made it his business to tell me what I could or could not receive in life. I speculated that he was just jealous because, as a freelance writer, he had to stick to a tight budget by living in a tiny studio apartment, and feasting only on boxed spaghetti and tomato sauce from a jar.

Tom never drank coffee; he always drank tea. Because he lived in London for seven years, he had acquired the habit of having tea every afternoon. He thought this made him English, but he wasn't. He was from Brooklyn. "He had no lips, most English people don't. At least he had that going for him," I thought.

To unruffle my feathers, I would often remind myself that Tom and David had been best friends since their high school days, so I kept the peace by just shrugging off Tom's antagonizing comments. I also made an effort to try and see the positive side of Tom. His extreme cynicism could be exceedingly funny, and it made Tom feel good when we laughed at his point of view. So I looked on the bright side about Tom coming to Europe with us. Tom knew where to find the cheapest hotels and the cheapest place to eat, and he was indispensably good with maps.

David and Tom were doing all the research, making all the arrangements, and planning the whole trip. All I had to do was come for the ride. My only request was that we ended up in Venice on my birthday.

Tom stole a handful of sugar packets off the counter table and slipped them into the top pocket of his denim jacket. I was in the process of buttering my bread, and when I squeezed the little packet of butter, it flew out of its foil and shot across the table onto Tom's sweater. We were all laughing so hard we couldn't breathe.

The night turned out to be pretty upbeat as we discussed all the possible hotels and sights we were going to see once we landed in Paris. I was looking forward to seeing the Louvre, and Tom and David were excited about seeing Jim Morrison's grave at the Père Lachaise Cemetery in Paris.

I began to sing the first verse of the song "Light My Fire" by The Doors to Tom as he sat across the table from me. I sang it off-key in an exaggerated way, moving my head and arms, and snapping my fingers.

Tom smiled despite himself, looked around embarrassed, and laughed, "Hey, what are you trying to do, get us kicked out of here?" David, still laughing, stopped the waiter going by, "Check please."

David left for work early and I stayed in bed. At eleven a.m., I reached across the bed to pick up the phone while rubbing the sandman from my eyes.

"Hello?"

"Hi, it's Carol. You got the job."

"What!" I asked as I sat up.

"You got the job!" she said again.

"I got the job!" I screamed.

"Yes, you got the job. You start next Monday. Be there at nine a.m. sharp," Carol calmly instructed.

"Oh my God! I got the job? What did they say?" I asked, curious about all the details.

"Tony loved you. He thought you were absolutely perfect. In fact, he had called my office right after you left to let me know that I did not have to send him any more candidates. I was out of the office most of the day but I called him this morning to confirm it and he said, 'You got the job.' Congratulations!"

"Oh, Carol, this is great. Thank you so much! Hey, I got the job!" I shouted.

"Good luck. If you have any questions between now and then, give me a call."

"I will. Thanks!" I sat there in bed for a moment trying to digest my unbelievable fortune. The phone rang and it was David.

"I got the job!" I shouted into the phone.

"Great! I knew you would get something sooner or later. Great! Congratulations! We can celebrate tonight. I got us tickets to see The Thompson Twins tonight."

"The who?" I asked.

"The Thompson Twins. They're a really good band. Oh, and guess what?" He asked pleased with himself.

"What?"

"We got tickets to see Tears for Fears at the Garden in September," he bragged.

"You got tickets to see Tears for Fears! How did you manage that? I thought they were sold out?"

"Tom got them for us at the record company he freelances for. You're gonna like the Thompson Twins tonight. I just bought their new CD. It's on the coffee table in the living room. I gotta run. See ya later. Listen to their new CD."

I jumped up out of bed and sang out loud a few bars from the Tears for Fears song, "Shout". I was so happy to finally land a great job and have a decent paycheck to look forward to each week. I was released from the chains of uncertainty and lack. Money meant choice and mobility. Now my life could finally move forward again. While in the shower, I belted out the lyrics from their song, "Everybody wants to rule the world."

After my shower, I slipped the Thompson Twins CD into the stereo and got dressed. I called my friend Alan at his photography studio in Soho to ask if he was still available to do some test shots with me for my modeling portfolio that weekend, and if he could throw in a roll of acting head shots for my acting resume.

"Yeah, sure. Do you have clothes for the photos?" he asked.

"I can handle it. I start a new job next week, so money won't be an issue. I can get some things at Bloomingdales on credit."

"Great, see you this Saturday at 10 a.m.," Alan agreed.

After talking with Alan, I scurried uptown to the hair salon, Alfreda-Kassandra, to get my bangs trimmed. This salon had stylists that were the best in the business. They worked for the top fashion magazines, making top models and celebrities beautiful. David was a client there as well. In fact, he turned me onto the Alfreda-Kassandra Salon. It was very expensive, $85 dollars for a wash, cut, and blow-dry, and then, of course, there was the tip. But it was worth every penny, because they made their clients look amazing, plus the trim upkeeps were free, so what the heck.

I was so happy to be out and about again. I especially loved having the opportunity to be in a fun environment to get pampered. The salon was bustling with great eighties music like Duran Duran, Echo and the Bunny Men, Simple Minds, and The Smiths. Fashionably dressed gay hairdressers scuttled across the floor here and there with their scissors and blow-dryers. Clients convened in their chairs sipping either coffee, tea, or champagne. Some read magazines, while others disappeared into deep porcelain sinks, as the interns rubbed soaps and conditioners through their wet locks. A few clients moseyed around the shop with large pieces of silver tinfoil in their hair for highlights. It reminded me of what my father used to say to my mother when she dyed her hair at home and wore the tin foil, "Take me to your leader."

Presley, my hair stylist, was a flamboyant svelte gay man. That day, he wore a Boy George inspired plaid kilt held together by a giant safety pin, accented by a black t-shirt and army boots. His hair was brassy red and styled high like a porcupine. He looked unusual and fun. Presley vigorously brushed out my long, straight, light brown hair with golden highlights. He checked my roots.

"Honey, I think you should come back in about another month and let us touch up these highlights. They look great now, but in another month you're gonna need a touch up, okay?" he warned.

I nodded as he went to work on trimming my bangs. He asked me about David and everything else that was going on in my life. Unlike most women, I hated to chat while in the chair, so I gave short quick answers and never elaborated much. I guess Presley might have enjoyed cutting David's hair more than mine, because David loved to talk and talk and talk, and yap away about anything and everything. With David, I could never get a word in edge wise. David was more like a woman than me. The way he fussed over his own hair, his appreciation for home decorating, and our mutual scorn for the beer guzzling spectator sports crowd was quite compatible with me. I was attracted to the kind of guy who you might say, *He's not gay, he's English.* Except, David was originally from Brooklyn.

Presley stepped back and looked at me with an approving nod, "Okay, sweet face, you're done. Don't forget to come back next month and have those highlights touched up."

The next day, I ran to Bloomingdales to try on some expensive clothes to purchase for my fashion shoot. I struggled to reach the elevator, maneuvering through the crowded and congested main lobby, strategically dodging all those wide-angle lens images of heavily made up sales girls pushing huge perfume bottles in my face. It was an unpleasant shopping experience but I was able to find everything I needed in one place, put it on a credit card, leave the tags on, and bring everything back the following week for a full-refund. It was the aspiring model's solution to having an affordable wardrobe selection for test shots.

I chose four different outfits, but my favorite was the sleek electric blue satin gown, with a low open back and a long train.

Shopping for clothes was fast and easy for me. Being the standard size six required for modeling, the clothes slipped on me like silk with no bumps or bulges. I had a dancer's body rather than an athletic body. My legs were lean, and strong, and my butt was firm and heart shaped. My breasts were on the small side but most models had small breasts at the time, and besides they were both exactly the same size and in perfect proportion to one another. I had a thin waist and shapely hips and a flat stomach. My arms were thin and willowy but I had a graceful stride. My ankles were thick but my feet had a very high arch as I balanced on my toes to imagine how the gown would look in heels.

I pulled my long, silky hair on top of my head to imagine a more sophisticated look. I swiveled a bit to see the bare back of the dress and gave a highbrow look in the mirror. I beheld my big brown eyes against my flawless skin, and puckered up my full and rosy lips. My hair wasn't as thick as I would have liked, and my nose was larger than the average celebrity model, but my attitude was "so what" nobody is perfect.

I had no hang ups about my body when I looked in the mirror. But I did not particularly stop to stare at it much to admire it either. I did not exalt my body in my own eyes nor did I criticize it. I could say to myself, "No scars, no broken bones, I still have only one head. Okay, everything looks good, let's go." With that recognition, I even had room for gratitude that my body was cooperating on a moment to moment basis in carrying out the daily functions of my life.

Physical beauty is all in time, it withers away, and so does the intellect, but love is forever – without dreaming – so let's dance. I thought to myself as I swirled around in front of the mirror admiring my new threads.

If I was proud of anything it was the fact that I could raise my arms high and bend over backwards until my palms touched the floor, and on even more flexible days, I could grab my ankles and just hang out there filling up my lungs with an extra supply of oxygen. I can't even call it pride. It just felt good to stretch my body in this way.

In school gymnastics, my favorite exercise was to hang on the rings and invert myself inside out with my chest expanded and my spine highly arched. I could hang there for hours like a bat in bell tower. As a kid, watching my favorite Saturday morning cartoons, Scooby Doo and The Bugaloos, I would lie with my back on the floor and push my legs straight over my head in between munching on Lucky Charms and Capt'n Crunch cereal. I wasn't trying to achieve anything. Spine stretching positions were just the most comfortable for me. So now all grown up, although I was often complimented on many of my physical features, my sexy back and curvy spine looked outstanding in the backless, electric blue evening gown.

I was comfortable in my own skin, perhaps because I was so physically active growing up. I was into swimming, dancing, roller skating, and on the school gymnastic team. Food for me was only fuel to burn. Also, I grew up mostly within the Italian side of the family. We ate a lot. I would be the first one at the dinner table and yet the last one to leave. My aunt would say, "Look at this kid. For Christ sake, give her some food. She's so skinny she doesn't even need an umbrella when it rains. Here have another cannoli." I could eat five or six cannolis in one sitting and still never gain an ounce.

Now, as I surveyed my nakedness in the dressing room mirror, I still had neither criticism nor admiration for it. Just a curiosity: *Who am I?* I was curious to know who was in there and whoever she was, how did she get in there? After leaving Bloomingdales, I headed off to Clairol for free highlights.

Many models got their hair colored or highlighted for free at the Clairol training center and corporate headquarters on Park Avenue. No music played at Clairol, the coffee was stale because it came out of a vending machine, and the place was as sterile as a doctor's office. But the technicians in their white lab coats always did a pretty good job.

In the evening David, Tom, and I went out to eat at the Hunan Balcony to celebrate and toast my new job. After, we cabbed it down to the Limelight, an old church that had been converted into a small concert hall and dance club. In the church lobby, chubby teenage girls dressed in black taffeta gowns and torn fish net stockings crawled around on the floor. They wore heavy black eyeliner, chains on their ankles, and bright orange streaks ran through their spiked hair. They were clearly drunk as they giggled with each other that they could not get up off the floor. Tom rolled his eyes with contempt and groaned, "The Jersey crowd is out tonight."

We moved into the main floor of the club, but it was too crowded, so we climbed our way up the red-carpeted staircase to the second balcony to get a better view. The lights went down, the curtain went up, the music began, and there were the Thompson Twins! The entire church was screaming.

It was now the weekend and I had everything prepared and ready to go for the fashion shoot, except that I awoke with my period and felt horrible. Not only was my stomach bloated, but my face puffed up and my skin looked sallow. Even worse, I broke out with one huge zit on my chin. Toothpaste would have gotten rid of the zit if I had been forewarned and had put some on the night before, but it was too late. I had forgotten to keep track of my cycle. I took two Midol with water and jumped in the shower. I dabbed some toothpaste on my zit, hoping it would not only cover it up, but clear it up before I got downtown to Alan's photo studio in Soho.

The rain was pouring down outside so rather than take the subway, I carried myself and a heavy garment bag, filled with the new clothes from Bloomingdales, into a big yellow taxi. The cab driver dropped my bag into the deep trunk while I collapsed into the cool leather of a lumpy backseat. The cabbie then jumped into the driver's seat while adjusting his cap, pulled the car away from the curb and seamlessly merged into the traffic, moving evenly down the avenue.

While listening to the sweet inspirational music playing on the radio of William Ackerman's "The Impending Death of the Virgin Spirit" intertwined with the swish swash of the windshield wipers, I peered out the blurry side window dripping with rain. The traffic light, pedestrians, architecture, and sky--all their colors and textures blending and swirling through the wetness like an impressionist painting struck me with absolute awe. Oh, life is so overwhelmingly beautiful at times, it can leave me speechless and paralyzed with an unspeakable reverence, the unbearable lightness of just being.

I soon found my heart now pounding in anticipation of today's event. I was excited about working with Alan because most photographers I worked with in the past preferred to accentuate my ethnicity which was fine, but it had its limits in the American market. Alan's photographs were crisp, simple, and honest, just like his personality. He could capture the All-American girl in me needed for landing catalog work and commercials.

I met Alan six months ago at an art gallery reception honoring the famous fashion photographer Richard Avedon. The young, clean cut fellow approached me in a friendly manner at the wine and cheese table to ask me if I was one of Avedon's subjects.

"No, I wish I was," I laughed.

"Are you a model?" Alan inquired.

"Yes. Are you a photographer or are you just trying to pick me up?" I asked tauntingly. Alan laughed.

"I am a photographer. I have a studio in Soho. I would like to photograph you. Here's my card. I'm legit. Promise," he smiled sweetly. Alan and I spent an enjoyable evening together perusing the Avedon exhibition.

The big yellow taxi wobbled and bounced on the cobblestone street awkwardly struggling and failing to get close enough to the curb as it parked. I climbed out of the back seat stepping over a puddle of water and oil reflecting a rainbow of brilliant colors. I looked up to a patch of bright blue sky peering through the clouds in the far distance. The black mass overhead was moving swiftly north. The rain was now a drizzle. I walked to the back of the cab, collected my garment bag and paid the driver.

Alan buzzed me in. When I walked into the studio, the place was in a shambles and Alan was slumped on the bar stool chair. He looked distraught.

"What happed?" I asked.

"I was robbed last night," he said, solemnly.

"What? What did they take?"

"They got my wide-angle lens, some money, and the gold watch I was shooting for a client's catalog. Luckily I had brought one of my cameras home with me last night. I always carry it around in case I run into something interesting to photograph. But they also took a bunch of antique cameras that I had been collecting over the years. They tried to pull out the stereo system, but it's just too big, or maybe they were running out of time, or something. I have an alarm system on the front door, but I think they managed to climb in through this window from the other building. He must've been Spiderman or something because it's not easy to get over to this ledge," Alan explained.

"Alan, I'm so sorry. Should we do this another time? You should call the police and get this taken care of," I suggested.

"The cops were here. They just left about thirty minutes ago. I've just been sitting here..." Alan swung his arm, and pushed the lamp off the kitchen island onto the floor. "Fuck!"

I didn't know what to say. Alan was clearly upset, and I didn't feel so well myself. There was a long silence.

"You know what? Let's do this," he stated.

"Are you sure?"

"No. Let's just forget about it for now. Forget it happened, and just do it. Let's just do it and have a good time," he insisted with a determined persistence.

"If you're up for it, I am," I agreed.

Shortly after, the stylist arrived and assisted me in choosing various outfits. He applied my make-up and experimented with different hairstyles. The rain had stopped, and the sun was streaming through the south windows. Alan pulled down all the shades and enthusiastically set up the backdrop and lighting. I appreciated and admired Alan's attitude and professionalism in pushing forward despite the obstacles and setbacks he had with this morning's burglary.

The stereo blasted great music of The Cars, Depeche Mode, Madonna, U2, and Cyndi Lauper. Once I was ready, Alan guided me to position in front of the backdrop. He adjusted the backlight and carefully maneuvered the strobe light to illuminate my face. I loved being in front of the camera. It was fun to project an image, and it was educational. I learned how different poses and projecting the right attitude could make a good a photograph. I loved photography, and although I was not a photographer myself, being a painter, I could learn from photographers how composition, color, lighting, and shutter speed affected the final product.

Once Alan was ready to shoot, I began to pose to the music. With my dance background, I could be free with my body and contribute an interesting composition to the overall photograph. Modeling was a fun experience for me, and a kind of mini-theater endeavor. It led to other aspirations I would not have had otherwise if I did not pursue it.

The photographer and I merged into the tempo and energy of the music. It turned out to be an inspiring photo session, and we had a great time. Hopefully, these would be the shots that would finally get me in the door.

CHAPTER THREE

TO BE OR NOT TO BE

THE NEXT MORNING, David and I went to our weekly scene-study class to perform a ten-minute scene from the Tennessee Williams play, *Cat on a Hot Tin Roof.* David played the character Brick Pollitt and I played his wife Maggie. David and I had been exploring the characters and rehearsing together for a few weeks now, and we felt we were ready to perform.

David usually gravitated towards more comedic material such as Neil Simon plays, but the instructor wanted David to stop relying on his comic personality and stretch his range, so he had assigned us this particular play.

We were the first set of students on the list to perform that morning. I hate being first. Being first makes everyone in the class nervous, but being last is even worse, because then you have to sit for two hours with sweaty palms and white knuckles in anticipation. I can't concentrate on the scenes ahead of me, because I'm too busy going through the lines, the beats, and the stage blocking of my own scene in my head. As a result, I'd miss out on the other students' work. When the instructor picked on me to comment, I didn't have a clue. I was too busy imagining what my scene was going to look like before I even got up on stage. "I liked it," I'd say. "Why did you like it? What did you like about it?" the instructor would ask. I'd just shrug my shoulders, "I'm not sure. I just did."

David and I quickly selected different prop furniture from behind the curtain, moved it onto the stage, and placed it just so. Then we organized the personal props we brought from home to scatter around the set: clothes hangers, a perfume bottle, lipstick, a hair brush, shaving materials, and a hand fan. I speedily undressed and jumped into my costume backstage, placing the silk and lace slip over my head, shear stockings on my legs, and then finally struggling with the zipper on the back of the pink dress that got caught in the fray of the lining. The sound of restless, impatient students amplified the anxiety. David came to my rescue and all was well. All David had to do was go barefoot and take off his shirt revealing a white t-shirt underneath.

David had strategically placed himself downstage in his pretend bathroom, so that the imaginary mirror he was looking into while shaving was facing the audience, what actors refer to as *the fourth wall*. I plopped myself on the bed upstage, and positioned myself in a cat like pose while holding a delicate lace hand-fan next to my cheek.

"Are you ready?" the instructor asked. David and I nodded.

"Okay, now I want you both to breathe. Take a few moments. Get conscious of your breath. Get anchored. Take as much time as you need, and let me know when you're ready," the teacher instructed.

I started the scene with the first line. My voice sounded shaky to me and I was vibrating inside of my body like an unstable washing machine. After the first line, I realized I had twenty more lines to go before David had any dialogue to respond back to me.

I suddenly realized that I was doing a monologue that could carry us both into a very intimate relationship with one another, but physically, we seemed miles apart. We had rehearsed back at our apartment in our much smaller living room space. Now, the stage we were on was much larger, emptier, and more expansive. The stage blocking had to be reconsidered and I had to acclimate immediately, which created a new challenge.

My insides kept rattling and rumbling like a battered plane engine trying to take off. My awareness moved directly to the sensations in my body. This is not me, I kept telling myself. It is only a reaction. Don't try to control it, but use it as an opportunity to really observe yourself in this moment. Breathe. This reaction is not me. Breathe. It comes from suppressed fears that bubble to the surface. Keep quiet. Don't panic. Observe. But I feel lost. It's okay. The beingness is only burping up old insecurity. If I am free from my mind, will I lose it? Will I look unattractive?

Forget about that. Breathe, trust. Play your truth. Don't panic. Breathe while engaging fully into your physical activities. Use the nervous energy to move toward your objective. Let the eruption happen. Don't panic. Observe it and on the other side of it, you'll find a space filled with peace. You'll enjoy playing and all will become effortless. I played all the uncomfortable emotions and traits of the character Maggie with abandonment and joy.

As I embraced the expansive space, using every square foot of it with my entire being, I performed my tasks with clear deliberation, while making full use of the props, the bedroom furniture, the imaginary closets, and surrounding windows and balcony as I rambled on about Brick's family and Brick's best friend Skipper.

I made sure that every word I uttered landed with emotional impact. But with David facing the audience downstage, I had no clue if I was influencing him. I had to trust my intuitive awareness and moment-to-moment intention in the scene. I had some idea that my acting was effective because the audience was quiet, but the energy in the room felt positive, the kind of energy that lets an actor know that the audience is fully participating with the characters on stage.

Brick made no attempt to look at Maggie and kept shaving as he delivered a brief line here and there. The way he shaved was just as interesting as his silence. I could not see the subtle nuances in David's performance, but the audience received information about Brick and Maggie's relationship through David's mannerisms and facial expressions which he directed into his *fourth wall* mirror.

When Maggie tried to forcefully make eye contact with Brick by moving downstage toward the bathroom, instead of looking at him in the face, I instinctively looked at his reflection in the imaginary mirror on *the fourth wall* as I spoke to him. The students and instructor appreciated this as a thoughtful, artistic choice of detail on my part. It wasn't planned. Every choice happened naturally without thought and without effort.

Afterwards, the instructor commented that the history, connection, relationship, and tension between Brick and Maggie were very strong. My comfortable use of the entire stage, and deliberate use of the props, was interesting to watch. David's subtle nuances in his shaving communicated a great deal of dialogue about his relationship with Maggie, even though he had very few lines to speak.

Both the instructor and students were very impressed with our work, and felt we had achieved the assignment.

"There is no need to redo the same scene next week. I would like to see new material from the both of you next time. Remember, keep challenging yourself," the instructor implored.

I had been training and performing for five years now, so it was not that I had learned anything new that day, because it's not learning, but rather an "allowing" that either happens or doesn't. Theater training is not a finite, text book education. Rather, it is a "state of being". Art is about understanding technique in order to throw away technique, and just "be". With each new endeavor, I used technique as the skeleton or foundation, and then broke away from it to allow a state of being. An actor may appear like a novice one day because they are still exploring the text. But, on another day, something clicks and his or her work can be pure genius. It has nothing to do with an inborn talent. We become skillful at something based on our interest and our consistent attention to it, not because we have an elusive quality called *talent*.

I particularly enjoyed this class because the instructor encouraged everyone to be a curious actor willing to take risks and do what is new and different. He pushed us into uncharted territory in order to stretch our instruments. If it lands well, so be it. If not, so be it. He was more interested in having us risk failure, instead of always succeeding.

When the class was over, most of the students pitched in to clean up the deli food wrappers from the floor, dump their empty coffee containers into the trash, store furniture and props neatly back stage, and stack up the folding chairs before leaving.

"I have an extra set of tickets to the play *The Burning Bed*. It's a pre-performance. Does anybody want them?" the instructor asked.

"Who's in it?" some of the actors yelled out.

"Farrah Fawcett," the instructor replied.

"From Charlie's Angels?" I asked.

"Isn't *The Burning Bed* a very, dark drama?" David inquired.

"Yes. She took a huge risk by taking this play on," the instructor commented.

Bob, a middle-aged actor, with a receding hairline, always dressed in a dusty suit--because he moonlighted as an on-the-go real-estate agent, took up the offer. "She's hot. I grew up madly in love with Farrah."

"They're yours. The last one out, make sure the door is locked." The instructor left with Bob and some other students.

Jimmy, a robust guy in baggy jeans and a grease-stained T-shirt, rolled out the green plastic garbage can to the middle of the room, "Hot pants Farrah Fawcett taking on the lead in a play like that? The critics are going to slaughter her," he warned.

Mark, tall, handsome, gay, and smartly dressed in a tweed jacket, black pants and an ascot, perched his chin lazily on top of a broom stick. "It's unfortunate that Hollywood celebrities get type cast, but maybe if she does well it will resurrect her career."

"I hope so, but once an actor establishes a certain image or persona, it's very hard for critics to embrace it," David replied.

"Industry people find a formula that works and keep banking on it in the same way chain stores populate the world. We have Duane Read, Wal-Mart, and McDonalds. They find a recipe and duplicate it, but now everything looks, feels, and tastes the same. My neighborhood is becoming one big shopping mall. I can't find a decent cup of coffee anymore," Jimmy fumed.

"Where do you live?" Mark asked.

"The Eastside. Murray Hill. ...What?" Jimmy asked wide-eyed.

"You don't look like a Mid-Towner?" Mark replied.

"Oh yeah, wise guy. What do I look like?" Jimmy challenged him.

"You look like a rough and tumble bad boy from the Bronx who has a girlfriend with big hair," Mark smiled teasingly.

Jimmy pushed the broom out from under Mark, and handed it back to him, "Stop posing like a GQ model and help us clean up."

Mark giggled, "You're so cute when you're angry."

Jimmy rolled his eyes and walked away. "Lillian, could you help me out here," he pleaded.

"Sure," she giggled. Lillian in her stocking feet, stood high on her ballerina toes and tippy-toed over to Mark. Her handkerchief dress and cascading crimped hair flowed behind her. She reminded me of a forest nymph. She explained in her squeaky voice, "It's like this Mark. In my opinion, the public still decides what they like."

"And you know what I like?" Mark asked.

"*Two whole beef patties, special sauce, lettuce, cheese, pickles, onions on a sesame seed bun.* The problem is that Madison Avenue sniffs out those popular public opinions so that they can market, brand, and package a good thing over and over again, and worldwide, so that it becomes a religion rather than an experience," Lillian suggested.

"No. Tell this schmuck I'm not gay!" Jimmy yelled out.

"Ssssh, I'm getting to that," Lillian replied.

Lillian moved her hands seductively across the back of Marks shoulders, and along his face. "You see Mark, we get easily sucked into the formula because it's the human condition, or I should say, human frailty, to want all aspects of our lives to be convenient, dependable, secure, and familiar all the time. We all need a secure foundation in order to step out into the unknown. Jimmy needs that. You need that. I need that. Be patient with him. Be patient with me!" She grabbed his collar tightly.

Mark jumped back. "Wooh! Lillian, look I'm sorry about what happened between us last Friday at the party. I was drunk, it was dark. I was lonely. I'm sorry. I thought you understood it was a mistake.

"I thought you were gay?" Jimmy blurted out.

"I am gay!" Mark exclaimed.

"Then what the fu... Never mind," Jimmy mumbled as he rolled the garbage pail out into the hallway.

Spike, dressed like an urban Point Dexter, and wearing two different colored socks, sat on the single chair left in the center of the stage. He ruminated out loud to himself, "The security that protects us from danger, if taken to an extreme, also imprisons us, and puts chains around our ankles. It makes our lives predictable, boring, suffocating, and impoverished, which totally omits even the possibility of a black hole, let alone a gnome. Yet, it is quite likely that sock gremlins are living in my dryer." The door slammed behind Spike, as the last student filed out of the room.

Outside the theater David and I, along with Jimmy, Lillian, and Mark, piled into a cab which took us from the West Village towards Union Square.

Jimmy continued, "I'm not saying sell out. I'm just trying to make a point. Being a successful actor in Hollywood has its virtues. One can have enough money to buy a good suit, get a hair-cut, go to the dentist, buy a house, marry and raise a family, afford health insurance, send one's kids to college, and take care of elderly parents. These are good and valid reasons for being talented and successful."

"I could never consider myself a talented actor or an untalented actor. It becomes irrelevant when I'm discovering that the technique and the craft of acting itself is a kind of prayer. It's an exploration of finding one's own voice, questioning one's own existence and reason for being," I responded.

Mark played an imaginary violin as I spoke. Jimmy cupped his hands to his mouth, mimicking patriotic background music. I joined in, raising my arm in triumphant Norma Ray style.

"It's about having the courage and commitment to look deep down into the abyss of the human psyche in order to understand the longing, guilt, joys, sorrows, hopes, dreams, and fears embedded in the human condition, and that, for me, is a kind of prayer. How can we expect only success when the willingness to explore all those areas must include the risk of failure?" I asked.

Jimmy responded, "This is true. If a Hollywood star experiments and fails, he may lose his reputation and his career. Not a good thing. I agree but --"

"But if *I* explore and experiment and fail, no one cares. No one knows who I am. It's not going to be on the front page of the *New York Times Arts and Leisure* section. In that sense, there's great freedom in being unknown. One can play and successfully fail without any reservation. If I'm playing in an obscure, hole-in-the-wall theater, and my prayer and meditation for the day does not get answered, who's going to write about it? No one is making a full-blown report that I failed to receive enlightenment or understanding that day," I replied.

Mark stuck his head out the window, and shouted out onto the sidewalk, "Ladies and Gentleman!!! The greatest actress of our time gave the most horrendous performance of her life today, and absolutely, destroyed . . . I tell you, absolutely decimated the words and the great poetry of our beloved Tennessee Williams! She sucked! She sucks. Off with her head, I say! Off with her head!!!

"Stop making an ass of yourself," Lillian snapped at Mark, as she pulled him by the shirt back in the window.

"Yeah Mark chill, will ya," Jimmy agreed. "David were you about to say something?"

"I was just going to say that Hollywood is so intertwined with business and profit that an actor's performance becomes an established, money-hording institution rather than a spiritual exploration. It's a business and they have to make a profit. Regardless, there are some great Hollywood films out there even though the bottom line is money," David replied.

"I agree. There are a lot of great Hollywood films. I just think the public needs to be educated on the craft of acting rather than reporting only on what some celebrity is wearing and who they are dating, divorcing, or what rehab clinic they checked themselves into," I explained.

Mark sighed, "I don't know. I think it might be tragically romantic to see a photo of myself slumped in some dark alley, bare-chested, hair all disheveled, with a needle in my arm, taking a splash on the cover of *Rolling Stone*. You know what they say, *Bad press is better than no press*."

Lillian replied, "I'm amused, but also sadly surprised when a common citizen thinks that acting is about being beautiful, photogenic, controversial, or popular in the press, rather than being good at one's craft."

Mark sighed again, "They want you to look good and act bad. It sells theater tickets, and it sells magazines. They only fire you when you cause them to go way over budget from being habitually late, or if you keep forgetting your lines."

"You're not supposed to memorize your lines. Mark, you're so irritating. Acting is about doing with a purpose – not reciting with a purpose. Acting means *act, do, be,* and *perform* with a clear intention, with a clear objective and a clear purpose. It is the doing and how one does something that brings dialogue to life. Memorizing lines before exploring the behavior comes from the novice who doesn't know any better," I snapped.

"You take the high road, I'll take the low road, and I'll be in Hollywood before you," Mark sang with a smirk.

"Now, now, girls stop fighting. An empty stomach is a cranky stomach," David warned.

"Hey where's Spike?" Jimmy asked looking at Mark.

"Last I saw him, he was in the theater," Mark replied.

"You left him there?" David laughed.

"Oh, Mark, man. You know how Spike is? He's going to think we abandoned him," Jimmy warned.

"I did abandon him! Do you know he sleeps with a pyramid on top of his bed? He says it helps him communicate with extra-terrestrials. This week he claims gremlins are living in his laundry basket. The kid freaks me out," Mark retorted.

"And you don't freak people out?" I asked.

"We should go back and get him," Jimmy suggested.

"Nooo!!!" Everyone screamed in unison.

"He'll be fine. He'll either take the subway or walk to the bar if he wants to hang with us," Lillian suggested to Jimmy.

"Why can't we just go back and get him," Jimmy suggested again.

"Nooo!!! Everyone screamed again.

"We're starving here," David chimed in.

"Yeah, we're starving. Spike's got money in his pocket and two legs. He's old enough to vote. He can come on his own," Mark argued.

"I'm not going back for him. I have to get to the airport." The cab driver threw the words over his shoulder.

As the cab stopped and waited on another red light, before turning onto Park Avenue, Mark's stupid comments about acting swam through my head.

Memorize lines! Mark can be so infantile. He always dressed like he had just walked out of an old Cary Grant movie, and he pranced around the stage like a runway model. I suspected that his only reason to be in the theater was to pick up men or women, or both.

Thanks to exhibitionists like Mark, even professional artists in other mediums don't have any idea about the actual technique of acting and think of it in superficial terms. A musician once asked me if I looked in the mirror while rehearsing my lines. I thought, *How absurd!*

"Do you look in the mirror when you practice playing the guitar or the key board?' I asked. "Well, no of course not. That would be ridiculous," he agreed.

When all is said and done, since I am poor and I do want to work at my craft and support myself as an actor, I may have to become rich and famous, simply because that's the nature of the beast. An actor doesn't have the choice to make a modest middle-class salary of $50,000 a year, each year. One is either making $2,000 a year as an actor or $80,000,000 per film, often doing three films a year! There is no middle ground. When an actor says he or she wants to be rich and famous, I can't argue with the idea. Mark may be right that actors need to create a bit of mystique and publicity to sell tickets, even if it's bad publicity. If they don't, then they won't end up rich and famous, and the only other option is to be poor and obscure – not much elbow room for anything in between, I thought, as I squirmed in the car seat for more space.

The cab finally delivered us to our favorite Sunday afternoon stomping ground, The Old Town Bar, a landmark that has been around since 1892. We all loved going there because the beer and the burgers were delicious, and the historical setting was rustic, cozy, and relaxed. Its original décor of a mahogany and marble bar with the original beveled mirror, and tin ceilings was still intact. It was like stepping back in time. During Prohibition, it was a speak-easy, and I could still smell the romantic aroma of stories flying up from the dusty corners and crevices every time the creaky front door swung open as a new patron walked in.

We moved to the middle of the room and slid into a capacious wooden booth. The waitress immediately took our drink orders.

"Did anyone watch *The Tales of the Dark Side* on TV the other night?" David asked enthusiastically.

"The episode called "The Case of the Stubborns" written by Robert Bloch?" Jimmy asked, excited.

"Yeah, yeah!" David agreed.

"That was fantastic!" Jimmy cried.

"It scared the hell out of me," I added.

"Which episode was it? I missed that one," Mark inquired.

"It takes place in this old country house in the South, and a woman and her son--I think the boy was about fifteen--anyway, they are sitting in the kitchen having breakfast," Lillian explained.

"And the boy's grandfather comes downstairs to join them, except he's dead. He had died the night before," I added.

"No!" Mark gasped. "Does he know he's dead?"

"No. The Mother and the son know he's dead. The small-town doctor and priest know he's dead, but the grandfather has no idea that he, himself, is dead," Lillian explained.

"Yeah, and he's wearing his burial suit with the white carnation in his breast pocket, and eating, and talking, and making a fuss like he was still alive," David added, amused by it all.

The waitress listened in as she served our beers.

"Everyone is trying to tell him he's dead, but he doesn't believe them. So he just eats three meals a day with them and spends his time on the front porch talking and acting the way he always did," Lillian went on.

"So what's the problem?" Mark asked.

The waitress chimes in, "He has no heart beat. He has no breath. His face is as white as a ghost. By afternoon, his face starts to decompose. By dinner time, his face--it's like half gone, and he's still walking, talking, and eating like everything is just fine. Rigor mortis sets in, so he walks down the stairs as stiff as an ironing board. His decaying body smells the house up and flies are swarming around him."

"Uuuggh!!! Everyone screamed, laughing.

"He sneezes at the dinner table, and his nose falls off!" David said, laughing hysterically.

"Uuugh!!! Gross!!!" Everyone screamed again, laughing harder.

"Are you guys ready to order?" the waitress smiled.

After everyone placed their various orders of deluxe burger platters, the waitress disappeared again.

While scraping off the beer bottle label, I asked, "So where do you think we go when we die?"

"That's the big, unanswered question. Nobody knows that," Jimmy answered.

"Into the great unknown, I suppose," Lillian replied.

"Do you think there is such a place?" I asked.

"Check it out, check it out, check it out..." Mark whispered to the group.

"What? Why are you whispering?" I asked.

"The actor Rob Lowe just came in with a bunch of people," David explained nonchalantly.

Lillian crawled up onto her seat in the booth and swiveled around, shouting, "Where?"

"Ssssssh. Don't look. Don't look. He's coming this way," Mark whispered as he pretended to peruse his menu.

The group of new comers passed our booth and sat at a table near the back of the pub.

"How can you be sure it's him?" Jimmy asked.

"Everyone in the bar is staring at him," Lillian replied.

"What's he doing?" Mark asked.

"He's just looking at everyone. He's smiling, but he looks a bit nervous about it," Jimmy responded.

Mark stretched up from his seat, craned his neck over the booth, and then ducked down. "He is so gorgeous!" he whispered.

"Mark, would you chill out. He's just a person," I said.

"He's such a hunk of one though," Mark sighed, his eyes a bit shiny.

"Hey, look at that. They're already serving him and his friends' food and drinks. And we're still sitting here waiting," Jimmy said.

"He probably called the place ahead of time to let them know he was coming," David explained.

"He probably doesn't even have to pay the check. Everything is on the house for these celebrities," Mark added.

"Mark would you stop trying to take a peek. You're embarrassing us," I pleaded.

"Yeah, Mark. He looks more uneasy with you gawking at him like that," Jimmy agreed.

"The waitress just took away his plate. She's taking all their plates away already. She's packing up their food," Jimmy reported.

"Why?" Lillian asked.

"Because you and Mark won't let the man eat in peace," I said.

"They're putting on their jackets and leaving," Jimmy added.

Two waitresses arrived to deliver our burger platters and then disappeared. Jimmy turned around towards the front door and back again. His voice was flat. "They just left."

A bald guy in a black raincoat retrieved a credit card from one of the waitresses, and she stacked a tall pile of doggie bags in his arms. He held the pile of brown bags awkwardly as he staggered towards the front door.

Jimmy turned and watched the bald man leave, then turned back around. "Their food just left."

A mixture of emotions floated around the table ranging from embarrassment to relief, to disappointment, and even a bit of sadness with unreasonable feelings of being snubbed.

Mark poured more beer into his glass and raised it high, "I would like to make a toast to David and Whitney for an outstanding and most memorable performance of *Cat on a Hot Tin Roof!* And to Jimmy and Lillian for their absolutely, fabulous, funny performance of Craig Lucas's play *Reckless.* And to me, for being fabulous!

"Salute!" Jimmy agreed as he raised his beer bottle.

"Cheers to us!!" We shouted as we raised ours.

As I bit into my burger, I thought to myself: "Yes, this is nice: to go anywhere and be anywhere I want to be without being noticed, without being recognized. I am invisible, obscure, and unknown. I have no reputation to protect. I have no resume to live up to. I can be fluid and ever-changing. I have no box to fit into, because I have not yet become a packaged product."

"Hey did anyone catch the last episode of *Lifestyles of the Rich and Famous*," David inquired.

"*Champagne wishes and caviar dreams*? Never miss it," Mark replied.

"What did you think of the thirty-room mansion with the sip-and-dip pool and the private zoo?" David asked.

"That hand-beaded couture dress was to die for," Lillian gasped.

"I think Barbara Streisand wore that dress on an awards show, and she looked absolutely stunning," Mark added.

"I want that ultra-sleek sports car. Did you see the engine on that thing?" Jimmy asked.

"I fell in love with the Tuscan Villa on the private Caribbean Island," I professed.

"Do you think millionaires are really happy all the time?" Lillian asked.

"One thing I can be sure of is that they don't have a boredom problem. If their 100-acre estate gets too claustrophobic, they can always wind up the propellers on the private jet, and take a holiday in Cannes. And just think of all the incredibly interesting people they get to meet, run around with, and have to keep up with," Mark stated.

"Yes, but does that make them perpetually happy?" Lillian asked.

"How do I know? Who's to know? But the good news is that they don't have to spend much time thinking about it," Mark explained.

"So the key to happiness is shopping?" David laughed.

"No. The key to ward off unhappiness is shopping," Lillian corrected.

"Well said, Watson," Mark replied.

"So, you're saying that the only way to be content in life is to be continually distracted? David chuckled.

Everyone laughed.

"Yeah, like Spike. He's probably still back at the theater ruminating over his lost socks!" Mark bellowed. Everyone laughed louder.

For me it was all food for thought. I contemplated the idea of why people have the strange misperception that the goal in life is to achieve an on-going, non-stop, experience of perpetual happiness, even though all evidence points to the fact that no one even knows of any such person, either directly or indirectly, who has achieved it. Nor can anyone point to any person who has lived a full life on this earth, living or dead, who has achieved it. Why would the majority of people who can't even solve the continual and mysterious disappearance of the lost laundry sock expect and hope to achieve it?

CHAPTER FOUR

MY NEW JOB

FOR MY FIRST day of work at the financial firm, I wore a short skirt, a bolero jacket, and a soft pink blouse. I lost the glasses, put on my contact lenses, and let my hair loose. I looked much better, but I still felt like someone else. The clothes are just not me. If I had put on some pearls, I would have looked like someone's little daughter playing dress up. I was twenty-four years old, but I still looked like a thirteen-year-old waif.

Upon arriving at MWR, Tony took me into the adjacent room to meet his partner Jim. Jim's office also had a large fireplace, but it was sparsely furnished with an Oriental carpet and two desks. Jim's large wooden desk and Susan's smaller desk sat opposite each other on separate sides of the room.

Jim was much older than Tony, perhaps in his late fifties, and he was the opposite of Tony in every way: conservative, stuffy, and reserved, with a husky build, and a ruddy face that suggested he drank a lot of scotch. His secretary, Susan, complimented his style with her dowdy suits and long-pleated skirts. Her rosy lips and cheeks and porcelain skin with no make-up still hinted of potential seduction. I suspected there was a glamorous, erotic creature hiding underneath.

Susan seemed to be a bit ruffled by my new look. Jim, meeting me for the first time, graciously welcomed me aboard, but he gave Tony a look as if to say, "You rascal", or was he saying, "You fool. I hope she can type." Tony, never blinking, escorted me into another large room at the front of the building. They called it *The Computer Room*. The room was filled with large computers and servers which made loud humming sounds--printers spewing out long reams of paper covered in numbers cascaded to the floor. There were seven other employees in *The Computer Room* who called themselves technical analysts and programmers. Tony enthusiastically introduced me to all seven of them--Doc, Dopey, Happy, Grumpy, Bashful, Sneezy, and Sleepy.

Susan breezed in at that moment, clutched my hand, and pulled me into the kitchen to show me how to use the coffee maker and where to find the china.

"I like your hair color, the blonde highlights. I used to be a strawberry blonde myself," she said. I must have looked at her surprised because she paraded on with greater enthusiasm. "Oh, yes it was. It was long and blonde, thick and wavy. I was pursuing a career in the theater when I was a younger girl. I gave up dancing and singing, though. It just wasn't practical, and I needed to pay the bills. I live in Westchester now. I'm renting a small one-bedroom on the ground floor of my parent's house. It's kind of nice because I have a yard. I used to live in Manhattan, but it was too expensive, noisy, and dirty. Luckily, I found this job. Jim is a friend of my father's, and well, I haven't gone on an audition in years."

"How long has it been since you were a blonde?" I asked.

"Well, let's see, I started with Jim, five years ago. I think about six months after working here he kind of talked me into going back to my natural color, and it's just been a lot easier. You know, not having to touch up the roots. Only a few months ago, I turned thirty, so I decided to cut it short. I'm glad I did because it's so much easier to maintain, and so much cooler in the summer time."

"Do you like working here? I mean you must, you've been here awhile," I asked.

"Yes, I do. It can get pretty boring at times, but when Jim and Tony go out of town for a whole week, I can bring my portable TV in to watch soap operas. Do you watch *Days of Our Lives* or *One Life to Live* or *Search for Tomorrow*?"

"I was on *Search for Tomorrow*." Oops! I let that slip out of the bag.

"Oooh! You were on *Search for Tomorrow!*" she gasped with surprise.

"Yeah, umm, I was just an extra. No big deal. This was a few years back. Umm, I used to study acting in school, too. And, well, I don't pursue it anymore. I mean, I haven't. I don't," I stuttered.

"At least you got to be on TV! It must have been exciting."

"Yeah, well, I outgrew it, you know," I muttered.

"Oh, don't be silly. What are you nineteen, twenty? You can still do it. I can't. I just turned the big three 'O' last year. But you look like you're just starting out," Susan said.

"I'm not. I'm twenty-four. I mean, like you said, it's just not the most practical thing to do when one has to pay the bills, and I have to pay the bills. Mmmm. Susan, this is good coffee."

I thought, "Good grief that was a close call!" I had to be careful what I said, especially around Susan. If anyone found out I was an actor, they would have had second thoughts and let me go. No one at an interview ever says it, but it's an unspoken rule with the employment agencies and the office employers to never let them know you are an artist. They want someone dependable and with longevity who won't suddenly run off like an irresponsible gypsy if Hollywood calls. Plus, what were the chances of that happening anyway?

Actually it could happen, because John Travolta had called me in for the lead in a film last year. I met him and the film Director, Jim Bridges, at the posh Carlyle Hotel on Fifth Avenue.

It was a warm, spring day. All the trees were budding. The neat rows of yellow and red tulips were in full bloom along Central Park.

I thought I was only going to meet Jim Bridges, but when the hotel suite door opened, to my pleasant surprise, there was John Travolta standing there bigger than life, greeting me with his starry blue eyes and warm smile. He was a large man and extremely tall; I felt like I was looking up at a giant. Fortunately, he was not my type as far as having any kind of crush, so I was able to stay composed. John served me a tall glass of ice tea, and we had a brief chat. I wasn't nervous at all, and we had a congenial interview. The story line and overall film project sounded a bit cheesy to me, so I was not too disappointed when I did not get called back.

I had much higher aspirations. I dreamed of working on films like *Reds,* an epic romance set against a historical backdrop during political turmoil--written, produced, and directed by Warren Beatty. The script was brilliant, the cinematography was flawless, and the acting was absolutely breathtaking.

The film *Tootsie*, with Dustin Hoffman, was my all time favorite comedy. I was in awe of the perfectly arched script, punchy dialogue, and the comedic timing of all the actors.

My interview with John Travolta was brief. I was not the right "type". It turns out Jamie Lee Curtis got the part, and the film was called *Perfect.* It bombed at the box office, but gave Jamie Lee Curtis a lucrative career as an exercise guru. Susan suddenly interrupted my flashback of meeting John Travolta.

"Have you been in any other soap operas or films?" She inquired.

"No, no. It was nothing really. Just that one job and I was only an extra. Like you say, it's just not a practical career path. So I plan to be here at MWR for the long haul and collect the gold watch. These are very good cookies, did you bake them, Susan?" I asked, once again trying to change the subject.

"No, Jim's wife baked them. They are delicious, aren't they?" Susan agreed.

Over the next few days, the office was hectic and I found my job difficult. We had a deadline to compile monthly and quarterly financial reports and get them out in the mail before the end of the month. At the same time, I had to learn the office procedures and what this company actually did. I discovered it was a private investment firm, specializing in hedge funds, and managed wealthy people's money. I assembled and mailed out the financial reports for some very famous models and celebrities.

In a week's time, the storm was over. After that, there was little or nothing for me to do on the job. I realized by my second month of employment that I only had one week out of the month where I was busy and actually working. The remaining time I spent reading a book, and was only interrupted by maybe three or four phone calls during the day. About once a week, I picked up Tony's dry cleaning or his shoes from the shoemaker. Tony was always in and out of the office, or sometimes gone for days, and I took messages for him. He called me once or twice a day so that I could read his messages to him over the phone.

When Tony was in the office, he was always on the phone interacting with his high-profile clients. He sat only a few feet away from me, and I loved to watch him laugh and chat on the phone. His enthusiasm was contagious. I was attracted to artistic types, and never to the upwardly-mobile businessman, but Tony was something else. He was so handsome, charismatic, and full of adventure.

The next day, Tony was out with clients. It was an unusually windy day in July, so I ventured out onto the patio to close down the sun umbrella. Once I finally secured the umbrella, I forcefully drew the French doors shut and pulled down the latch. I sauntered to my desk, and fell back into my comfy leather chair. "Aah, safety and quiet at last," I thought. The bell rang and startled me. It was a delivery boy with a large bouquet of flowers. Then the phone rang. It was Tony calling in for his messages.

"Tony, are you coming back to the office soon, because we just received a delivery of some beautiful red roses?" I asked.

"I won't be in for the rest of the day. I'm taking a client up in an air balloon. It's the perfect day for it. It's absolutely beautiful out here!" he replied.

Yeah, that sounded like Tony. He and his client were probably also eating caviar and drinking champagne. It tickled me inside to know someone who lived their life like it was a glamorous movie. I loved the idea that I was able to work for someone who could show me that it was possible, and not just a dream.

"Just read the card that came with the roses over the phone," he asked. I assumed the roses were from a client, but when I read the card to him my heart fell to my stomach. I became intensely disappointed, and a little jealous.

"It says, *Thinking of you today, and always, Love Karen.*"

"Oh, that was sweet of her. Thanks, I'll give her a call to thank her. Could you please put them in some water for me?"

I read the card over and over again as I brought the flowers into the kitchen to find a vase, *Thinking of you today, and always, Love Karen*. Mmm, it could be a client. It could be one of those wealthy old ladies, who think of Tony fondly, like he's her handsome young son or something.

Tony was very nonchalant about it when I read the note to him. It could be a client. Tony and his client's are very friendly and social. They have lunch at Le Cirque. They go up in air balloons together. Maybe it's a female client that has a crush on Tony. Who wouldn't have a crush on Tony? I mean, any woman at any age would have a crush on Tony. I laughed out loud. The poor fool. She probably ran out to have a facelift just to try to win over his affections, and now she's sending him roses. "Who is she? Who is Karen?" I thought.

Susan blew in from lunch with a few shopping bags from Bloomingdales. "Oh my! What beautiful roses." She leaned over the kitchen counter and inhaled the delicate red petals as I arranged them in the Waterford crystal vase. "Who are they for? Who are they from?" Susan inquired.

"They're for Tony. Karen sent them. Do you know who Karen is?" I asked.

"Oh, yes. That's his new girlfriend," Susan answered sarcastically.

"His new girlfriend? I didn't know he had an old girlfriend."

"Tony has had a few girlfriends," Susan smirked.

"I'm sure he does. I mean has. How new is this one?"

Susan poured herself a cup of coffee while delivering the gossip. "I met her for the first time last night. It was late, about six p.m. You had already left for the day. At first I thought it was his niece or something, because she's very young," Susan laughed.

"How young?"

"Twenty or twenty-two--tops. But he's thirty-eight. So I think that's robbing the cradle," Susan snapped.

"Really, I'm surprised. Does he always date them that young? I just pictured Tony with someone more his age, not necessarily old and stuffy, but sophisticated, you know," I added.

"Oh, yeah, his last girlfriend was about twenty-nine or should I say, thirty-five. You know the anorexic kind with the long fur coat and high heels? But she was a real bitch. That didn't last long."

"What's this one like?"

"Just a girl. You know, very young--very pretty. Blonde--kind of short, but chesty--blue eyes, fair skin. Very different from the last one he was dating."

"What does she do?" I asked.

"Nothing. She's an artist. Her parents support her. Actually, she lives right across the street from here. I think that's how he met her, probably at the traffic light on the corner."

"That's nice. When did this happen?"

"Like I said, I only met her last night, but I'm pretty sure that this is a recent development, and he's only known her a few weeks."

"Was she nice?" I asked.

"In the past five years, I've met all of Tony's girlfriends, and none of them are nice. They're all bitches. This one's bitchy too. She's a snotty little rich kid. Supposedly her parents bought her the co-op that she lives in across the street," Susan snapped.

"How do you know about that?" I asked nonchalantly.

"Tony told me."

"He did?" I asked, surprised.

Susan sounded angry or at least a bit frustrated. "Tony is a bragger. He brags to me about all his girlfriends."

"He does? Wow!" I was even more surprised.

"Yes, he does. There are a lot of things about Tony you don't know. He loves to brag and he loves to show off. He's not as secure a person as people tend to think he is," Susan admitted. I was shocked to hear Susan's honest opinions about Tony.

"Really?" I asked.

"Really," said Susan.

While venturing back into Tony's office and placing the dramatic display of exquisite ruby roses on his desk, I was beginning to wonder if Susan perhaps had a crush on Tony, too. Tony was always bragging, showing off, and looking for attention. Insecure? I had never seen it that way, until Susan pointed it out. Tony seemed more vulnerable and more accessible to me now.

The next day, I sashayed into work dressed up. I wore a short black skirt and the *Wonderbra* underneath a tight-fitting, white angora sweater with a low scoop neck. The heels on my shoes were higher. I had blow-dried my hair to make it look much fuller, and wore plum-raspberry lip gloss. Luckily, Tony was in today, so I walked by his desk at every opportunity to show myself off.

I swished by him to file papers, get myself coffee, get him coffee, or go to the rest room. I swiveled by him to talk with Susan in Jim's office, and I slithered past him to go into *The Computer Room* for no reason at all but to say hello to the computer people, and see what they were working on. I had no idea what those elves were talking about. I politely excused myself so I could get back to Tony. I slivered towards his desk and leaned over him to ask if he wanted more coffee. After I fetched his coffee, I perched myself on his desk and crossed my legs, my synthetic *Hanes* hosiery barely touching his face. He looked up, smiled, nodded, and said, "Thank you." He turned his back away from me and continued on with his phone conversation.

I did this most days, because I had nothing else to do. Some days I got all dressed up for nothing, because he was out the whole time with clients, and only called in at the end of the afternoon for messages. When he was in the office, I subtly tried to get his attention in any way I could. This went on for about three or four weeks, but it seemed like the only person I was getting into a tizzy was me. There were days on end when Tony was rarely in the office. When he was, he was on the phone laughing and chatting with friends and clients. It was starting to piss me off. It was now late autumn. Finally, one day I realized I was barking up the wrong tree which I probably had no business barking up it to begin with. So I stopped flirting with him. I was just not interested anymore.

Shortly after, one late afternoon, Tony's girlfriend Karen stopped by the office looking for him. It was the first time I had met her, and she was as exactly as Susan described: short, blonde, and bitchy.

"Tony's not here. He'll probably be back tomorrow," I said.

Karen appeared agitated, and I could tell she had a bone to pick with Tony. She looked me over a bit and snapped, "Well, just let him know I was here," and then bolted out the front door slamming it with a huge bang.

The next afternoon, Karen returned and Tony was surprised to see her walk in. She stomped over to his desk, and asked him to have her resume revised. She appeared very irritable again.

"Sure. No problem," Tony agreed, as he walked over and handed me the resume. I looked at the white piece of paper, which lists her personal information, art exhibits, and schooling. The obnoxious little brat wanted me to tweak her resume. I agreed as if it was no problem at all.

Karen stood over me for a few minutes dictating how she wanted her resume laid out. The tone in her voice was bossy and condescending. I gave her a dirty look, so she walked over to Tony's desk, but he was on the phone with a client. "Karen, I'm busy. Please, I'll call you later," Tony snapped.

Karen turned to me and gave me a dirty look, "No problem. I'll just come by and pick it up tomorrow." She stormed out of the office slamming the front door again.

Out of nowhere, over the next few weeks, Tony started conversing with me, making jokes, and being very attentive and charming. He even fetched me a cup of coffee, brought lunch in, and invited me to join him on the patio. Did he break up with Karen? Was he actually into me instead? I felt awkward, and bit petrified.

After our lunch together, Tony got a call. He told the person on the other end of the phone that he could be at their office in about a half an hour. Then he looked at me apologetically. "Sorry, but I have to go see this client."

I thought it was strange. Why was he apologizing to me for having to go see a client? It made me nervous. Was he actually going to make a move on me pretty soon? I had not heard of or seen Karen in quite a few weeks. Did they break up?

Now, I realized that what I had been secretly fantasizing about, I really did not want. I was afraid. The flirting was fun, and even though I felt frustrated that it had been one sided, it was safe. Now it was beginning to feel too real, and it could get complicated, and things could get out of control.

Tony had his jacket off and his shirtsleeves still rolled up. He had to get himself together for his meeting. He struggled to put on his cuff links, and asked me to help him. It seemed like a very intimate request, but I didn't hesitate. He stood up from his desk, and I walked over to him, maneuvering the gold cufflinks through the holes in the fabric of his shirt. My knees felt weak, my armpits were sweating, and my heart was pounding. He looked at me very attentively. It was a moment of awkward silence that felt like an eternity. I managed to secure and clip the links, and straightened his shirt cuffs. Tony smiled softly at me. "Thanks." He slipped on his jacket, grabbed his leather briefcase, and ran out the door and down the stairs.

CHAPTER FIVE

NEW DEVELOPMENTS

BACK AT HOME, while watching *Dynasty,* David came up with the idea of taking a trip to California for the Christmas Holidays.

"What do you want for Christmas?" I asked.

"I don't want anything," he yawned.

"Neither do I," I agreed.

"I have an idea. Let's not buy each other any presents this year. Let's make our presents to each other a trip to California. We can stay with my sister and her husband in Montecito to cut hotel costs, and the airfare is only $250 round trip," David suggested.

"That's a great idea. Then we can drive back down to L.A. and stay with my cousin in Beverly Hills for a few days," I said, excited.

"That would be perfect – we can see Montecito and L.A," David agreed.

"I'm just wondering if Tony will let me take off from work for a week. I've only been working there six months."

"Tony will give you the time off. Business is dead for everyone during the holidays," David assured me.

"You're right. Tony probably won't even be around. He might go to Aspen to be with his family during the holidays. Let's talk to your sister and my cousin first before I even bring it up at work," I suggested.

"I already talked to my sister today. She says she and her husband would love to have us."

"Okay, I'll call my cousin tomorrow," I agreed.

"You need a haircut." David flopped my hair around with his hand.

"Oh, that's what looks different. You got yours cut today!"

"I was waiting for you to notice. He did a good job, didn't he?" David brushed his hand through his thick straight black hair.

"Yeah, it does look great!"

"I was nervous to learn that Presley left the salon. They gave me this new hairstylist, Leonardi, but he did an excellent job," David chimed.

"Presley left the salon?" I asked surprised.

"Yeah, I was surprised too. He went to a competitor, Pierre DeMar Salon, but this new guy Leonardi is really good. Actually, I think I like him better. When you make an appointment, ask for Leonardi, and let him know I sent you. I already told him you would be coming," David insisted.

"Cool. Yeah, I'll make an appointment for some time next week," I agreed.

The following Monday at work I was still thinking about the possibility of going to California for Christmas. I thought it was *amazing* that I would be taking two trips in pretty much the same year. One trip to L.A. and onto Montecito for a week, and then we had the trip to Europe coming up in late spring or early summer. David and I always had a great time on our trips together to the Caribbean, so I was really looking forward to our next adventure.

I was only in the office for about ten minutes when the phone rang. It was some guy from *The New York Post* asking for me.

"Yes, this is she," I said.

The man sounded very excited, and happy for me when he asked, "Do you have today's *New York Post*?"

"No," I said, thinking that he was trying to sell me a subscription to their newspaper.

"Run out and get it, because your picture is in the paper!" he urged.

"What? What do you mean?"

"Your name and picture are in the paper for Eileen Ford's Face of the 80's Contest," he explained with excitement.

"Are you serious?"

"Yes, I'm serious. I'm calling from *The New York Post* to let you know about it. You need to run out and get today's paper."

"But, how—"

"Did you submit your modeling photos for the Eileen Ford Modeling Contest?"

"No, but... Oh, my friend Alan, a photographer may have submitted them," I said.

"Well, your beautiful face is in the paper on page nineteen. So get yourself a copy," he urged again.

"Does this mean I'm in the running for the actual contest?"

"No, no. Sorry to say, that's up to the Ford Modeling Agency, but they will probably contact you if you are one of the finalists. We just thought your photo was a knockout and we wanted to print it. Best of luck to you. You better go now before this morning's paper sells out."

"Wow, yes, yes, I will. Thanks again."

I grabbed my purse. "Susan! I'll be right back. I just need to run to the store and pick something up. It'll take me five minutes. In case Tony shows up, let him know I'll be right back," I yelled into her office.

"Is there a problem? Is everything all right?" she asked concerned.

"Everything is great! I just need to pick something up pronto!"

On my way to the newsstand on Lexington Avenue, I remembered how I had stopped by the Eileen Ford Agency a few years ago and the talent scout had turned me down because I was in inch too short, or not the right look for their agency. I am 5'7" and too "European looking." Eileen Ford preferred the All-American girl look that her clients Cheryl Tiegs, Brooke Shields, and Christie Brinkley have.

I opened the newspaper to page nineteen, and there I was. They even printed my name below the photo. It was a great shot. I held the paper up to the newsstand proprietor. "Look, that's me!"

He stepped back and, in an Indian accent, said, "Yes, that's you! Nice, very nice! Oh, beautiful, beautiful. Now I know a celebrity, yes?" he agreed, shaking his head up and down.

I walked the half block back to the office, all the while looking down at my photo in the newspaper. When I got there, I found Tony sitting at his desk.

"Tony, look, I'm in today's paper," I said as I placed the newspaper on his desk in front of him, and pointed to my photo.

"Eileen Ford's Face of the 80's Contest?" he read with surprise.

"My friend Alan submitted my picture."

Tony smiled and looked surprised. "Wow, yeah, look at that! That's great."

Susan ran into Tony's office wanting to know what all the excitement was about. Tony turned the newspaper around on his desk, "Whitney is in today's newspaper."

Susan picked up the paper. "Where? Where? Oh, wow! Eileen Ford's Face of the 80's Contest. Do you think you'll win?" she asked with wide eyes.

Tony's partner, Jim, walked in and looked over Susan's shoulder to see the photo. "So, we have a celebrity in the office now?" he asked suspiciously.

"I doubt I'll actually win," I said, trying to pacify Jim, but he had already gone back to his desk in the next room.

"You might. You never know," said Susan. Then she laughed. "Hey Tony, you may end up managing your secretary's financial portfolio soon."

Tony smiled at Susan's comment, but he also had a concerned look under his smile, which made me uncomfortable. I closed the paper and headed back to my desk.

I was feeling really good about the whole event, and thinking that perhaps Tony might see me in a different light now. Whether he was attracted to me or not, at least maybe he would see I was someone who could end up being as successful as anyone else in his world, and not just his secretary who picked up his dry cleaning.

Right after lunch, we got very busy because it was nearing the end of the month, and we needed to get our clients' financial portfolios mailed out. I folded and tore the statistical spread sheets, collated, then stapled them under the fancy green cover adorned with the gold lettering of our company name and logo. Collate, fold, staple. Collate, fold, staple. Tony started to talk to me about one of his clients as I was collating, folding, and stapling.

It was really hard not to look at Tony; he was just so damn handsome. I tried to look and listen to him at the same time, while putting these folders together, and suddenly I slammed the stapler down on my finger. "AAAAAAAAAHHHH!"

He looked at me calmly but curiously. "What did you do?" he asked.

"AAAAAAHHHH! I stapled my finger! AAAHH. Oh my God! Tony, I stapled my finger! I have a staple in my finger! Tony, I have a staple stuck in my finger," I cried out.

"Come here," he said calmly.

I opened my hand, and he looked at the staple in my finger, and then he looked at me. "You have a staple in your finger," he chuckled softly.

"AAAAOOH! Don't push it that way. It hurts," I screamed.

He held my hand firmly. "Okay, I want you to close your eyes, and look away. I'm going to pull it out really quick," he warned.

"Oh no! Oh God!" I cringed and I shut my eyes.

"Relax. Just keep your eyes closed, and look away," he instructed as he yanked it out.

"AAOH!" Oh, Goddamn. Thank you," I sighed.

"There's some hydrogen peroxide in the bathroom. Go clean it off before it gets infected," he warned.

I wobbled past Tony's desk, shaking my head in disbelief before exiting to the bathroom. "I never did that before. I stapled my finger. I can't believe I did that. I'm such an idiot," I mumbled under my breath.

During the rest of the week, I noticed that Tony's behavior towards me had changed after seeing my photo in the newspaper. At first, I thought he was struggling with personal problems. Karen seemed to have disappeared and I never saw or heard from, or about her since the day she had brought in her resume. Maybe someone in Tony's family was ill. Tony never mentioned anything and I never asked. Either way, my excitement over having my modeling photo in the newspaper was dampened, because Tony did not seem to be really happy for me.

Over the following weeks, Tony wasn't so charming anymore. He now constantly asked me to run personal errands for him. I was always sent to the dry-cleaners to pick up his suits and shirts, to the drugstore, and to the shoe repairman. His bossy and condescending attitude towards me when he requested these things annoyed me more than actually doing them. I really had nothing else to do most of the day except run errands for him, but his indifference and coldness towards me made me feel separate and alone. I lost interest in him again. The infatuation and false hope were gone for good. He didn't even seem attractive anymore. I felt more confident and secure about myself. I no longer saw him as better than me, or more important than me, *or* more deserving than me. I wasn't even angry at him or disappointed. It did not matter to me anymore if he had any kind of attraction for me or not.

By the end of the week, David, Tom, and I went to a concert at Irving Plaza to see the singer David Burne and The Talking Heads. I could never master the Michael Jackson moon walk, but I could always make David and Tom laugh while imitating David Byrne's eccentric dance style, hitting myself in the forehead with the palm of my hand, and balancing on my heels as if I was falling backwards while singing his hit song, "Once In a Lifetime".

The Talking Heads opened up the show with one of their popular tunes, "Burning Down the House". The theme of the song made me feel uneasy--a foreboding sense of things to come. I couldn't shake off the premonition that my life was about to be caught up in flames, leaving me lost in a heap of ash.

CHAPTER SIX

COME UNDONE

I HAD BEEN putting off getting my haircut, so one day I decided to make an appointment with Leonardi and finally get it done as David had suggested so many times over the past few weeks. I was not worried about having a new hairstylist replace Presley. Since David was a fanatic about his hair, and he trusted Leonardi, so would I.

On a balmy September day, I finally found my way to Alexandra-Kassandra Hair Salon. While I waited in the chair wearing only a soft haircutting cloth over my bare torso, and the latest *Vogue* magazine in my lap, the delicate hairs on my arms stood up from a sudden chill. An assistant with canary-yellow spiked hair whizzed by me spinning like an animated cartoon character. "Leonardi will be with you soon. He is a little overbooked today. Would you like a cup of coffee, or a Mimosa?"

"Just a coffee with milk and sugar please, thank you," I replied. In a blink of an eye the assistant whizzed away, spinned back again with my coffee, and swirled away again.

As I looked down, still perusing the magazine, someone's finger touched my chin and gently pushed up my head. He looked me directly in the eyes and said in a slight English accent, "Hi, I'm Leonardi. Sorry to keep you waiting. I'm overbooked today. You can see how crazy it is in here," he apologized.

He appeared to be taken aback a bit by what he saw when he looked at me. I was not sure what to make of it. His hands began to play with the locks framing my face. He pursed his lips in the form of a kiss and his stare rested on my face, then in my eyes. I was expressionless as my eyes locked into his. He very quietly said to me as though his breath had been taken away, "You're so beautiful". I felt extremely vulnerable all of sudden for reasons I couldn't understand.

Although I had been pursuing modeling and acting, I had never felt or thought that I was as beautiful as he expressed.

Leonardi was not traditionally handsome, but I thought he was *magnificent* looking. He was about thirty years old, and he stood tall and lean—with a soft but strong handsome face, a Roman nose and full lips, all framed by a delicious cascade of loose black curls. Leonardi had a keen rock-n-roll energy about him. If he wasn't a hair stylist, he'd most likely be a guitarist in a popular rock band. He donned an elegant white poet's shirt with a ruffled sleeve. Above his ankle-high leather boots, his taut black jeans accentuated his sexy behind. His clothes were expensive and well-pressed, and Leonardi himself was well manicured and impeccably groomed. His skin was a rich shade of golden bronze that gave him a healthy sun-kissed glow. I thought he was *beautiful*.

Leonardi now stood behind me, his strong hands resting on my shoulders. His touch induced a pleasing quiver down my spine. He adoringly studied me in the mirror ahead. He dug both his hands deep into my scalp and pulled my hair high up, creating tension at the roots. My forehead tingled. My breath deepened. He gently pushed my head down and perceptibly moved his hands through the tender nap of my neck before swooping my mane forward. A relaxing sensation shot from the top of my head to my toes. He lightly pressed his thumb into the side of my temple while pulling the mass of locks sideways. My eyelids now felt heavy. He then moved in front of me observing my face. His fingers directed my chin upward, and he slid the brush from my forehead and down the back of my neck. His breath so close I could smell cinnamon. "What would you like me to do with your hair?" he asked softly, almost pensively--his fingers fluttering through my tresses.

"Just the usual straight, long cut with short bangs that Presley used to give me," I said quietly and self-consciously.

"Yes, a very straight angle on the bottom, no layers, and very straight short bangs. Cut sweet and sexy, but cold as ice. Decadent. Yes, I like that very much," he agreed.

"Wow, what a description for a haircut", I thought. "Yes!" I agreed with him.

Leonardi kept tossing my hair this way and that way to see how it would fall over my head and my face. When his fingers lingered behind my responsive ear lobes, a mild shiver prickled through my spine. His hands dug deeply into the mass of hair and then out again. The rhythmic beat of "Killing Moon" by Echo and the Bunnymen sunk me into a deeper trance. Leonardi moved my bangs around, and his hands ran through the locks on each side of my face again. He kept pursing his lips and resting his eyes on mine making it obvious to me that he was admiring me. I felt uneasy and awkward. Leonardi appeared uncomfortable and awkward with me, but mostly inquisitive.

I wasn't sure what to make of this, because I always assumed that all hairdressers were gay, especially the successful ones like Leonardi who worked on celebrities and top models in the high fashion magazines. So it took me a moment to realize that Leonardi may, in fact, be attracted to me. I was wondering if it were possible--could he be a heterosexual male hairstylist or perhaps bi-sexual. I could not imagine him to be straight, but then he did not seem gay either. And why was I feeling like I was becoming undone?

Leonardi floated around the chair and glanced at me often. He did not talk while cutting my hair, but I could hear him speaking all the time by the curious way he looked at me. He firmly tilted my chin up again as he moved a comb through, from the top of my forehead, down the back of my head--the stiff teeth of the comb stimulating my scalp. My head followed as my neck stretched back, my eyes reluctantly closed. As he combed through the right side of my hair, my head fell to the left. I felt both his hands cup my face to move it straight and forward. My eyelids flew open, and our eyes locked--Leonardi's stare stayed fixed on me. Leonardi had tenderness in his eyes and a sincere appreciation, and even awe at the object of his affections which appeared to be me. I felt the same intense attraction to Leonardi that I sensed he felt for me, but my rational mind kept saying that it was only in my imagination. His face loomed close to mine again, he puckered his lips as if to kiss me, but only the light scent of musk landed.

My body fell limp as his strong and steady hands pulled my hair up and back again, the music amplifying the hypnotic trance of his touch. The gentleness of his temperate palm covered my listless eyes while he sprayed a soft mist of rose-scented water on my bangs. His sweet breath on top of me again as he leaned close.

Leonardi was confident in what he was doing with my hair, but I could sense his silent hesitation about what he wanted to say to me, how to say it, or if he should say anything at all. Perhaps it was because he already knew I had a boyfriend. After all, David was his new client, and David had already told Leonardi that I would be coming to him sooner or later to get my haircut.

Finally, Leonardi asked me, "Are you a model?"

"Yes, I'm an actor, and sometimes I do some print work as well," I said awkwardly.

"That's great. You are very beautiful you know," he said again.

I was quiet for a moment and became even shyer after hearing this from him once more. "Thank you."

His whole body moved smoothly around the chair. His hands flowed and danced through the air with a scissor and comb. His movements were elegant without being feminine. Leonardi continued working on my hair as if he was in a creative frenzy painting the Mona Lisa. Whenever he stopped to look at me to check his work, he puckered his lips again like he was going to kiss me, but he didn't. There was only an awkward silence between us.

Just as the awkward silence and the intense electricity between us became unbearable, Leonardi excused himself to check on another client. The song by Duran Duran "Save a Prayer" began to play. Tears welled up in my eyes because I was thinking that perhaps I had gone insane. Just a few months ago I was attracted to my boss, who appeared to just play with my emotions, and now I was attracted to a gay man. What in God's name was going on with me? Why was my attraction to Leonardi so much more intense than my brief infatuation with Tony? A few tears trickled down my face.

Leonardi was silent and apprehensive with me, but as I observed him interacting with the other stylist, assistants, and clients, he smiled broadly and laughed deeply and loudly. He was down-to-earth and funny. His laugh was genuine. Watching him from a far, I could admire his confidence. His innocent sense of play was not only refreshing to behold but also comforting and healing. I was *enchanted* by him. His euphonious laughter made it easy to blink back and dry my oncoming tears. I smiled and chuckled quietly as he returned to my chair.

Now that the assistant was ready to take over and blow-dry my hair, Leonardi insisted on doing it himself. The way he continued to touch me and look at me made me want to touch him too. The appreciation of each other's presence appeared to be requited. But was it? I couldn't be sure. Were my mind and emotions just playing tricks on me again? I was confused. I felt so repressed and held back that I wanted to break down and weep again.

My session with Leonardi was almost over and I dreaded the thought as his wizardly fingers styled the last few fluffs of my hair. He then removed the cloth and tenderly cleaned the back of my neck, reminding me to drop by the salon whenever I needed to get my bangs trimmed. He continued to move his hands deeply into my hair, using the brush to fluff and style as if he were stalling for time.

Finally, he leaned his hands firmly on my knees and looked directly into my eyes. "Some of my friends and I are planning to do a fashion music video. I thought maybe you would like to be in it."

"A fashion music video? What kind?" I asked.

He leaned back against the counter, and reached out his hand to play with my bangs. "It's going to be a very cool video. We're just at the beginning of the planning stage, but so far we have this idea to dress up beautiful models in wedding gowns, and have them dance through the rooms of a burnt out abandoned building."

"Wow, that sounds very cool."

"Would you be interested?"

"Yeah, I would! Of course I would. When is it?"

"We don't know yet. Like I said we're still in the planning stages. But if you keep in touch and call me, I'll hopefully have more information in the next coming weeks. Would you do that?" he asked. Before handing me his business card, he scribbled another phone number on it. "You can call me at home, if you like," he added with a strong intention in his eyes.

"Okay, great. Thank you Leonardi," I said as I took the card.

A week later, I rang Leonardi at the salon, rather than at his home. I figured he would be at work during the afternoon hours, but the receptionist told me he was in London on assignment. I called again the following week, but learned he was still out of town. Another week skipped by and I called again. He was at the salon, but they told me he was too busy to come to the phone, and asked if I wanted to leave a message. I left a message for him to get in touch with me.

In the late afternoon Leonardi rang me back from his apartment to apologize for not being available, and asked me to join him and his friends at a nightclub that night for drinks. "I would love having you," he urged.

I asked him about the video, but he said that because he was out of town working on some magazine covers, things got delayed, and it might take a few more months to put it together. "Come with us to the club tonight, it'll be fun," he enthusiastically pleaded.

"Leonardi, I really can't do that tonight. David and I have already made plans. We're going to the Tears for Fears concert at Madison Square Garden."

"Do you guys live together," he asked with a pensive tone in his voice.

"Yeah, we do," I replied with a sigh and disappointment in my voice that surprised me.

"Maybe another time then?" he proposed. There was a silence between us now.

"Leonardi..."

"Yeah, what is it?" he asked softly.

I loved his voice. He has this slight English accent which was so sweet and melodic. There was a certain pitch in his voice that touched a pulsing nerve in my body that I did not know I had before. "Uuum..." My words stumbled and froze. I really didn't know what to say.

"What is it? Is there something you want to tell me?" he inquired quietly.

"Uumm. Yeah, but... I don't know, Leonardi. I don't know what to say," I said nervously.

"Don't worry; we'll see each other again," he consoled.

My whole body trembled, and I got butterflies in my stomach. I didn't have to say anything to him. He knew what I was feeling, because perhaps he was feeling the same way. Then I was silent with fear and guilt.

"Goodnight beautiful girl," he whispered softly.

"Goodnight Leonardi." I gently hung up the phone.

David came home a few minutes later. He was in a good mood, and eager to try out the new restaurant that opened up in Soho for dinner before heading to Madison Square Garden to see Tears for Fears. David saw me sitting on the bed looking down in deep thought.

"What's wrong?" he asked.

"Nothing. I just zoned out for a minute. I had a long day, and I'm hungry."

"Well, let's go," he said.

I did not call Leonardi again after that. I did not hear from him either. Maybe he was afraid of getting David on the phone, or maybe he tried calling only to hear David's voice on the answering machine. Maybe he just knew better than to pursue a girl who was already living with another man. If I wanted to talk to Leonardi again, I would have to call him. That was way too much responsibility for me to handle. But I kept wondering about my feelings for Leonardi. The thoughts were driving me crazy.

Finally, two weeks later, I stopped by the salon with the excuse of picking up some hair gel that Leonardi had recommended during my last visit. As I asked the receptionist about the hair gel, Leonardi spotted me as he whizzed by. He skidded a bit on the shiny floor, and stopped short in front of me. "Hi!" he exclaimed.

"Hi!" I replied, noticing how extremely hip and suave he looked in his crisp shirt, tapestry vest, silk trousers, and soft velvet loafers.

"I was thinking about you. How have you been?" he asked.

"Great. I just came by to pick up that hair gel you recommended."

Leonardi stood directly in front of me, playing with my hair.

"Your hair looks great. You look great! Go sit in the chair, I'll get the gel. I want to show you how to apply it properly." He escorted me to a chair.

With a spray bottle he dampened my hair, and combed the water through, all the time pursing his lips. He uncapped the tube of gel. "Just put this much in the palm of your hand, only a little, the size of a dime, and move it through your hair like this. You'll see how much volume and bounce it gives once you blow dry it through." Leonardi's exquisite hands moved through my tresses, rubbing the gel through like he was working on a clay sculpture.

Standing in front of me again, Leonardi placed his knees slightly bent between my legs, while his fingers flew down through the locks framing my face. He pursed his lips again as he always did, as if he was going to kiss me, and then -- he actually did! On the lips! -- A soft, but strong and tender kiss that felt like marshmallow and tasted like bubble gum. I suddenly felt like a brilliant blooming sunflower against an azure sky, the air filled with the scent of gardenias and rain.

Leonardi gave me the bottle of gel, told me it was on the house, and refused my tip. "Call me sometime if you just want to say hello. You can call me at home you know?" His chin dropped down and his eyes went up a little to see my reaction to his request.

I was surprised. He wanted me to make the first move. I realized that he would never call me while I was living with David, and I did not want to initiate anything by calling him. The only reason I could call him with any clear conscious was if he was going to cast me in the music video. The video would give me a legitimate reason to call him and see him again. Other than that, I would feel too guilty to do so. "I don't know if I can do that. You know..."

He nodded in understanding and agreement. "Call me anyway; we have the music video to work on," he prodded.

"Oh yeah! When will we be doing that?" I asked. Leonardi moved towards me and held my hands firmly in his.

"I've been out of town a lot, and not able to coordinate it yet." He intently looked into my eyes, and gently moved a strand of hair from my face. I felt light headed, and had to catch my breath.

Leonardi broke the silence, "We still want to do the video, but it may take some time. Please call me and keep in touch. Will you do that?" he pleaded. My voice was caught in my throat.

He fluffed my bangs. "Come back for a trim in a few weeks, okay?" At that moment, I still couldn't speak so I found myself taking his hand and squeezing it firmly too, and I found it hard to let go.

"Okay, thanks Leonardi. Bye," I said nervously and headed towards the glass doors.

I looked back for a brief moment to see Leonardi leaning against the counter, his arms clasped around his chest, and his head down in deep thought. He saw me look at him and immediately straightened up, waved goodbye, and whizzed out of view into the energetic and frenzied traffic of the high-profile hair salon.

From that day on my mind was preoccupied. If I broke up with David tomorrow, and got my own place, it could be a big mistake, because my feelings for Leonardi could be nothing but a passing fancy, just as my crush on Tony Scott had been. I had never spent enough time with Leonardi to figure out what was really going on inside me, and if Leonardi did desire me, maybe his attraction was fleeting.

David and I were going to California for the first time in a few weeks and then to Europe next summer. I had never been to Europe and it was the trip of a lifetime. David and I got along so well, and I never questioned David's devotion to me. David adored me, and only me. David was my best friend.

Leonardi, on the other hand, had beautiful women around him all the time. The most beautiful models in the world were always accessible to him. What if Leonardi and I became lovers but within a few months, on a fashion shoot, he met some ravishing creature and he found me easily replaceable? I didn't really know Leonardi. His lifestyle was fast and glamorous, full of temptations, seductions, and attractions. He lived in a world of exotic food, world travel, and jet set people. I felt very intimidated by Leonardi's world. He seemed to be inviting me into it, but I wanted to feel safe and truly loved in that world too.

I tried to wrap my head around the reality of the situation. Leaving David would be irrational and not something I could allow myself to even consider. I put Leonardi out of my mind. I did not call him again. Because he never called me, not even in regard to the music fashion video, the matter was put to rest.

CHAPTER SEVEN

DEEP DENIAL

WHEN THE WEEK of Thanksgiving rolled around, I had to get my bangs trimmed. I looked like a sheep dog, and I could not see well anymore with the hair in front of my eyes. I arrived at the salon on a miserable icy-cold, wet and windy Saturday. I struggled to get in the doorway with my soggy umbrella, over-sized shoulder bag, a pair of gloves in my mouth, all the while fighting to untangle the wire earphones from the walkman wrapped around my scarf. Since I was holding up traffic at the entrance, an assistant hurried over to help me get settled.

Once she got me untangled, she took my coat, escorted me to the chair, and fetched me a hot cup of cocoa and a magazine. Out of the corner of my eye, at the other end of the salon, I saw Leonardi working on a client. I flipped the magazine on my lap with frenzied anxiety. I was not reading the articles or even looking at the ads. I wacked the pages over one by one, slammed the magazine down, picked up another magazine, and then another and then another, and skimmed through them all in the same way.

When Leonardi finally pranced over to my chair, I was distant and aloof.

"Hi! Long time no see. Where have you been hiding?" he asked all bubbly and cheery.

"I've been busy. I just came in for a trim," I replied flatly.

"I wish you had given me a call or dropped me a line," he replied.

"Why? Did you do your fashion video?"

"No. I've been way too busy. Traveling a lot. It's been so crazy. Most of my assignments this last quarter have been out of town. I've got so much jet lag. I like to be busy, but this is ridiculous," he went on.

I was quiet and did not respond.

Leonardi sensed that I was upset about something. "I was thinking of you, but I just did not have any free time, and now with the holiday season, we have been booked solid. I haven't had time to come up for air, let alone call anyone and make any plans," he explained.

I was silent.

Then he kneeled down in front of me and took my hands in his. He brushed the hair from my eyes. "I'm sorry. I really, really wanted to call you." He said it in such a genuine and sincere way that my face softened.

An associate called Leonardi over to another chair to check on a customer's highlights. "Excuse me, love, I'll be right back." He kissed me thoughtfully on the cheek, and disappeared.

I felt dizzy. By the time he returned, I had put up a wall to protect myself from the confused and overwhelming feelings for Leonardi that were flooding back.

"So what are your plans for the holidays?" he asked.

"David and I are going to California to visit his sister and her husband in Montecito and then onto L.A. to stay with my cousin in Beverly Hills," I responded. I think I was trying to impress Leonardi with the fact that I had a life too and did not need him or want him, and wasn't waiting around for his call. "And shortly after that we'll be going to Europe for a couple of weeks," I added.

"Wow, that's great. Where in Europe are you going?"

"France and Italy. We want to start our trip in Paris and then work our way around the surrounding cities like Beaune and Dijon, then after take a train through the Swiss Alps and into Italy," I replied.

"Where in Italy?" he asked with interest.

"We want to see Rome, Venice, Florence, and we plan to stay in a few little towns just outside of Florence before seeing Tuscany. We may stop in Verona and Lake Cuomo."

"That's fantastic." Have you ever been before?" He continued to move the brush through my hair and smooth it with his hand.

"No, I haven't. This is my first time!"

"You are going to absolutely love it!" he said, sounding genuinely excited for me.

"Yeah, I know. I'm very excited," I agreed.

"Enjoy your trip to California, and Europe."

"I will. We're actually not going to Europe till the late spring or early summer. But we're having a great time planning it in the meantime."

"I'm sure you are!" Leonardi agreed. He pulled off the cover around my neck and I handed him a tip. This time he accepted it. I walked out with my head held high like I was never going to look back.

When I found myself back on the street, I did not feel good at all. I felt like a phony. I was not lying or exaggerating to Leonardi about my plans to go to California, and I was not lying about my impressive European itinerary. Everything I told him was true. It was my aloof and indifferent attitude towards him that made me feel phony and very melancholy. I did not want him to think I had feelings for him anymore, because *I* did not want to believe I had feelings for him anymore.

Tony happily agreed to let me take Christmas week off to visit family in California. He would be in Aspen, Colorado skiing with his family and so would most of his clients. There was no reason for the office to be open. If they needed a warm body, Susan was more than happy to be there and pass the time by bringing in her portable TV to watch her favorite soap operas.

I was sure that my attraction to Tony was long gone and now I also felt that my infatuation for Leonardi had died. I went through the motions of my routine: going to work every day, attending acting and dance class on the weekends, and theater rehearsals on weeknights. On my nights off, I hung out with David and Tom in the Eudora coffee shop. I shut my emotions down to deal with the mediocrity of my day-to-day existence. Yes, I was working for a man that was better looking than Robert Redford, and yes, I had done some modeling, and gotten some extra work in films. And yes, David and I studied acting together, and ate out every night, went to clubs, and saw the latest rock bands. Yes, I had experienced fun trips to the Caribbean with him. Yes, I was excited about going to California with him and then to Europe. My life was very different and much better than it was when I was a teenager in Queens. In fact, most people would say it was very exciting and sort of glamorous compared to the average person. But I felt a longing and emptiness inside me. A philosopher once said, "One should see the glass half full, rather than half empty". What they don't consider is that the glass may appear half full on the outside, but can feel half empty on the inside.

I was not making my living as an actor. I was still a secretary with boring and unchallenging tasks, and enduring long, uneventful days. Also, I was still very much financially dependent on David. Tony was so aloof now that my position at MWR did not feel secure.

Both Tony and Leonardi were making a lot of money doing what they loved and enjoying the good life. I wasn't jealous, I just felt left out. I wanted to be as alive and excited about my life as Leonardi and Tony were about theirs. However, I didn't want their life, I wanted my own life. I wanted to make a living with my talents as an actor, and to be financially independent doing what I loved to do.

I felt ashamed that I did not know how to do what Tony and Leonardi knew how to do naturally and instinctively with no blockades or opposition. David and I spent so much time and money running around to production companies, writing letters to film directors, and auditioning at workshops, but I still only landed the occasional extra work on movies, or small catalogue print jobs.

Upon reflection, I judged my attraction to Tony as stupid and in very poor judgment. I felt extremely guilty for feeling the way I did about Leonardi. I decided that I needed to get a grip, but the only way I could do that was to shut myself down, and not feel anything at all.

I went to work every day feeling bored and numb. Everything irritated me. When Tony and Jim were both out of the office for a few days in a row, Susan brought in her portable TV set with the enthusiasm of a naughty rebellious teenager. Susan's prissy prude, conservative view-point combined with her attraction to sleazy day-time drama made her obnoxiously hypocritical. I wanted to yell at her, "Get a life!" Dye your hair blonde again! Go out and dance! Get drunk! For the love of God...get laid! Just get a life will yah!" Instead, I smiled and said nothing. Inside my head I was screaming though, screaming at her, and realizing I was really screaming at myself.

I needed to get a life! *I* needed to go out and dance. *I* needed to get drunk, and *I* needed to make love. Not just with anyone, though. I needed to dance, and get drunk, and make love to the person I felt passionately about, and I couldn't do so.

It was the second week of December, and I looked out onto the patio, which was now covered in snow and sheets of ice. I felt as frozen and numb inside myself as what I saw outside my office windows. The icicles that hung from the planters and the trees were like frozen tears that would not move, or melt, or flow. They hung there, stuck in suspended animation like my life, my feelings, and my world.

David did not notice my dissatisfaction and I did not notice his. I had failed to recognize the signs of his discontent, which had been brewing for quite a while. David's way of dealing with his unhappiness was to keep himself distracted and occupied. We went to numerous clubs, and saw a lot of bands simply because it was something to do, whether we liked the band or not. We stayed up late and watched lots of boring TV. On the nights we didn't have enough energy or enough money, we sat in the coffee shop with Tom, often until three in the morning. The conversations were argumentative, negative, and dispiriting.

At the coffee shop, I got restless and found myself getting extremely agitated. The negative talk was often about how marriage is a miserable, phony institution and having kids is the end of one's life. It was a point of view I had heard a hundred times over. The constant yapping rolled on and on about scandals and the misfortunes of celebrities we didn't even know, and how corrupt the government was, and how we were all probably dying or going to die from this or that, and the government was doing it on purpose...blah, blah, blah. The only thing David and Tom were upbeat and positive about was our upcoming trip to Europe.

Finally, I just yelled out, "Enough already!"

Tom and David froze and looked at each other.

"What the hell's the matter with you?" David asked.

I flipped my paper napkin around a bit on the table, and looked down. "Nothing. Can we go back to talking about something more positive, like our trip to Europe or something?"

"Sure. Are you tired? Do you want to go home?" David asked as he looked at his watch. He then looked at Tom and said, "It's almost two o'clock in the morning. Do you realize we've been sitting here talking for over four hours?"

"Yeah, well what else is new? We always do this," Tom chuckled.

"Exactly my point," I snapped back.

"She's tired. Let's get going," David said.

We all got up and left. I walked on ahead of them feeling more miserable than tired, or was I tired because I was miserable?

....

At the office, the only project I could find to keep my mind occupied was thinking about what I would get Tony for the office Christmas party. It had to be something he would like, that wasn't personal, but had a personal touch. I walked around the city on my lunch hour and came across a book about golf. Tony played a lot of golf with his clients. I knew nothing about the game, but the book was written so tongue-in-cheek even I laughed at most of the golf jokes.

I did not know what to write on the inside cover of the book. I felt sentimental, but I thought humor would be the best way to communicate something to Tony. I wanted to write something funny, but I did not know enough about golf to come up with a pun related to the book. So I called Tom. Tom suggested I inscribe it with: *For those idle moments in the sand traps, Season's Greetings,* or *Happy Holidays.* That sounded good. Tom could be tastefully funny when he wanted or needed to be. After all he was a writer; a cynical bastard at times, but still a talented writer.

Our office Christmas party was small and intimate. Susan, Jim, and I decorated the seven-foot tree by the fireplace in Jim and Susan's office. Everyone brought in a plate of food of some sort from home, or picked up pastries from Dean and Deluca along with a bottle of wine. The computer people from *The Computer Room* filtered in and out occasionally to grab some holiday snacks and refreshments. They actually wore the red Christmas elf hats I had bought for them, yet they thought of themselves as "too cool" to participate in the tree decorating festivities. Tony's excuse was to stay at his desk and be on the phone with clients and friends.

Near the end of the day, Jim called everyone into his office to share a toast, and watch Susan open the present he had bought her. It was wrapped neatly in a huge, long, heavy box, and everyone was curious as to what it could possibly be. Susan unwrapped the gift very slowly and neatly, as if she wanted to keep the paper intact to use over again.

"Good grief, that's one big present Susan, quick open it up," I urged. Susan kept tearing the paper slowly, and folding the sections cautiously. I jumped in tearing the paper off aggressively. "This is how you do it Susan."

"Oh, my God!" she yelled out. "It's a Casio keyboard!"

Jim stepped in, opened the box, pulled out the Casio keyboard, placed it on the table, and plugged it into the wall.

Susan postured at the keyboard and played a slow Baroque tune, singing in a high, operatic voice. The song was sober and reverent. She was in key, but her voice was flat, with no richness or real expression. She sounded like a prudish church lady. Everyone stood around with their glass of wine in their hands trying not to laugh. Jim looked on, smiling like a proud father.

The computer people had strained smiles on their faces and their eyes widened trying to hold back the laughter. Tony and I looked at each other and smirked. We were all in a lot of pain listening to Susan and praying to God for the song to end soon, but it paraded on forever.

When the song finally ended, everyone clapped with great enthusiasm and left the room immediately to seek shelter far enough away from Susan to let loose their laughter.

Tony opened my gift. He seemed to be sincerely impressed and appreciative of the golf book, but he apologized for not getting me anything, saying he had been too busy to shop. Not even an impersonal bonus check--I was a bit bummed. *Whatever*, I had the week off and I could look forward to my first trip to LA. I guess that was my gift, I reasoned to myself.

CHAPTER EIGHT

CALIFORNIA DREAMING

I CLIPPED ON my wings and off we went to the airport. I always wore wings pinned to the lapel of my jacket whenever I flew. I have a tremendous respect and appreciation for aviation and pilots. I think the airplane is the greatest invention ever known to mankind other than, of course, the telephone. I always look forward to shaking hands with the pilot and co-pilot. For me, pilots always looked in real life like they do in the commercials—tall, tan, with thick salt and pepper hair, blue-eyes, and a friendly white smile. They have a special aura about them, a certain charisma and joy in their spirit that one can feel in their presence. I think it's because they get to experience the freedom of being in the unobstructed and spacious sky all the time.

Some people might think this is crazy, but I love plane food. I enjoy the blue trays with their tiny compartments, the baby-sized portions of meat and potatoes, or perhaps chicken and cranberry sauce, and the little cup of dessert. I adore the petite sugar packets with the printed airline logo and the white coffee stirrers with wing tips on their tops. There was something fun and even exciting, about anticipating and then finally getting my meal on an airplane. I know the food sucks, but the presentation just makes me happy.

I was just as excited about the trip on the way to the airport and waiting on the plane as I was about getting to my destination. My only disappointment stemmed from the fact that people don't dress up to go to the airport anymore and make it an event like they did in old movies. These days, the terminals are a bit old and dirty. They look as bad as bus terminals. When the industry began to call airplanes "airbuses", it took the magic out of flying and made the perception of air travel mundane, uneventful, and finally stressful. But I still had my imagination, so I pretended that it was the 1940s and air flight was still glamorous and exhilarating.

The flight was smooth and we landed two minutes early. The weather in L.A. was warm and sunny. David and I were in good spirits as we hopped on the nearby bus for the three hour ride north. Although David and I had a pleasant experience visiting his sister and brother-in-law in Montecito, overall it was low key and uneventful. Montecito was picturesque with its Spanish Colonial Revival Style architecture, vineyards, green hills, and horse ranches, but it was a quiet sleepy bedroom community with not much going on.

Only a few days into our trip, I felt an unbearable loneliness that I hadn't felt since I was a teenager. Perhaps it was the lighting that made me feel melancholy. It was a late Sunday afternoon kind of light, casting deep shadows across the lawn and grassy hills. The kind of lighting that often reminded me that the weekend was almost over and a new school week would begin. It was the kind of light that echoed a throbbing numb pain in my heart for no particular reason.

That evening, David and I went out to dinner together at a seafood restaurant near the beach and ordered lobster tails. As we waited for the meal, David's voice became increasingly irritating. Throughout our relationship, David did all the talking, and whenever I tried to get a word in edge wise, he just talked over me, interrupting me and my train of thought. I realized it had always been that way. He talked and I listened, nodding in agreement, with the hopes that he would shut up and let me say something. He never did. Instead, he kept yapping on and on. I felt quiet and withdrawn. I wasn't eating my food. He got angry with me.

"That lobster cost twenty-five dollars, aren't you going to eat it?" he snapped. I've never seen him angry with me, especially about not eating my food.

"I'm just not hungry," I said quietly.

"What do you mean you're not hungry?" he asked confused.

"I don't know. I thought I was, but now I just don't have the appetite I thought I did." He banged his fist on the table with frustration.

"Hey!" I yelled out, "I'm not hungry, okay?"

"Well, you should have thought of that before you ordered the lobster," he snapped back.

"You're the one that kept recommending I order the lobster."

"Because that's what I thought you wanted," he claimed.

"Sometimes you don't want what you think you want. Sometimes you change your mind about what you want. Sometimes you just don't have the stomach for what you thought you wanted. Isn't it my prerogative to change my mind?" I explained.

"That's an expensive prerogative," he replied in a more light hearted way.

"We can bring it home in a doggy bag, okay. I'll have it for breakfast if it makes you feel any better."

"That's not the point. We were supposed to eat it here, together. I thought you *loved* lobster," he sighed.

"I do! But for some reason, out of nowhere, lobster just doesn't do it for me. Did that ever happen to you? Didn't you ever love something so much that you ate it all the time and you looked forward to the smell, the taste, and the texture, and all of sudden, bam! It just didn't do it for you anymore?"

"Yeah, I had that experience with Milk Duds," he agreed.

"Milk Duds?

"Yeah, I would eat them all the time. One day, I couldn't even look at them. Just the thought of them made me nauseous." We both laughed.

While chomping enthusiastically on his lobster, David rambled on and on again about everything under the sun and I just sat through it yawning excessively. David was obsessed with talking about the personal lives and scandalous stories of celebrities constantly being reported by the media. I did not care about the lives of celebrities. They did not know me, so why should I care about them? I found these conversations boring, irritable, and a complete waste of my time. It dawned on me for the first time that my inability to participate in the conversation on any subject and share my viewpoints was always a struggle and a losing battle. Maybe that's why I felt so lonely.

I pushed the pink and white fish around my plate hiding it under a heap of spinach. Although I appreciated David's aim to please, he was always in search of the perfect experience, and if it failed to be perfect, he turned into a very crabby person who was difficult to be around. Unless I was always, each moment, enthusiastically embracing every event and hanging on his every word, he considered himself and his life a failure.

David would never eat dinner at home and he was very particular about his dining experience. More often than not, that required hours of walking around Manhattan before finally deciding on which new establishment to try. I would always be tired from the long hike, and get cranky from an empty stomach and a migraine headache. Once he found a place, he had to sit at the best table in the house. If the table location, the food, and the service did not turn out to be the ultimate dining experience, he would be very disappointed and upset. He would get upset with himself for making a bad decision and upset with the restaurant for being a bad choice. There was no such thing as having the ultimate film, concert, or dining experience on a continual basis but for some strange reason, David believed that there was. As a result, he was constantly being disappointed and upset by this inconsistency in life that he had absolutely no control over, and everyone around him had to endure the irritability of his disillusionment.

Although the five years had been great with David, and I felt appreciated and safe compared to my teenage years, I kept thinking, "What if?" It was not Leonardi I was thinking about so much anymore--it was the, "What if".

While David slept soundly that night in his sister's guestroom, I lay awake listening to the crickets and staring through the glass doors at the moonlight reflected on the fish pond in the courtyard. I thought if I decide to move out, I would need to save enough money to do so, but David made that very difficult.

Although David was funny and good natured, I could sense his underlying unhappiness. He bitched and moaned about not having enough money on a daily basis. As soon as he made some though, he would spend it right away. He would often make $500 to $3,000 in just a few days on some freelance design project as an Art Director. But instead of putting some of this money away, he would spend it all before landing his next assignment. After he spent everything, his fear and anxiety from not knowing where he would acquire his next job and/or his next paycheck came back. Because we lived in a rent controlled apartment, he could have put some of his earnings in the bank to relieve the stress and anxiety between jobs, but he refused.

Tom and I pointed out to David that he could save $100 per month just on cutting out the daily trip to the *Häagen Dazs* ice cream parlor to buy his favorite triple scoop coffee-mocha chip, sugar waffle cone. We also suggested that he take the subway rather than spending $200 per month on taxicabs.

I told David that we didn't have to eat out every night, and although neither one of us knew how to cook, we could whip up something decent a few nights a week at home. David hated to eat at home. The idea made him not just angry, but furious.

Rather than seeing every film that came out, I recommended that we be more selective, but David loved his movies, even if many of them turned out to be bad. David also loved to shop for knick knacks and toys. One day, I came home and found seven stuffed *Cat in the Hat* toys sitting on the sofa, smiling at me like village idiots. His toys weren't expensive but it all added up over time and cluttered the house. Whenever David had more than enough money, he would blow it right away on something totally useless: a brand new $4,000 leather couch, custom shelves for his entertainment center, or top of the line stereo speakers. He bought the most expensive camera equipment to capture those "special moments" at home and during our travels.

David refused to keep track of his money, and he refused to change his lifestyle and spending habits, but he continued to sing the same sad song of not having enough. He was so stressed out about it that his back often gave out, and then he would end up spending another few hundred dollars a month seeing a chiropractor.

When I was working a steady job, after taxes, I took home only $287 a week. Almost a third went to subway fare, breakfast, lunch, and dry cleaning bills for my business suits. I gave myself $50 per week for pocket money and then left $140 in the bank, inevitably investing most of that money on classes, pictures and resumes, a visit to the dentist, or an occasional pair of shoes. Since most of my day jobs never lasted for more than six months, whatever little money I did manage to save was for those rainy days of being unemployed.

David's endless grumbling about money always made me feel frustrated and guilty. It felt like he was blaming me for not making as much as him. Although he did not want me to share in the rent expenses, I felt like he wanted me to pick up the slack of his reckless spending. If I had been able to make $3,000 in a few days like him, he would have found a way to have us both blow it. The few times I did manage to save more than $1,000 he saw it as an opportunity for us to take a trip. He could easily come up with his airfare and hotel expense by working only one or two days. It took me months to save that amount, and months of working at jobs I hated, but I felt guilty for not being willing to pay for my half of the trip, because he paid the bills and the rent. Since we both loved to travel, and traveling made him optimistic and happy, it was easy to share the enthusiasm. For both of us, traveling was an escape from all the stress and uncertainty.

I sat up in bed to take a drink of water from the glass on the nightstand. I took a few gulps and held the glass up observing the reflections of blue light. Is it half empty or half full? I realized that if either of us were to ever establish acting careers and become wealthy, David would have us buy a huge Manhattan penthouse apartment, the one with the biggest mortgage, still beyond our means, simply because he loved the view.

I felt restless and wide awake. The moon was hanging bright and low in the black purple sky. I got out of bed, quietly slid through the glass door and stepped out into the courtyard. A shooting star flickered down and disappeared behind the lemon trees. I sat on the floor, starring into the pond at the chubby goldfish meandering in the glistening water.

I loved David and I cared about him, but I questioned whether I was *in* love with him. David and I were very close friends but not lovers, so where was this relationship really going anyway? At the beginning of our courtship, we had tried having sex a few times but it was too painful for me. David was like a jack hammer invading a slab of cement. There was no kissing, romantic gestures, nor gentle exploration. He wasn't a rough person, and he wasn't trying to intentionally hurt me, he was just awkward, unaware, and hopelessly incompetent. He complained of my inability to relax. It wasn't in me to hurt his feelings and tell him that he just didn't know how to play the piano. Nor could I give him lessons. I was too young and indifferent about sex to teach someone. It never stopped us from being best friends. An orgasm may last for a moment, but a friendship can last a lifetime, and I believe that's how we both processed this glitch in our relationship, by shoveling it under a heap of spinach.

A strong breeze caressed my face and blew through my hair. A light rain began to fall. I continued to sit at the edge of the pond watching the drops of rain merge into the pool of water. Even if all had been well with our finances and sex life, there was still the fact that David never wanted to get married to anyone, ever. David often expressed to Tom and I that marriage was just a piece of paper, and once people get married it always ruins the relationship. He claimed that all his friends who got married ended up divorced, or they stayed unhappily committed to each other for the sake of the kids.

Marrying someone had never been on my mind all these years. I began to consider that maybe as I got older I might change my mind, but I was in a relationship with someone who was totally opposed to the idea. If I was to ever meet someone I could eventually marry, how would I meet them by living with David?

The rain was heavy now and I basked in the experience of being washed clean of all my misconceptions.

David and I celebrated New Year's Eve with his sister and brother-in-law at a quiet, local restaurant by the pier. At twelve o'clock, we blew our horns into the starry sky, but we heard only a few voices in the far distance shout "Happy New Year! – Happy 1985!" Even being home watching Dick Clark in Times Square on TV had more energy and enthusiasm than this.

"It's California. It's, uumm, laid back?" his brother-in-law sighed.

On our way home, as we strolled past the silhouette of a wooden house with a white picket fence, with the sky so clear and moon so low, I thought I was in a Charlie Brown animation. Montecito was enchanting, but too quiet and boring to envy as a place to live. I looked forward to driving back down to L.A. for a few days before getting on a plane and heading home. Maybe Los Angeles had a bigger pulse.

. . . .

Although I appreciated my cousin's enthusiasm for showing us around town, I hated Los Angeles. L.A. was plastic, tacky, and cheap. David loved it for all those reasons, and I hated it for all those reasons. Also, the city was too spread out and the fumes from the constant bumper to bumper traffic gave me a headache. The city itself looked like one huge parking lot. I love palm trees, but the sight of them standing next to tall buildings made me uneasy, it always had, even when I saw them in brochures or photographs.

The Santa Monica pier was not very impressive either. It was a dirty beach with a beat up boardwalk, a few dusty carnival rides, and an ancient Ferris wheel. The old woman in the ticket booth struck my heart with both deep sadness and fear. The colors of her thick make-up matched the carnival park's colors, a dusty red rose and antique beige. The deep cracks in her face mirrored the paint cracks of the rides and the ticket booth she sat in. A bit of bleached blonde hair peeked out from under her red kerchief. Had she been, at one time, a young Hollywood starlet, her dreams now reduced to a faded old amusement park? She looked unbearably lonely as her expressionless face starred out the porthole window into her own "What if".

David and I strolled around the rest of the boardwalk which was populated with elderly, low-income hippies selling bad art and iron pumpers parading their biceps. Pedestrians in clown-colored clothing streamed by on roller skates and skate boarders flipped over cement steps. The lonely image of the old woman's face in the ticket booth continued to haunt me.

After exploring downtown L.A. we hiked to the top of the Hollywood Hills. I looked down onto the thick fog of pollution hovering over Los Angeles. It gave me the impression that the entire city had been hit by a nuclear bomb. I realized I could never live in L.A. It was not for me. I was glad I had come to L.A. just to realize how much I loved New York, and how happy I was to finally be going home.

During the plane ride back to New York, I pondered the idea of making more money in order to move out and get my own apartment. Perhaps I could resurrect a better working relationship with my boss Tony and within the coming year he would give me a raise. I did not know how I could strategize my position. There weren't any opportunities to climb the corporate ladder. The administrative tasks required were minimal, and the remaining duties left were picking up his dry cleaning, taking a few messages, and adjusting his cufflinks and shirt collar.

Getting a substantial part in a decent film would solve my entire economic crisis, but how, when, and where that was going to happen was beyond me. My mind went back to figuring out more immediate and practical ways to raise my income, but I came up blank and fell asleep.

The stewardess's announcement to fasten our seatbelts for landing woke me up. I peeked out the plane window to see the approaching New York City lights twinkling in the night sky with a soothing and familiar vibrancy. They filled me with a renewed hope that I could somehow find a way to gain my independence. I felt relieved to be coming home.

CHAPTER NINE

A MAGICAL POTION

WHEN I ARRIVED at the office on Monday, Tony was not around. I didn't think much about it. Jim called me into his office and Susan disappeared into the kitchen. I sat in front of Jim's portentous desk. A conspicuous traditional oil painting of some regal looking guy hung on the wall behind him in a gold ornate frame.

"Tony wanted me to break the news to you that we have to let you go," Jim blurted out with satisfaction.

"Let me go? Why?" I asked shocked.

"Tony and I have been discussing some issues together, and decided to make some changes, and we're just doing some re-organizing. Sorry."

"Where's Tony? Why isn't he here to tell me himself?"

"He's out with a client. Tony wanted me to be the one to tell you."

I could tell that Jim was lying to me. He did not seem sorry at all that Tony was letting me go. In fact, I think it was Jim's decision and not Tony's. I was upset because I could sense there was something going on that Jim wasn't telling me and Tony wasn't around to tell me.

"You'll be getting two-weeks severance pay and Tony will give you a good reference," Jim added.

"I just don't understand, Jim. I just came back from a week in California. Tony didn't give me any indication or warning that this was going to happen when I left. I would like to speak to Tony about this. Will he be back at all today? I asked again.

"No." Jim looked at me with little sympathy, and he seemed almost angry at me. I was wondering why Jim was so angry, but it didn't seem like he was going to tell me anything. "What are your plans now? Are you going to continue to pursue the entertainment business?" I thought it was a strange remark to make. I had given no indication to Tony or Jim that I was pursuing an acting or modeling career, other than the fact that my photo was in the paper for a modeling contest.

"My plans? I'm sorry to lose my job, but I guess I have to look on the bright side and see it as an opportunity."

"Opportunity?" Jim inquired.

"My boyfriend and I were planning a two-week vacation in Europe this coming summer, but since I'll have more time off now, we can extend our trip to possibly six weeks or longer," I explained.

Jim's alcohol-pickled face turned a brighter red than it already was, and his mouth crunched down very tightly. I could almost see the steam coming out of his ears and blowing out the top of his head. Jim was clearly angry, but it still made no sense to me why.

I spoke to Susan in the kitchen before collecting my things to leave the office. I asked her point blank, "What happened? What's going on?"

She looked down guiltily as she stirred the cream in her coffee. "I think they thought you had gone to California for a big film audition, or to meet an agent or something."

"Why would they think that? That's not true. I went there to visit family for the Holidays. I didn't have any film audition. It was Christmas for God's sake. Even people in Hollywood shut down their offices and leave town. They go to celebrate Christmas and New Year's in Aspen, Colorado like Tony does, for God's sake."

"Well, with that beautiful modeling photo that was in the newspaper, maybe they thought that's why you went to California," Susan suggested.

"Where's Tony," I asked Susan, annoyed.

"He's not coming back for a few days. He's still in Aspen."

"Yeah, he's in Aspen, where Stephen Spielberg probably is and Aaron Spelling and anyone else who's anybody. There's no one to audition for in L.A. during the holiday season, even if I knew anybody to audition for. I was visiting family like I said I was," I exclaimed.

I looked at Susan and realized she had given Tony and Jim the idea that I was in L.A. auditioning for a film. Or was it Tony who was upset that my modeling picture was in the paper? Maybe it was both of them; maybe it was all of them. "Susan, I hope you did not have anything to do with this," I warned.

"No, I didn't know that they were going to let you go." She looked into her cup with guilt all over her face.

"Thanks a lot, Susan. But don't fret your little head over it, because I'm going to Europe for the summer anyway. It actually worked out for the best. I just feel really bad that Tony is such a coward that he could not be here to do it himself." I marched out of the office with just my handbag and a small, green folder.

Once home, I turned on the stereo blasting The Smiths song, "What Difference Does It Make?" and danced around the living room. It usually takes about three days for the reality to set in that I lost my job.

It was now a few weeks into a stone-cold January with a wind-chill factor of seven degrees below zero. I had worked for Tony for only six months. I did not have enough money saved up to live on and definitely not enough money saved to be able to go to Europe in May. I did not know how long it would take me to find another job and I needed money. The arctic winter weather amplified my misery.

David and I agreed that I should find temporary office work and look for a permanent job after we came back from Europe. We also agree to extend our trip to five weeks, because the trip became cheaper the longer we stayed. The major expense was the airfare: $2,000 round trip. But once we got to France and Italy, hotels were about ten dollars a night and meals were only five dollars.

I applied for unemployment and signed up with every temporary agency in the city. I rarely got any calls for work, but when I did, the assignment lasted only a few days. Then I would be out of work again for weeks.

I was very lonely and frustrated being at home and I felt betrayed. I was angry that Tony, Susan, and Jim had not been happy or supportive about my modeling photo appearing in the newspaper. Maybe they had more faith in my success than I did and thought for sure I would become a super-model, or land a movie role.

I needed the job at MWR Inc., not only to support myself, but to continue my acting classes, get new pictures, and to have money in my pocket. They had pulled the rug out from under me.

While David was at work, I was on the phone throughout the day calling the temp agencies to see if there was any available office work. When something came up, it was usually a low-paying, sweat-shop assignment in a typing pool at an office where people did not smile or laugh and behaved like zombies with no personalities. I got my check at the end of the week and realized I was making more money collecting unemployment and staying home than going to work.

I went through days where I was so frustrated that I threw things across the room and scared the dog, Buddy Hackett - he would cower under the couch. I walked around the neighborhood just to get out of the house and I kicked trees. When I returned to the house, no matter how organized and clean I had managed to get it, all the knick-knacks, newspapers, and over-stuffed closets made me feel overwhelmed and hopeless.

Whenever I felt that I had little control over my life, I found it therapeutic to create a sense of order and openness in my living space. That was impossible with David. Most of the stuff was David's so I couldn't throw it out. David was a pack rat. He never got rid of anything. Even if I threw out my own stuff, like old clothes or shoes that I never wore, he found them in the garbage and brought them back in the house. He got upset if I threw anything out. He still had clothes that his ex-girlfriend had left behind. He wouldn't even let me give things to Goodwill. It made me crazy.

When life got frustrating, I needed to clean and organize my space, but it wasn't my space, and these weren't my things, they were David's and he didn't like things organized. He claimed he could not find anything when things were in order.

When I was in an anxiety crisis, I also liked to rearrange the furniture. He would come home and find the couch over here and the dining table over there. Sometimes he liked the change and sometimes he didn't. When he didn't, we would move everything back to the original position. He would laugh because he did not understand how my petite frame could lift the couch without any help. I never dared move any of his records, CD's or stereo equipment, because next to the dog, stereo equipment was man's best friend.

By the beginning of April, the ground had thawed, but I hadn't. Being out of work for too long is a strange experience. It wasn't just the poverty but the lack of income kept me from participating with the rest of the world. I was isolated. Nothing was coming in or going out on all levels, not just money. Not having an income created an emotional void, a physiological void, and a creative void in my life. Things became stagnant. It was like I didn't exist.

After months and months of sending out my picture and resume, I received a call for a few days of extra work on a coming of age film, *Heaven Help Us*, starring Donald Sutherland, John Heard, and Kevin Dillon. Since I was a member of Screen Actors Guild, the extra work could pay me a union scale of up to $150 per day, and there was the possibility of working four to six days or more. I was relieved. It would not solve my long-term financial problem, but at least it would put me in the company of other actors, and give me something to look forward to. Extra work was usually pretty boring because it really had nothing to do with exercising one's craft as an actor, but it was a nice break to hang out on the set with other actors and watch the production crew in action. I was still naïve enough to think that it was an opportunity to get noticed by the director or producer, which meant I had to look my best.

The ends of my hair were scraggly and my bangs were way past my eyes. I could not afford to get my haircut, but I did not hesitate to make an appointment. This was my career, and even if it was just extra work, I had to look my best. I was not going to trust my hair to a cheap salon. I called the Alfreda-Kassandra Salon to make an appointment. I had no romantic thoughts about Leonardi at all when I was making the call--this was just business.

The receptionist told me that Leonardi was off for the day, so I called him at his apartment. It sounded like I had woken him, because he answered the phone in a low, soft voice.

"Hi Leonardi. It's Whitney."

"Hi." He perked up. "I mean, Hi! This is a pleasant surprise!"

"It sounds like I woke you up."

"No, no. I was just sleeping in late because it's my day off. I was up, but just kind of lying here in bed staying cozy under the covers. How are you? I miss seeing you come by the shop."

"I lost my job this past January, and so things have been kind of frustrating and a bit difficult for me financially. I've been having a really tough time," I blubbered.

"Oh, I'm so sorry. Is that why you haven't been to the salon?"

"Yeah, I guess."

"You sound so unhappy." he sighed.

"I am. I need a haircut though, ASAP. The shop told me you were off for the day so I thought maybe I could catch you at home. I'm going to be doing some extra work on a film. It's only for four or five days, but my bangs are getting really long, and so is the rest of my hair. It looks too messy to leave it like this for the movie," I explained.

"When is the film work?"

"The day after tomorrow? So I need to come into the salon tomorrow. I know its short notice, but can I come by the salon tomorrow?"

"I'm off tomorrow also, but I can still do it for you. Just come to my apartment," he offered.

"We can't do it at the salon?"

"I'm off tomorrow. If you need it done that soon, I'll have to do it here. I cut hair for my friends all the time at my house. Really, and I'll do it for you for free. I don't mind helping you out. It's no problem really. Just come over at noon," he offered again.

"Wow, Leonardi, thanks. That's so great of you. I really appreciate it," I said relieved.

"Don't worry about it. I would love to. Oh, and make sure to bring your modeling portfolio with you. I want to see it. Don't forget to bring it," he insisted.

Later in the afternoon, I called Central Casting, and they instructed me to bring one casual outfit and to wear any color but red. I guess the star was wearing red, so they didn't want the extras wearing the same color. I was excited about the film project even if it was only extra work. I felt alive again. I felt hopeful. I suddenly had somewhere to go, something to do, and somewhere to be. That evening, I ironed some clothes. I love to iron, especially to music, it relaxes me. I enjoy the smell of the steam floating up off the fabric and watching the creases and wrinkles disappear.

The next day, I showed up at Leonardi's building, a high-rise in the West 60's. The lobby was all mirrors and chandeliers. The doorman called Leonardi on the desk phone, announced me, and sent me up to the penthouse.

Leonardi opened his door. He was barefoot, wearing sexy jeans and a loose-fitting white button-down shirt. I was surprised at myself for recognizing, once again, how sexy and handsome he was. He motioned me in with his hand as he talked on the phone, and then disappeared into the bedroom for privacy.

The apartment was a spacious two-room loft decorated all in pristine white accented with color by a cobalt blue vase on a white marble coffee table, vibrant contemporary paintings, and scattered sea shells. The massive living room window revealed an unobstructed view of blue sky and white clouds. The sun light showered in enhancing the brightness of the entire space. A sweet fresh scent of Patchouli incense filled the air.

I picked up an electric guitar leaning against the platform couch, turned and spun it on the soft white carpet, and leaned it back down again. I could see Leonardi in the adjacent room lounging on his platform bed chatting on the phone while smoking a cigarette. He smiled at me, and pursed his lips.

Within a moment, Leonardi sprinted out of the bedroom to greet me.

"Sorry I'm late. I had a few errands to run for the film shoot tomorrow. God, I feel so sticky and sweaty," I said nervously.

The phone rang. Leonardi ran into the bedroom. Within a split-second, he darted out again, grabbed my modeling portfolio from my hand, and at the same time, he threw me a white terry cloth robe. "Here, go take a shower and put this on. Excuse me, sorry, but I have to take this call," and he ran back into the bedroom.

I stood looking down at the robe in my hand. Leonardi peaked out, and pointed to the bathroom. "Go. Quick. We don't have much time," he ordered.

The bathroom décor was white with lavish gold accents. I kicked off my boots and quickly undressed. My nose investigated the different types of gels, soaps, and shampoos. My hands explored the softness of the plush terry cloth towels sitting on the shelf. The water felt warm and refreshing, and my hair now smelled like fresh spring flowers from his shampoo. I dried off and slipped the velvety robe over my emollient bare body, tied it at my waist, and drifted back into the living room.

Leonardi was off the phone by now, smoking another cigarette, and plucking notes on his electric guitar against old Beatles songs from the early 60's playing on the stereo. He had my modeling portfolio opened next to him on the platform ledge.

"I like your look and the photos are nice, but you need better photographers. Who took these shots, because they just don't do you justice?"

I picked up the book and sat next to him. "Just photographers I was able to get test shots from, you know. I'll work with whoever will work with me," I said with a smile. Leonardi handed me a glass of red wine. He lit my cigarette.

"That's good, but you need a real professional guy who can put you on the map. You need photos that pop. These don't pop enough. This one over here is quite good though, but you need more photos like this one here, and even better. They need to jump out. Pop! You know what I mean? Pop!"

"Yeah, I know. Pop!" I agreed. We clicked our wine glasses together.

"Come here," he said, as he led me to sit in the salon chair. He firmly pulled the robe down around my bare shoulders, and electricity moved through my whole body. He fluffed my hair around with his elegant, graceful fingers, "You want the same cut right? Straight with bangs, cold as ice?"

I nodded unable to speak.

While working on my hair, Leonardi cajoled me into small talk about my Christmas Holiday. He was looking at me in the same way he had looked at me the first time we met at the salon. He gazed into my eyes, and pursed his lips as if he were going to kiss me. Instead, he continued combing and cutting my hair, and sang to me softly the lyrics, "Yes It Is" by the Beatles playing on the stereo.

I was memorized by the calming and melodic tone of his voice. As he stood behind me cutting my hair and drawing his sorcerous hands through my tresses, his whisper of lyrics into my ears lulled me into a quiet sleepy trance.

At times, he bent down in front of me and looked into my eyes and sang with the extra emphasis of an English accent. My heart was melting as he sang to me. I enjoyed the way he looked at me. His hands touching my neck and shoulders were exceedingly soothing and his voice was deeply tranquilizing. He trimmed the bottom of my hair, and as he proceeded to cut my bangs he moved his legs between my thighs to get a good angle with the scissors, which caused my robe to open and reveal more thigh. I felt his groin against my leg and my body went limp, yet filled with fire. The stereo stopped playing music for a brief moment, and then there was the click and drop sound of a CD, before the Duran Duran song, "Save a Prayer" played.

Leaving my bangs only half-cut on my forehead, Leonardi placed the comb and scissors down on the table. While cupping my face in his hands, he slowly kissed my lips, my world now narrowing to the dark focus of his sensual mouth. Conscious of nothing else, but the hot pressure of his cushiony lips, my mouth melted and surrendered into his as I drew my arms around his virile waist. Both our hands slowly roamed each other's body while we explored the various ways our parting lips could come back together--each joining, increasingly more passionate.

Leonardi picked me up and carried me onto his bed, gently laying me down on the fluffy white down comforter. The right side of my bangs and the bottom right side of my hair were cut, but the left side was undone.

My robe fell half open. He removed it completely as he looked down at me. Then he leaned over to continue kissing me. He lay down on top of me and our bodies fit perfectly together. I could feel his heart and the blood in his veins. His soul felt so close to my heart. I looked at him, mesmerized by the angelic beauty in his face. I started to unbutton his shirt. He got up quickly, slipped off his jeans, and came back on top of me in a gentle embrace. We kissed each other for a long time and kept looking into each other's eyes. I felt that I was finally home. I had found my other half. He stopped for a moment, looking deep into my eyes, and whispered, "You are special." He looked down at me in awe and wonder. I looked at him in the same way, and I felt myself ascending somewhere in space. We made love slowly. Any fear or shame I had felt melted away. I realized--if I were to die right now, it would be perfectly fine. To be with Leonardi in that moment, in that way, was more than I could have imagined experiencing in a whole lifetime. I knew I loved Leonardi. I had loved him from the first moment I laid eyes on him, as if I had dreamt about him twenty-four years before I saw him. I did not know what he was going to look like, or who he was to going be, but here I was in heaven on a white cloud in the bright blue sky with an angel.

Later, he finished cutting the rest of my hair, which felt like a continuation of him making love to me. With my hair done, we sailed back into the bedroom and drank more wine. He looked into my eyes and sang the lyrics of another favorite Beatle song, "Here There and Everywhere" softly into my ears. We then rested on the bed quietly for a long time in each other's arms. As I looked out the window, my spirit was flying into the wide open sky. The wind was soft and cool. I could even have wings or I could walk upon the clouds, and jump up and down. My dreams soared. The music was in my soul and I was free. Man loved, and his love was light, and light is life, and life lives eternal -- without dreaming.

Just as the sky was turning a deep pink and orange, the phone rang. Leonardi leaned over me and picked up the white receiver. "Hi! Actually we're starved! My girl Whitney and I..." Leonardi laughed into the phone occasionally as he listened to the voice at the other end.

"Are you hungry?" he asked me.

I nodded and kissed him on the mouth. He brushed my head with the back of his hand as he spoke to his friend on the phone. "We can be downstairs in half an hour or so. Okay. Bye."

"That was my friend Guy. We're going to meet him at Fiorelli's for dinner. Quick. Go jump in the shower. I'll go after you."

"Guy who?" I asked.

"Guy Peellaert," he replied.

"Guy Peellaert? You mean the artist Guy Peellaert? I asked excited.

"Yeah, he's a friend of mine. He lives in Paris and just came into New York for the week."

"Oh my God. Leonardi, he's one of my favorite artists. He designed the Bowie and Rolling Stones album covers. I still have his book of illustrations *Rock Dreams*. I wrote a paper about him back in school. That's so wild! You know Guy Peellaert?" I shouted.

Leonardi laughed, "You wrote a school paper about Guy!"

"Yeah, isn't that crazy," I giggled.

"Quick, we don't want to be late, get in the shower," Leonardi urged.

The restaurant was a short walk from Leonardi's apartment. Fiorelli's was a simple Italian restaurant. Each table was covered with a white paper cloth and supplied with a short glass filled with crayons. I observed people at the nearby tables drawing on their table cloths, so I drew a quick caricature of Leonardi with a purple crayon. It was a very good likeness, with simple lines that captured Leonardi's oval face, his Roman nose, and long curls.

"Wow, that's really good," Leonardi looked at it with surprise.

I just smiled and winked at him.

Just then Guy Peellaert wandered over to our table to join us. Leonardi introduced me and then pointed to my drawing, "Look Whitney's an artist too."

It was a little embarrassing and intimidating for me to hear Leonardi say that to the legendary Guy Peellaert. But Guy appeared to have other things on his mind that he wanted to discuss with Leonardi in private, so I sensed that he was disappointed to see me there.

I did not know what Leonardi and Guy were rambling on about throughout dinner, as they talked about people and situations only familiar to them, and sometimes they spoke in French. I felt left out, and became withdrawn. Occasionally, Leonardi asked me something to include me in the conversation, but I still felt uncomfortable by Guy's lack of enthusiasm.

"Whitney says you were always her favorite artist, she even wrote a school paper about you. Isn't that wild?"

Guy's reaction was dry. I squirmed in my chair. Leonardi looked awkward.

Shortly after the chocolate mousse, we all left the restaurant to go our separate ways. Leonardi and I stood off the curb in the cool evening air. He hugged me close while he quickly hailed down a cab. Leonardi opened the car door and as I slid in the back seat, he gave me some money for the fare and shut the door. He then stuck his head in the window, "I'm off next Thursday. Call me in the morning," he urged, grasping the back of my head with his hand, and slipping me one more steadfast kiss before letting the cab peel away.

A quarter past ten in the evening was not a suspicious time for me to come home, so I was not worried about needing any kind of alibi. When I tip-toed into the apartment, I found David asleep on the couch with the TV on. I looked around the house, and for the first time none of the clutter bothered me. This is wonderful, I thought. The house was fine; the clutter was great. I didn't care. Life suddenly looked sweet. I wasn't angry anymore, I wasn't anxious, or hostile, or frustrated. The heaviness that I had felt over the past few months was miraculously gone.

I shut off the TV and woke David up. He let out a moan. I led him into the dark bedroom where he stumbled onto the mattress. I pulled the covers over him and climbed into bed myself. As I lay my head down on the pillow, the reality of the situation struck me, "What am I going to do now?" But I was too tired to think about it, and too happy to worry about it. All the anger and frustration I had felt since losing my job at MWR dropped from my mind like the last grains of sand passing through an hourglass, and I fell fast asleep.

CHAPTER TEN

HE LOVES ME HE LOVES ME NOT

WORKING AS A film extra over the next few days was relaxing and enjoyable. All the extras were given hair, make-up, and wardrobe, and asked to play sixteen year old students at a Catholic Boys School dance in Brooklyn, circa 1965. No big character stretch for most of the extras, as all of them were in the age range of about 15 to 17 years old. I was the only 24 year old playing a sixteen year old. I enjoyed the experience though, because I got to dance with the cutest boy in the school. He was an extra also, but he was dreamy: tall, blonde, and handsome. His face had an uncanny resemblance to my first boyfriend, my first love back in high school, who was now deceased. Unfortunately, to my disappointment, this boy did not have the same witty and charming personality that my first true love had.

Other than that, most of the time was spent sitting around all day waiting for the crew to set up a five-minute scene. To pass the time, most of the extras read books or plays. Some knitted and some did needle point. Others chatted with each other all day about the business of acting, and some just ate a lot of bagels and sandwiches at the craft table. A few extras walked around talking to themselves as they rehearsed monologues for their upcoming auditions. That always looked insane to me, even though I knew what they were doing. I had little in common with the young kids on the set, so I tried to strike up a conversation with the actor John Heard who was playing the part of a Catholic priest. I got cheeky with him about his black robe and white collar, but he just chased me away in good humor telling me it was way past my bedtime, and to go on home and do my homework. My *Dippity-do* hairstyle and 1965 teenage clothes probably gave me the appearance of being much younger than even 16. He might have thought I was 14 year old jail bait. So I made friends with a young comedian named Doug who knew card tricks and how to make animals out of balloons.

To survive in New York City, Doug worked at a *Häagen Dazs* ice cream parlor, because he loved ice cream. The problem was that his salary was low and his New York City rent was high. He was subletting a room which contained only a floor mattress and an old dresser. All he ate was the free ice cream from *Häagen Dazs*. A few nights later, he called me crying that he had gone blind. He had, in fact, gone temporarily blind from having a diet consisting of mostly ice cream for breakfast, lunch, and dinner. At first, I got angry with him for not telling me or anyone else that he was starving to death. He was too optimistic and proud. I calmed down and convinced him to call his sister in Minnesota to ask her to either send him money, or take him in for a time.

Doug regained his sight the next day, but decided to pack his belongings in a duffle bag and return to Minnesota that afternoon. He called me the following day to let me know that he was well again and grateful to be home, close to his family and friends. Perhaps one day he would return to New York to pursue his acting career. I don't know if he ever did, we lost touch.

Thursday morning, as soon as David left the house for work at about 8:30, I jumped out of bed and into the shower. I could never talk to anyone or start my day until I had taken a shower. I quickly dressed, put on my make-up and gave Leonardi a call. He told me he had to go to the salon for just a few hours, and to meet him in front of the shop at about 11 a.m.

On a warm but overcast day, I stood in front of the salon building. Shortly after, Leonardi jauntily bounced down the steps and onto the street looking as saucy and sexy as a pirate -- his long black eighteenth-century military coat tails flying behind him in the wind. He had on jeans, short black boats, and a long royal purple shirt.

The alluring sight of him reminded me of Isadora Duncan's passion for her lover. I had been studying the dance style of Isadora Duncan for five years. Her life was dripping with passion for dance, music, art, and the love of her life, the famous theater designer, Gordon Craig.

> "Here stood before me brilliant youth, beauty, genius, and all inflamed with sudden love. I flew into his arms with all the magnetic willingness of a temperment which had for two years lain dormant, but waiting to spring forth..." *My Life* by Isadora Duncan.

Leonardi came up quickly behind me, grabbed my hand, drew me close to him and kissed me hard. Still holding my hand, he then twirled me away from him and led me down the street in a bouncy strut. He stopped short, pulled me firmly into his arms and kissed me again.

> "...more like an angel of Blake than a mortal youth he appeared. Hardly were my eyes ravished by his beauty than I was drawn toward him entwined, melted. As flame meets flame, we burned in one bright fire," *My Life* by Isadora Duncan

We smooched for a long time in the middle of the avenue and then Leonardi swung us around into an exuberant strut again. *We were dancing.*

Once we reached the corner light on 57th Street in front of Carnegie Hall, Leonardi pointed to a woman in a bright red hat. "Look at that. Isn't that incredible?"

"What?" I asked.

"That woman in her hat! She's incredible," he gleamed.

Leonardi found inspiration anywhere and everywhere. He was on fire. I loved that about him. His excitement about life excited me. He was so free and alive that I thought I was going to burst open and let loose a rainbow of colors.

"He always entered in a state of wild excitement over a tree or a bird or a child he had seen on his way. One never spent a dull moment with him…," *My Life* by Isadora Duncan.

We strolled back to his apartment, and once in the door, Leonardi immediately got on the phone and ordered lunch to be delivered. Leonardi then led me to the middle of the living room. We danced close together as he placed his burning smooth cheek next to mine. He showered me with butterfly kisses and sang softly in my ear more lyrics to "Here There and Everywhere" by the Beatles.

"This was not a young man making love to a girl. This was the meeting of twin souls. The light covering of flesh was so transmuted with ecstasy that early passion became a heavenly embrace of white, fiery flame," *My Life* by Isadora Duncan.

The food arrived and Leonardi ran into the kitchen for some glasses, utensils, and a bottle of red wine. I opened the aluminum plates filled with cheese and meat tortellini covered in red sauce, a fresh garden salad, and fried calamari. We sat on the wide ledge of his platform living room, rather than the couch.

"Where are you from originally?" I asked.

"Brooklyn," he smiled.

"Why do I detect a slight English accent?"

"I travel a lot. Where are you originally from?" he asked.

"Queens."

"Nothing wrong with that you know."

"Did I say there was?" I playfully bantered.

"I can see you being a very famous actress one day," he replied with an approving nod.

"Thanks."

"No, really I mean it. You have a quality, a presence, that special something. Do you have an agent?"

"No, that's the most frustrating thing. It's so hard to get one. I think once I have one, and they send me out for auditions, I will get work."

"You need one. You'll get one. You have to have faith," he assured me.

"How come I haven't found one yet?" I asked, frustrated.

"The thing is you're very different. You don't have the average American look. You're very unique."

"I hear that a lot. The few agents that have met me have said that I'm either going to be very rich or very poor, because my style and look is considerably different, although quite interesting, and only the right part will get me in the door."

"I agree. You just have to hang in there, and be ready when it happens. I see you being picked for a very specific type of role that very few people would be able to play. Getting that part could make you a star, if it's a good film. Your look is unique and you have a special presence. The photography work in your portfolio wasn't that great, I mean it was okay, but your face is so beautiful and photogenic that I can see you in a very specific European type film, a more artistic genre. Here have some more calamari," he offered.

"You really think so?"

"You look a bit like Isabella Rossellini, but different. You have that same quality though. My ex-girlfriend looked a lot like that also."

"Did she look like me or Isabella Rossellini?" I asked.

"Actually she looked almost as beautiful as you," he said before kissing me.

"What happened to her? What was her name?" I probed.

"Maria. We broke up. You both look so much alike though, like sisters. I wanted to marry her, but things didn't work out. She was a high fashion model I had met in Milan, but she was being kept by a wealthy Mafioso. He never would have let her go. It happened some time ago, but let's not talk about it."

"That's sounds intense, and a bit scary, so yeah, let's not talk about it," I agreed.

"How long have you and David been together?"

"Five years. We met in acting class," I said, feeling uncomfortable.

"Do you love him?

"I'm here with you right now, so what does that say. I shouldn't be here with you. I think I love him. He's been so good to me, but I'm also thinking that maybe I'm not in love with him. I don't know. I'm very confused right now. Leonardi, I should not be here with you. I feel very guilty. I don't want to hurt anyone. David's a good guy. He would never do anything to hurt me. I feel very... I can't hurt him. I don't want to hurt anyone. I..."

Leonardi brushed the tears from my face and held me close. "Let's not talk about it right now. Okay? Just relax. You have calamari on your mouth," he chuckled. He licked my mouth and kissed me again. He held my hand to his heart and rested my head on his shoulder then sang more verses of "Here There and Everywhere" by the Beatles. We drifted into the bedroom, made love again, and fell asleep in each other's arms.

"There are joys so complete, so all perfect, that one should not survive them. Ah, why did not my burning soul find exit that night, and fly, like Blake's angel...," *My Life* by Isadora Duncan.

When I awoke, it was late in the afternoon. Leonardi was asleep beside me. I suddenly felt terribly frightened. I knew I could not cheat on David. I wasn't the type of person to lie and sneak around, but that was exactly what I was doing. I knew for sure that I wanted to be with Leonardi, but did Leonardi really want to be with me? And if he did, how was I going to tell David?

I was afraid of telling Leonardi so soon that I loved him. I thought it would scare him away. We had only been together twice in the past seven days. It would be insane to tell Leonardi that I loved him. There could be no other reason for me to cheat on David. I would never get involved in a casual or meaningless affair and jeopardize my relationship with David just for a fling. Leonardi obviously meant something to me, or I would never have done this.

When Leonardi woke up, we spent the rest of the day talking. The more I learned about Leonardi, the more frightened I became. Although he came from the same lower-middle class background in Brooklyn, as I had in Queens, his past was filled with joy, acceptance, and appreciation. He had three older sisters who had cuddled him. His mother adored him. He never questioned the idea of pursuing what he wanted, and never questioned getting what he wanted. He just followed his joy and knew it would all work out. No one close to him disapproved of him as a person or who he was at his core.

My parents did not understand my ambitions as an actor or my passion for art. Nor did they care to know anything about it. They waited for the day when I outgrew my childish dreams and settled down in one office job as a secretary for the rest of my life, married to a lawyer.

"Leonardi. I'm scared. I can't do this to David. I can't lie to him, and sneak around with you. I mean it's wrong, and I would not want anyone to do it to me," I confessed.

I was hoping Leonardi would say, "I love you. Please come live with me." It was too much to expect so soon, but I wanted desperately to hear it. I wanted to say it to him.

"Leonardi, I never cheated on David before. I never cheated on anyone. I would not want anyone to do it to me. How am I going to go home and pretend that nothing has happened in these past few days? I'd be living a lie and it doesn't feel like me to do that. I don't know what to do now," I explained.

Leonardi got very stern with me. "Whitney, you need to move out."

"I need to move out," I repeated softly as I looked up at the ceiling. They weren't the words I wanted to hear. I wanted to hear, "I love you, and you need to move out."

"How am I going to do that? I don't have a job. I don't have enough money in the bank."

"Listen to me. This is your life we are talking about. You have to move out. I agree with you that we can't sneak around. You have to do something about it. You will get a job, and then you'll find an apartment and get out. You can do it," Leonardi insisted.

I knew Leonardi didn't understand my situation. I had been through too many office jobs, and none of them ever worked out. MWR was a better experience in comparison, but it had only lasted six months. Most of my previous office jobs had been crazy experiences of physiological and emotional abuse from either a manager or co-worker which left me traumatized.

Besides, with the Savings & Loan Crisis and so many banks failing, there weren't many jobs to be had. I learned from my job seeking efforts that the few jobs available in my field, with my experience and skill set, were now reserved only for "recent" college graduates, preferably from ivy league schools. The average skilled woman could no longer acquire the same modest position of secretary in a good company with decent pay unless she was "fresh out of college" and well-connected to affluent people. Even office temp jobs were almost impossible to come by during this recession, and the temp assignments available were few and far between.

Many people who were already well-established in freelance work had a less painful time riding out the recession. David was still doing well freelancing as an Art Director for advertising agencies. I also noticed that people in high paying positions in law and medicine were not hurting. People who were already well-established in highly lucrative positions in the media and entertainment industry were not affected by the recession at all. It was the lower middle class that got affected first, and affected the hardest from a severe economic down-turn. Most of Leonardi's clients were extremely affluent, and he also catered to wealthy celebrities in the entertainment business. For Leonardi an economic crisis did not even exist. For Leonardi—*business was booming.*

Yet, I had to admire Leonardi's success, and I was even a bit dumbfounded at his ability to become so prosperous. Most hairdressers only made about $35,000 a year or less. Leonardi was thirty-one years old and made over $100,000 a year styling hair for models and movie stars. He hadn't experienced working in an office or a factory with dull zombie-like people or abusive people who bullied him and put him down. He did not have a family that communicated to him that his talents and dreams were worthless, or that he was worthless.

David was the only person in my life who saw me as worthy and deserving of something better in my life. He was always there for me. I felt guilty and ashamed for not being in love with him. I loved him like a brother. The romantic and physical compatibility was just not there. I wish it was, but it wasn't.

Leonardi and I rested on the bed quietly. I stared up at the ceiling as he explored my face running his fingers across my forehead, down my nose, then resting them on my lips. I delicately nibbled on his finger tips. He leaned forward holding my face in his hands caressing my temples and eyelids with tender kisses. He then dropped his head back on the pillow and brought my hand to his mouth, kissed my fingers lightly and then rested my palm to his warm chest.

The thought came to me that maybe I needed David to show me my value when no one else would. Maybe now that I had grown up a little, and had the experience of comfort, safety, and healing, it was time for me to move on to a grander phase of my life, but why did I feel so guilty?

Leonardi stretched out his left arm to grab his cigarettes and a lighter on the nightstand next to him. He lit one in his mouth and passed it onto me, and then lit one for himself. "It's not such a big deal you know. You'll find a job and move out. People do it all the time," Leonardi whispered.

I said nothing as I gazed up at the ceiling exhaling a puff of smoke and watching it float above me. Even if I was able to find a steady job, it would not enable me to afford the rent by myself, because Manhattan was so expensive. I would have to find a roommate, and live with a stranger who might be totally incompatible. How could I explain all this to Leonardi? I was too ashamed to admit that I could not keep a regular job long enough to take care of myself. I was too ashamed to admit that I did not know how to get what I needed to do the work I loved, as he did. I was also ashamed to tell him about the dark world I had escaped from in Queens, and why I had wanted to escape, and finally did when I met David. I was too ashamed and afraid to tell him I loved him. I did not know how to get grounded in my life the way he had. More importantly, I didn't know why I could not do it, no matter how hard I had tried. Leonardi was now looking at me intently.

"I don't know when or how I will find a job, Leonardi. And if I do, then I have to save up money and find a place to live. That's going to take time, and in the meantime, that means we have to sneak around until I can make any kind of move. I'll be living a lie for three months, six months, eight months. I can't sneak around until then," I admitted.

Leonardi stroked my hair, and looked down at me, "You need to move out honey." I was very frustrated and depressed when he said it again. We didn't talk much anymore, just held each other, and shortly after, I got dressed and went back home.

The next day, I walked around the tranquil tree-lined streets of my Gramercy Park neighborhood with its beautiful, historical, four-story brownstones, each accented with flower pots on the window sills and pretty little gardens near the foot of the front steps. It was a far cry from the ugly, dirty, drug-ridden, neighborhood in Queens that I had left behind five years ago.

I entered the tall iron gates of Gramercy Park itself, and sat on a small bench under a hovering willow tree. I looked out onto the small park with its many multi-colored flower beds. A warm breeze blew through the air and cherry blossoms floated gently to the ground. A squirrel scrambled up a nearby tree. Another squirrel dashed across the pebble walkway and onto the grass. Tiny birds frolicked and bathed in the marble water fountain. It was a beautiful park. Even the pigeons were handsome.

The only other person in the park was a woman at the far end, rocking a baby carriage back and forth. I assumed that she was not related to the baby at all, but hired help--a Nanny.

I speculated that as an Administrative Assistant, I only cleared less than $300 a week after taxes. A studio or one-bedroom apartment in Manhattan started at $1,200 per month. Even if I did find an office job, how long could I hold onto it and continue to keep my head above water. I would never be able to afford to continue to pursue acting. I would spend whatever money I made on rent, eating tuna fish out of a can, and washing my clothes in the sink. Did Leonardi love me? Would he stay with me? There were no guarantees.

And what about my trip to Europe? I've never been to Europe. It was my dream. We had already purchased the tickets, made hotel reservations in Paris, Rome, and Venice. David was going to be crushed. He was going to be devastated, not only if I moved out, but if I ruined our trip. He didn't deserve this. It was all up to me to figure out. This was turning my life upside down and inside out with no guarantees. Leonardi and I could break up months from now and I would be lost on the street, living in poverty, or worse back in Queens with the drugs and violence of my old neighborhood. No, I couldn't do this. I wouldn't do this. This had to stop. I was out of my mind.

I returned home and called Leonardi. "I'm sorry. I can't see you anymore. It's over."

"Whitney, don't do this. You need to move out of there. Listen to me, you need to get out of there and get your own place," Leonardi begged.

"Leonardi. I don't have a job. I don't have a place to go to, or a place I can afford," I argued.

"You will get a job. You can find your own place. You can do it. I know you can. You need to get out of there," Leonardi pleaded.

"I can't. I know I can't. Where am I going to work? What am I going to do?"

"You just go out and get a job. Just get a job and find a place. I'll help you. I'll ask around," Leonardi insisted.

"Leonardi, you don't understand. I can't see you anymore," I snapped.

"Well, if you can't see me anymore, you still need to move out of there, whether you see me or not," Leonardi snapped back.

"Why?" I demanded.

"Because you don't love him!" he yelled out.

The words hit me like a ton of bricks. Both of us were silent on the phone for a long moment, then we called a time out and both hung up.

A few days later Leonardi called me. "Sidney, an associate of mine at the salon, is looking for a roommate. A few of us are going out clubbing tonight, why don't you come along and I can introduce you to Sidney."

"I can't Leonardi. I can't do this. If I went out with you tonight, I would have to tell David where I was going, and why. I can't sneak around."

"I understand," his voice was mellow. "Only you know what you need and want. I really don't want to force you into anything you feel uncomfortable with. I'm just trying to help. I just want to help you, okay?"

I was quiet.

"Whitney, are you there?" he asked quietly.

"Yes. I'm just feeling bad right now."

"If you need to call me, I'm here. Okay… Okay?"

"Okay," I muttered.

A week crawled by. I did not call Leonardi and he did not call me, but I was hoping he would call me again. I realized that I might not hear from him again. He wasn't going to come after me and yet that's what I wanted him to do. I wanted Leonardi to whisk me away, but I also wanted to forget about him.

CHAPTER ELEVEN

SAYING GOODBYE

A MONTH HAD now gone by since I last heard from Leonardi. I had not called him and he had not called me. I tried to keep my mind occupied by looking for a job, but I was unable to find one. I had temporary office assignments for a few days here and there, but nothing lasting. No other acting jobs came up either. I was depressed and didn't eat or sleep.

David would talk to me, but my mind was far away. We got into arguments over nothing at all, because he could not understand my lethargic behavior and attitude. I always looked melancholy and disconnected from him and everyone else around me. Tom and David's negative conversations and depressing cynical view point went on and on and made me irritable. When we spoke about Europe, I wasn't as excited anymore. I thought of how much I wanted to fly away to Paris or Venice with Leonardi.

My mind was now focused on looking for a permanent job and moving out rather than on going to Europe. Being home alone all day made me restless. I threw things across the room just like I had done before I got the job at MWR with Tony Scott. This time though, I was overwhelmed with grief and slumped to the floor weeping like a baby. I cried out "God, please help me!" I couldn't stand to be without Leonardi. I missed him so much. Did he miss me? If he did, why didn't he come and get me?

David and Tom wanted to go downtown to a club to see some band. I told them I didn't feel well and that they should go without me. After they left, I rested on the futon listening to a John Waite song "Missing You" on the radio. I finally broke down and called Leonardi at his apartment. He was home.

"Hi," I said.

"Hi. Are you okay? Leonardi whispered softly.

"Yeah, I mean, no... I miss you," I said in a monotone voice as I rested on the bed peering up at a small moth fluttering around the light fixture.

"Are you in love with me?" he asked.

There was a moment of silence as I thought, "What a narcissistic thing to ask! Am I in love with you? You're supposed to say, 'Whitney, I think I'm in love with you,' or 'I love you,' or 'I miss you too.' Or 'I love you, and I'm coming to get you.' What the hell kind of question was that! 'Are you in love with me?'" Instead I said nothing.

"Are you?" he asked again.

"Leonardi, how am I supposed to know? I'm confused. I know I want to see you again. And it's wrong. What am I going to do, Leonardi? I can't sneak around. I can't lie and cheat on David. I can't do it!"

"You need to move out, my lovely," he whispered.

"I know. I need to move out," I sighed.

"Meet me tomorrow night and come out with us. I'll introduce you to Sidney. She's a hair colorist at the salon and she's looking for a roommate."

"Where does she live?"

"On the Upper West Side. Near me. We would be close to each other."

"Near you?"

"Yes, not far away at all," he promised.

"What's her rent?"

"I don't know, but I'm sure it can't be too much between the two of you. Come out tomorrow night, please?" he begged.

"I need to think about this. I need to--"

Leonardi interrupted and was gentle but firm. "Whitney, you don't know what you're options are until you get out there and open yourself up to new experiences and people."

"I'll try to keep an open mind, and at least look into the possibilities. Is that fair enough?" I asked.

"Be at my place around 7 p.m. We'll eat first, and then go meet Sidney and some friends at the club. It's going to be all right, things will work themselves out. Just relax, okay?"

"Okay," I agreed.

After I hung up with Leonardi, I was relieved that I had finally called him and talked with him. I was still frightened, but he had eased some of the fear when he said, "It's going to be all right. Things will work themselves out. Just relax, okay?"

I thought he was probably right. The unknown is always frightening. Big changes were always painful and scary. I would get through this somehow. I didn't know how, but if Leonardi said I would, I would. After all, how did I come to live with David?'

Shortly after David and I met, David moved from a studio to a much larger one-bedroom apartment down the hall. I was there almost every day, so I brought in more and more of my clothes until within a few weeks, I was living with him.

Maybe that's what would happen with Leonardi and me. I'd find a job, and live with Sidney for a short time. Leonardi and I could see each other without sneaking around, and I wouldn't have to live a lie. I could live my life with a clear conscious. Leonardi and I would have the opportunity to see if we were, in fact, in love with each other. Then we could either move in with one another or get married. Who knew? That could happen. Why couldn't it? It was already happening. There was no reason to be scared, and if I was too scared, I didn't have to do it. I was just going out tomorrow to meet his friend Sidney to find out what my options were. It was not the end of the world. Meeting Sidney didn't mean I actually had to go through with moving in with her. I could just go to the club with them the next night, get more information, and feel it out.

I left the apartment early before David came home from work. When I got to Leonardi's apartment, he had his music blasting. I was surprised to find his close friend and associate from the salon, Maxwell, with him. Maxwell was a much larger, more muscular guy--nice looking, very out-going and vivacious. He was singing silly lyrics into a microphone and acting giddy with Leonardi. They were both goofing around with one another, and having a good time.

After the delivery guy arrived, Leonardi hurriedly placed Chinese take-out food onto dinner plates. He yelled out to me to fetch some utensils in the kitchen. I couldn't find the drawer where the utensils were. Leonardi already agitated, ran to the kitchen, and pulled open the drawer to get the utensils himself.

"I'm sorry. I didn't know where they were," I said embarrassed.

"Come on let's just eat quickly and get going," he snapped.

A cold chill flew down my spine. He had never spoken to me that way before. I figured maybe I was just being sensitive because I was so nervous about being there.

Maxwell dominated the scene with jokes and loud laughter, and he directed all his conversation to Leonardi while ignoring me. Leonardi laughed and jested along with him. I became shy and self-conscious.

I did not feel included in the improvisational games that were going on between them, nor the conversation. I had expected to see Leonardi alone when I showed up, or at least with just his friend Sidney. I had not expected to walk into the private party these two guys were having together.

They continued to laugh and I tried to laugh along with them, but my laugh was strained. After the meal, they both lit up joints and started goofing around again. Leonardi picked up his guitar and played against some songs on the stereo, while Maxwell sang into the microphone improvising his own ridiculous lyrics. They tumbled to the floor laughing uncontrollably. I kept hoping that Maxwell would leave.

We finally all left the apartment and piled into a cab heading to a downtown nightclub. I followed along, hoping for a moment to talk with Leonardi alone. That never happened. In the cab, I sat between Maxwell and Leonardi, and the only thing I remember Maxwell saying to me was, "Did you ever think of getting a nose job?"

I knew what he meant. My nose was large in comparison to what was considered beautiful in the American modeling market at the time. Models with small button noses were considered more attractive. I did not love my nose, but I did not hate it either. It was also a bit crooked, and although it photographed longer on the right side of my face, on the left side it photographed much smaller and even appeared little. So I could tilt my head to either side, just a bit, and get two different looks. Besides, models were just people who had imperfections. It was the clothes, hair, make-up, lighting and photography that gave the illusion of perfection. I was satisfied with my looks, and never felt the need to get surgery and change it. I was who I was, and that was fine with me..

Leonardi looked at me to see my response to Maxwell.

"No, I never ever thought about changing my nose," I stated.

"She has a nice nose Maxwell," Leonardi added.

"No, she does. I was just wondering if she ever thought that she should change it," Maxwell explained.

"No, I never did, and I never will have a desire to change anything about it. I like my nose," I said firmly.

"She likes her nose, that's good," Maxwell commented.

After that, I was sure I did not like Maxwell.

In the dark, crowded night club, we found refuge at one of the many small tables embellished with a little black lamp. The music was too loud for conversation. A waitress showed up to take drink orders. "Just a white wine!" I shouted. Leonardi and Maxwell sat next to each other and continued chatting, but I couldn't hear any of the conversation.

Within a few minutes, two other women showed up at our table. I immediately recognized one of them as being Sidney, the hair colorist from the salon. Sidney was a short, boney, forty-seven year old woman with an angry dry face. Tonight, she was dressed like an aging Phyllis Diller. Her dehydrated black hair was teased up electrocution style, and a red ostrich feather boa draped wildly over her gaudy spandex leopard print dress. She was a battered remnant from the 1970's glitter-rock drug scene. I secretly cringed. Sidney and I tried to speak to each other, but the music was too loud.

"We'll talk later!" Sidney yelled.

"Okay!" I nodded.

Sidney, Leonardi, and Maxwell did not look eager to leave the club. They kept mingling around in the crowd, occasionally coming back to the table to pick up their drinks or grab a cigarette. I realized it must be past midnight. David would be wondering where I was. I was alarmed now, because time was running out, and I still did not have any information regarding the possibility of moving in with Sidney. I knew I should have left the club a long time ago, but I could not seem to drag myself away. I kept thinking any minute we would leave this dark, smoky, noisy place, and I could talk with Leonardi or at least talk to Sidney. Finally, by 1 a.m. Leonardi said, "There's nothing happening here, let's go."

All five of us hopped into a cab, only to end up at another club further downtown. This night club was even more mobbed and boisterous than the one we had left.

I shouted in his ear over the music, "Leonardi, I should probably go"

"Why do you want to go, aren't you having a good time?"

"Yeah, but it's so late, David is going to be wondering what happened to me," I shouted.

"Just tell him you were out with some friends," Leonardi yelled back.

Leonardi excused himself to talk with some friends he saw across the room. Sidney and I tried to converse again, but the music was just too loud. Leonardi and Maxwell had disappeared for a long time. I realized it was now almost three in the morning, and I did not have an alibi for David. I wasn't even trying to think one up. What was I going to say to him when I walked in the door? I had no clue. My mind was blank. I felt frozen all night, and unable to enjoy myself while waiting for an opportunity to talk with Leonardi or Sidney. By three-thirty in the morning we left the club, and Leonardi hailed a cab.

"Where are we going now?" I asked.

"Back to my place."

"Leonardi I need to go home. It's really late. It's so late. I don't know what I'm going to tell David. I have to go."

Leonardi flagged down another car for me, handed me some fare money, kissed me goodbye and sent me on my way.

I reached home at four in the morning. David was sitting on the couch waiting for me. "Where were you?" he asked with anger in his voice.

"I ended up going to a club with some friends. It was a spur of the moment thing. Sorry I didn't call," I said.

David knew I was lying, and I knew he knew that I was lying. I never go out with so-called friends until four in the morning, especially friends with no names, and I never stay out until four in the morning without calling anyone or letting anyone know where I am.

"I called Darcey. I even called your parents. I didn't know where you were," he snapped.

My voice was nervous and weak. "I felt kind of restless, and decided to tag along with some friends to a club." I was a lousy liar. I had no practice at it. I knew lying was wrong, I never did it, so I had never developed the skill to do it well.

"I'm going to sleep." David exited into the bedroom and disappeared under the covers. I followed after him, and crawled under the covers on my side of the futon. I looked up into the dark of the ceiling. David had his back to me, and within a moment of our lying down together asked, "You were with Leonardi, weren't you?"

I sighed loudly, and said, "Yeah. I was with Leonardi."

David sprang up and looked at me in the dark. "I knew it! I knew you were with him! I knew you were with Leonardi!" Then he turned away from me, rolling over on his side.

I was quiet for a moment, not knowing what I was going to say, or how I was going to say it. "Nothing happened. We just went to a club, that's all," I said.

"I don't care. Don't talk to me right now, okay. I can't even look at you right now," he said keeping his back to me.

Still staring up at the ceiling and placing my hands over my face, I blurted out, "I'm sorry! I think I'm in love with Leonardi. I tried not to be, but I couldn't help it."

David turned his torso around and looked at me in the dark again. "You're what!"

"I'm in love with Leonardi," I admitted again. David rotated back on his side away from me again. There was dead silence. As I continued to gaze up at the ceiling I stated, "David, I need to move out." David didn't say anything. He just fell asleep.

He got up very early the next morning and left the house while I still slept. After dragging myself into the shower in the late morning, I called Leonardi at the salon. "He knows now. David knows," I said plainly.

"Hold on. I'm going to get Sidney and put her on the phone. Just hold on," Leonardi replied.

I spoke briefly with Sidney, and late that afternoon found my way up to her apartment on West 72nd Street and Amsterdam Avenue. It was a large one-bedroom in a pre-war building on the 10th floor. She had five locks on her front door.

There was a kitchenette on the left side of the hall entrance. Her living room had a sectional black leather couch and a glass/chrome coffee table. Her cast-iron bed, covered in a zebra print, sat on the other side of the room next to an antique wooden dresser decorated with a purple beaded lamp. All the walls in the room were a dark mauve color. It looked like a bordello. I assumed Sidney slept in the living room, and I was going to rent out the bedroom.

The bedroom was spacious, bright and unfurnished with white walls, but the bathroom entrance was in the bedroom. Sidney would have to come into my room if she wanted to use the bathroom, which did not give me much privacy. "A minor inconvenience," I thought.

I felt uncomfortable around Sidney. She appeared cold hearted. She dressed in cheap tacky clothes, and her face had a bitter frozen expression. Her entire being was icy.

Sidney told me my share would be $700 a month, not including utilities. I didn't tell her I could not afford it. I thanked her for showing the apartment to me and would let her know by the end of the week what I was going to do. I still did not have a steady job. I only had $2,000 in the bank, which I had been saving for my share of the trip to Europe. Maybe I just had to realize that I wasn't going to Europe. I was going to live here.

It was not in my heart to move in with Sidney. I was scared. She was not Leonardi and she was not David. She was a stranger to me, and not the type of person I would gravitate towards knowing, let alone live with. I guess I should have trusted my gut instincts, but I felt between a rock and a hard place. I did not want to live with Sidney, but I could not stay with David either. Also, I trusted Leonardi's recommendations, because he had known Sidney for some time, and had worked with her for quite a few years now at the salon. Perhaps it would be okay, but I had my doubts.

On my way back to David's apartment, I realized that I was not going to Europe. I realized that our relationship was over. When I walked in the door of our apartment, I found David standing there with a pile of my clothes on hangers, throwing them out into the hallway. All my stuff was all over the floor in the living room and hanging out of the bedroom dresser drawers. He kept grabbing stuff and throwing it out the door into the hallway, "You want to move out! Here move out!" he screamed.

The dog was all excited, barking at David and prancing around the hardwood floors in the living room. I retrieved my clothes in the hallway. As I kept picking them up, David kept throwing another pile at me in the hallway. "Here! Move out! Get the hell out of here! Go!" he cried.

I knelt down on the pile of clothes in the hall and started crying, "Stop! Stop! Please Stop! Please stop."

David stopped and looked at me. He dropped everything and slumped down on the dining room chair holding his head in one hand. "I don't want to hurt you. I'm sorry," he said.

I wandered back into the apartment. "I'm sorry. It's my fault," I insisted. I bent down to pick up the clothes in the bedroom doorway.

David came in, grabbed my hair, and banged my head against the plush carpet in the bedroom. The odd thing was that he kept moving my head against the carpet by holding my hair, but he broke the impact of my head with the floor by pulling back, so my head did not actually make contact with the floor.

He did not want to physically hurt me, and had no real intention of doing so, even though he felt like it. I almost started laughing, because he wasn't banging my head at all. My head hardly made contact with the floor and the carpet on the floor was too thick to hurt me anyway. David was obviously more hurt than angry. I still cried out for him to stop though, and to let go of my hair.

He moved away, holding his hands to his face. "What am I doing? God, this is crazy. What am I doing? Look at me. I'm a woman beater." He was shocked at his own behavior.

"No, you're not. Stop that," I said.

"But look at what I was doing?" he cried.

"You're being ridiculous now. You didn't do anything. Okay. It's all right. We need to just calm down, and talk. Okay?"

We sat on the couch and talked for a long time. It was not only a civil, conversation, it was warm and loving. David was hurt and upset, but he didn't hate me, and I didn't hate him.

"So now what?" You can't live here. Are you going to move in with Leonardi?"

"No, I'm not moving in with Leonardi. I am going to get my own place and be on my own. That's why I was out so late, because I was supposed to meet this woman Sidney who needs a roommate," I explained.

"This guy may not even be in love with you. Is he?"

"I don't really know. We were only together twice. What I do know is that it's not fair to you, and I should move out. I'm not going to move in with Leonardi. I'm just going to get my own place. I never had my own apartment. I went from my parent's house to your house. Maybe I need time to live by myself and get in touch with how I really feel and what I really want. Sidney, one of the hair colorists at the salon, needs a roommate."

"I know Sidney. Years ago she used to hang out with a mutual friend, Helen. They were good friends at one time. They met at the beauty school they both attended after high school," David said pleased.

"Oh, you know Sidney?"

"Yeah, Sidney and Helen go way back."

"So she would be okay to room with? She seems kind of weird," I admitted.

"Oh, Sidney is okay. Yeah, I think so. I mean. This was years ago when Helen knew her, but I always run into her at the salon and she seems cool," David assured me.

"Okay. That's good to hear, because I don't know her and I was wasn't sure if it was a good idea to live with her."

"No, Sidney's fine. I'm sure she'll be okay to move in with. What about our trip to Europe? David asked.

"I don't know. I just assumed that you wouldn't want to go to Europe with me anymore."

"We already bought the tickets, and we already sent in the money to reserve the hotels for you, me, and Tom. That's a lot of money to throw down the toilet. It's coming up in only a few weeks and I don't want to go without you. I don't want to go to Europe with just Tom. That would be a real drag. I still want to go to Europe with you," David insisted.

"But I'll be moving in with Sidney by the end of the week," I said confused.

"So what? You can still go to Europe with us. I want you to see Europe. I can't go without you. I'm not going, if you don't go with me. What about Tom? Tom is counting on it. If you don't go, I won't go, and then Tom won't go. It's just going to cancel out everyone's trip if you don't go," David argued.

"Yeah, but if I go to Europe, how am I going to pay the rent at Sidney's while I'm gone, and how am I going to have the money to pay for it when I get back?

"Sublet it for the month. People do that all the time," David enthusiastically suggested.

"You mean move in for the first few weeks and then sublet it right way for the next four weeks while I'm gone?"

"Why not? There's always someone on vacation looking for an apartment for a short time in New York, especially in the spring and summer," David suggested again.

"Do you think Sidney would let me do that?"

"Yeah, I don't see why not," David replied.

David and I went to the coffee shop for burgers and he offered to help me move what few belongings I had into Sidney's place that week. He fully expected me to go to Europe with him with no objections. I told him I'd see if I could work it out with Sidney. Sidney might not like the idea of me subletting the apartment to a total stranger only a few weeks after I had moved in. I was still unsure about the whole European trip, but I went along with it for the evening because it calmed David down and put him into better spirits. I saw things differently though. Rather than going to Europe with David and Tom, I would take a job, pay the rent, and spend time with Leonardi.

I called Sidney the next day to tell her that I would be moving in and that I might leave for Europe in the same month.

She said, "Yeah, sure no problem. Where are you going?"

I laughed. "Actually, I'm probably not going anywhere. But I *may* have to go to Europe because all the hotels have been booked and the plane fare is already paid for. I mean, everything is very out of balance right now and I most likely won't go. I want to go to Europe. I'm very confused. I just wanted to know if I had the option to sublet the place while I'm gone in case I did go."

"Yeah, sure. Are you going to come back?" Sidney inquired.

I laughed again nervously, "Yeah, of course. It would just be for a month. Plus, I most likely won't be going anyway."

I stopped by Sidney's place that evening to give her the first month's rent. When I scrambled home to David's apartment, I called Leonardi, "I just gave Sidney one month's rent and I'll be moving into her apartment in a couple of days."

"That's great!" Leonardi said with excitement, "You'll see Whitney. Everything is going to work out."

"Yeah, I think so too. Listen, David and I have already paid for our trip to Europe, and he keeps insisting that I go with him. It's coming up in a few weeks."

"Are you going to go?"

"No, no of course not. I mean I can't. I just haven't been able to break the news to him because his mind is totally set on me going. He won't take no for an answer."

"He hasn't let go of you yet," Leonardi replied.

"What do you expect? I mean, everything that's gone down between us has happened in only a matter of two weeks. And for David, it's only been a matter of a few days. I can't even imagine what it's been like for him. We already paid for the trip and everything." I explained.

"He needs to let go of you," Leonardi insisted.

"I know, but he's already paid for most of the trip, and our friend Tom, who is coming with us, already paid for most of the trip also. Everyone is going to be disappointed and lose a lot of money that they can't afford to throw away. I have to convince David to go without me and just take Tom with him. I haven't been able to do that yet."

"He needs to let go of you," Leonardi stated sternly.

As I packed my belongings at David's apartment, things were quiet and subdued. I only had some clothes, books, and a few knick-knacks to pack, along with my desk and a foam bed/couch. David was very quiet. He didn't whine, yell, or show emotion.

He handed me a little monkey puppet he had won for me at the Italian street festival in Little Italy one summer. "You may want to bring him with you," he said sadly. David had bought me many sweet little gifts over the years. "And here is your book to put you to sleep at night. *Good night, Moon*, he said quietly.

"Thanks." I gently placed it in the cardboard box with some other trinkets and books.

CHAPTER TWELVE

MY NEW HOME AND A NEW BEGINNING

SIDNEY GREETED ME at her apartment with the keys. There were five locks on the inside of the door in addition to a latch with a chain. I counted all the keys on the key ring, including one for the lobby door and one for the mailbox. David and Sidney made small talk. Before he left, he looked back at me.

"She'll be fine," Sidney said to him, as he slowly walked out the door.

I had hoped Leonardi would call me at Sidney's my first night in my new place. He did not call. I thought perhaps it was for the best, since I had a lot of unpacking to do. By 10 p.m., I was very tired and I fell asleep anyway.

In the morning, I walked around the neighborhood to locate the necessities: dry cleaners, grocery store, drug store and a bank. I spent the rest of the day rearranging my things. I assumed Sidney was at the salon all day working. There was no word from Leonardi during that day or evening. David did not call either. It was a strange feeling, but perhaps it was to be expected considering my new situation. By late evening, I was anxious, but consoled myself. Maybe everyone wants to give me some space, and give themselves some space too, especially David. I didn't call anyone either, and turned in early. I heard Sidney come home, finally, around one in the morning.

The next day, I called David at work to tell him I may have forgotten a pair of shoes in his closet. He told me he'd bring them by, because he wanted to drop off some more brochures for me to choose which towns in Tuscany to see just outside of Florence.

"David, I don't think I should go."

"What!" David bellowed.

"I can't go."

"You have to go! What's Tom going to do? We have a responsibility towards Tom too, you know," David shouted.

"I know, but it doesn't make any sense. I moved out because of Leonardi, and now I'm going to Europe with you? That's crazy."

"You can figure it out with Leonardi when you come back," he snapped.

"I can't go!" I cried.

"You've got to go!"

"I can't!"

"Don't do this to me. Okay. Don't do this. If you don't go, I'm not going and then Tom's not going. Everyone's tickets and hotels are paid for—we can't get a reimbursement, alright? You're going!" he demanded.

"I can't," I insisted again.

"Why not?" he asked furious.

"It feels wrong."

David got calm again. "It's wrong, if you don't go. Don't you want to see Europe? You've never been to Europe. Don't you want to see Paris, Venice, and Rome? God! This is crazy. I want you to see Europe. I want you to come with us."

"I can't go!" I pleaded again.

David snapped, "You need to think this over some more. I can't cancel anything. We're just going to sit on it for now. I gotta go, bye."

David wanted to go to Europe, and he wanted me with him. But I decided I was not going. David could sit on it for as long as he wanted to, because I was not going.

That night, with still no phone call from Leonardi, I sat in my room feeling isolated and lost. I called Leonardi at home, but only got his answering machine.

The next morning was Saturday, and Sidney was off from work, and hanging out around the apartment. She prowled through my room to go into the bathroom and stayed there for over two hours. I knocked on the door.

"Sidney, are you all right?"

Her voice filtered through the door, "Yeah, I'm in the bathtub."

I stood outside the bathroom door with my knees bent and legs scrunched together. "Oh, I'm sorry to disturb you, but I really need to pee."

"I'll be out in a few minutes," she called out.

I sat on the bed with my legs crossed, moving my body back and forth for about another twenty minutes trying to hold on.

Finally, Sidney stood at the open door, her anorexic wrinkly body, dramatized under a black sheer baby-doll nightie laced with faux fur trim from *Fredrick's of Hollywood*. Her fire engine red toe-nails peeked out through a pair of high heel slippers decorated with furry black powder puffs. Her brittle hair was piled high on her head with a red silk kerchief. She carried a small paperback book in her hand. My eyes popped out of my head in horror and disbelieve.

Sidney slithered out of the bathroom slowly and nonchalantly, "Wow, that bath felt great," she purred. "Sorry I took so long, but I was in there masturbating to Herman Hesse. Have you ever read Herman Hesse?" she added.

"No, umm I haven't," I replied with a gulp. I didn't know who Herman Hesse was at the time. I assumed she was reading pornography, because she was dressed like a Transylvanian hooker, and casually admitted to spending the time in the bathroom masturbating.

"Oh, you must read some Herman Hesse," she purred again, as she strolled back into the living room onto her bed.

I scurried into the bathroom, slammed the door, and quickly dragged down my jeans over my legs to finally relieve myself in the steamy bathroom. I was freaking out.

After I got out of the bathroom, I closed my bedroom door to call the salon for Leonardi, but the receptionist told me he wasn't in that day. I called him at home and got his answering machine. I left a message hoping he'd call me back soon. I called the salon again and asked where he was and when he would be in.

"Leonardi is out of the country," the receptionist stated.

"Out of the country? Is he on assignment? I asked.

"I don't know. Who is this?" She quipped.

"I'm a friend of his. He would be expecting my call."

"Well, I can't give you any confidential information."

"Can you just tell me when he'll be back in town?"

"Are you calling to make a hair styling appointment?" she asked, annoyed.

"No, like I said, I'm a friend of his, and he's expecting my call."

"Well, he left abruptly and no one knows when he'll be back."

"Did he go out of the country to do a magazine shoot or something? Is he out of the country working?" I probed.

"Ma'am, that's confidential information. I think you should call back sometime next week. Maybe he'll be back by then."

I sat back on my couch, thinking this was weird. This was really weird. I could understand that he may have had to leave the country on a fashion shoot, and I could understand that he may have had to leave right away because that's the nature of his business, but why didn't he call me at some point between here and the airport, or at least leave a message with the receptionist at the salon, to let me know he would be gone, and when he would be back? Sidney and Leonardi had worked together as associates at the same salon every day for years, and I was her new roommate. Why didn't he give her the message concerning his sudden departure?

I stood in the doorway that separated my bedroom and Sidney's room. Sidney was still lounging on her bed, displayed like a decayed corpse in erotic lingerie, reading her book.

"Sidney did you see Leonardi at work yesterday?"

Sidney never looking away from her book, "No, I didn't. I haven't seen him for a few days now."

"Do you know where he went?"

Still looking at her book, she said, "No, I have no idea."

I called the receptionist the next day to see if Leonardi was back in the States, and again she told me, "No." I called his apartment. He picked up the phone. "Oh, Leonardi. Thank God! I've been trying to reach you," I said relieved.

"I can't talk to you." He hung up. I stood in my room with my brain tingling. What the hell was that all about? He didn't sound angry. That was a good sign. He sounded hurried, but he did not sound upset or angry. So that was good. What did he sound like? I thought for a moment. I had heard a bit of panic in his voice, but I wasn't sure. Was it panic? Yes, it sounded like panic. I think I heard panic. Or was I hearing my own panic? No, it sounded like his panic. I wasn't really sure what I had just heard. I dialed the phone again. "Hello?" he whispered.

"Leonardi, why did you just hang up on--?

"I can't talk to you anymore." Click.

A stab of pain shot through my chest as I stood there with the phone receiver in my hand. I was in the twilight zone. I dialed the phone again.

Leonardi answered it again. "Hello?" he whispered.

"Leonardi what the--."

"Don't call me anymore. You can't call here. We can't talk to each other any--."

"But--."

"Do NOT call here!" Click.

I dialed the phone again, he picked it up, but I couldn't get a word in quickly enough. "No, I don't under --." Click. "What's going on?" I whispered to myself. I shook my head in disbelief and confusion. Yes, he did sound panicked, and he sounded scared but why? I grabbed my jacket and my keys and headed out the door to Leonardi's apartment.

Leonardi's lobby had a doorman at the front desk that screened and announced guests on the house phone. I had to find a way to sneak past him. If Leonardi wasn't going to talk to me on the phone and explain himself, he certainly was not going to allow the doorman to let me up to his apartment. Luckily, a group of five people were walking into the lobby, and I strolled in with them trying to blend in with the group. It was fortunate that the doorman recognized at least a few of the people in the group as regular tenants, so he didn't stop us. The doorman nodded and tipped his hat. I kept looking straight ahead trying to appear as if I was with the small party of people as we headed into the open elevator.

I stood in front of Leonardi's apartment door and rang the bell. He opened the door wide, saw me, and slammed it shut.

"Leonardi! What are you doing! What's going on? I banged on the door again, and buzzed his bell. "Leonardi please open the door!" He opened the door again but only half way, sticking his head out. He didn't sound angry with me. He looked frightened. "How did you get in here? You have to leave. You have to go now." He was closing the door again. I tried to keep it open with my hands.

"Leonardi! Please tell me what's going on! Please! Please, Leonardi! Leonardi spread his legs, planting his feet firmly in the carpet and pushed harder, finally closing the door on me.

"What the hell is going on? Leonardi, please open the door!" I pleaded. I kept banging on the door and ringing the bell, but he wouldn't answer or even talk to me from the other side. I leaned my back against the heavy metal door and slid down. I crouched on the floor, raised my knees, hid my head in my chest and wept. I sat forlorn, and he still never came out. I got up and knocked on the door a few more times. "Leonardi, I don't understand. Please talk to me. Help me understand what's going on," I said more quietly now. There was only silence. I sat down against the door again.

Maybe it was best to leave. Leonardi did not appear angry with me, just scared, so I started to realize that he might be in danger. There was no other explanation for his bizarre behavior. Whatever was going on, I wasn't going to know what it was until Leonardi was ready to tell me. I got up, walked to the elevator, and went home.

Home? I wasn't going home. I was going to Sidney's apartment. That wasn't home. I had moved out of David's house to be with Leonardi. Instead, I was going home to Sidney, a weird middle-aged woman who was like a character in a low-budget horror film. I was frightened.

When I got back to the apartment, Sidney was gone and I didn't know where she went or when she was coming back. I mulled around the house feeling drained and exhausted. I was afraid for Leonardi. What kind of danger could he be in? Was he in very serious trouble? What could it possibly be?

Who could possibly want to harm him and why? There was not a hateful or vengeful bone in that man's body. I couldn't see him doing anything bad to anyone that would make them want to go after him. None of it made any sense. My brain was on overload. I couldn't eat, and in the evening, I still wasn't hungry. Sidney was still out and I suspected she would probably not be back until the wee hours of the morning, so I called Leonardi's apartment again. He answered the phone. "Hello?" he whispered.

"Leonardi, don't hang up! It's Whitney. What is going on? Talk to me," I pleaded.

"It's over. I can't see you anymore, and I can't talk to you. Don't call here," he whispered loudly. Click.

I called him again and got his answering machine. I yelled into the phone. "Leonardi! Pick-up-the-phone! Leonardi! Pick-up-the-phone! I deserve an explanation! Leonardi! Leonardi, if you don't pick up the phone right now, I'm coming over there and I'm not going to leave until you tell me what's going on! I'll go to the hair salon. I'll go there and I'll make a big scene, Leonardi! I will Leonardi, I will! Leonardi!"

Leonardi got on the line. "I can't see you anymore," he whispered frantically.

"I heard that part. But why can't you see me anymore? I just moved into Sidney's house less than three days ago and now you're breaking up with me? Why?"

"I can't talk about it. I can't talk to you. It's over," he pleaded.

"But why!!" I cried.

"It's over. I'm not going to see you and I'm not going to talk to you anymore. It's over. Don't call me anymore. Please stay away," he begged.

"But why?" I wept.

"I'm sorry." Click.

God help me! I was going to end up in a straight jacket. This couldn't be happening. It wasn't happening. This was not happening. I wanted somebody to wake me from this nightmare. Now my brain and body were in over-drive. I reclined on the couch starring at the ceiling for some time. I then got up and turned on the radio to try and stop my brain. Madonna's song, "I'm Crazy for You," played.

I sat down at my desk and wrote a three-page letter to Leonardi, telling him how much I loved him, and I did not understand why he was refusing to see me or speak to me. I wanted to know what I could do. I would write a few pages only to tear them up and start over. I wrote and wrote until about three in the morning. I stayed up all night, and at about six in the morning, as the sun was coming up and the streets were very quiet, I went to his apartment building. I didn't see a doorman, so I scurried across the lobby and jumped into the elevator.

I knocked on his door and rang the bell, but no one answered. I tried to stick the envelope under his door, but the envelope was too thick and the space under his door was too narrow. I kept ringing the bell. Finally, I heard a noise on the other side of the door.

"Who is it?"

I recognized Leonardi's voice.

"It's me, Whitney," I said quietly but firmly.

"I told you to go away!" he whispered loudly from the other side of the door.

"Leonardi, I don't know what is going on, and since you're not going to tell me, at least take this letter. It's a goodbye letter, okay? Open the door, take it and I'll leave. I'll never come back, okay? I promise. Take the letter. Can you at least do that for me?" I pleaded.

"Then will you go away?" he insisted.

"Yes, yes, I will. I promise. Please just open the door and take the letter," I wept. Leonardi opened the door halfway, and I could see that he was naked under his white, terry cloth bathrobe. I placed my hand in the door with the letter, and he quickly snatched it.

"Are you alone?" I asked.

"Yes, I'm alone," he replied. As he was closing the door, I found myself pushing it open again. "Leonardi, please. I just need to talk. I need to understand. Please tell me what's wrong. Please," I begged. Leonardi was furious as he grabbed my wrist and pushed me back out into the hallway. "Get out of here, now! And don't come back! It's over!" he yelled. Scared, I ran down the hall, into the elevator, and out into the street. It was so surreal, I couldn't even cry. I was traumatized.

I returned to Sidney's apartment. Sidney was still asleep and probably would be for most of the day. I don't think she came home until around three in the morning. I thought, "Oh, my God. What's happening to me? Somebody wake me up from this terrible nightmare." Without having any sleep in the past twenty-four hours, no food, having this bizarre experience with Sidney, and then with Leonardi, my mind and my body were in shock. I had to make some very fast decisions. Now that Leonardi was out of the picture, and out of my life, for reasons I could not fathom, I could not stay with Sidney. Sidney was a nut job. But I couldn't go back to David's house either. It would be wrong to ask David to take me back, and I wasn't sure if I wanted to be there anyway. I was more confused than ever about everything.

It was seven thirty in the morning and I knew David would be up taking a shower and getting ready to go out for the day. I could still catch him at home.

"Hi! What's up?" He sounded wide awake, chipper, and happy to hear from me.

"I'm coming with you and Tom to Europe," I proclaimed.

"Well, yeah, of course you are, silly. I never thought that you weren't coming with us," he chuckled.

"I thought I wasn't coming."

"That's because you're Polish," he joked.

"Yeah, I'm also half Italian. I grew up eating spaghetti."

"Well, then, you're a spaghetti head. I knew you would change your mind. It's Europe. You've never been there. It's going to be great. Of course, you're coming."

"I need to sublet my bedroom at Sidney's while I'm gone," I said.

"Okay, just put some advertisements up in the local health food stores, and anywhere else you can find a bulletin board. You can put an ad in the Village Voice. I'm sure you'll find someone," David suggested.

"You think so? We only have twelve days until our flight."

"Yeah, yeah, just make up some flyers. Don't worry about it. Either way, you're coming with us, so just try to get a sublet in the meantime. I'll give you a call later. Okay?" David promised.

"Yeah, okay?" I said, curious.

David's behavior was odd, but I was grateful to have him in my life. I was grateful for his stability and his loyalty. He was grounded and unusually well-adjusted, considering the circumstances. His humor brought back my sanity. He was being so nice to me after the terrible thing I had done to him. He really wanted me to see Europe with him. I felt even guiltier because I had hurt him by moving out. I had broken his trust in me and now he was handling it so well. Why was he now handling it so well? Why was I asking so many questions! *Stop it!*, I said to myself.

I fell asleep for most of the day and woke up around six in the evening still hungry, but I wasn't sure if I would be able to eat. Sidney was nowhere to be found. I guessed she might be at work or just out. I hurried downstairs to a local Chinese take-out and ordered fried dumplings, fried rice, an egg roll, and a coke to take back up to the apartment--just what I needed, MSG. I had to eat something though, and I couldn't focus on shopping for anything healthy.

David called me a few hours later and we talked for awhile. I didn't mention anything about Sidney or anything that had happened between me and Leonardi. I wanted to wait until I saw him, so I asked if I could come by his apartment the next night.

"Tomorrow night's not good because Tom asked me to go with him to a party at one of the record companies he works for. But how about the following night?" he asked.

"Okay." I agreed. I was disappointed and felt a bit snubbed by David. He had never turned me down like that or put his own plans before me. But I realized, "Come on, what do you expect? Give the guy a break. You're the one who slept with another man and moved out."

"Is anything wrong?" he asked.

"No. It can wait. Go to the party. Have a good time. We can talk the day after. Sidney just walked in the door, and I need to talk with her about subletting my room for a month. Let me go, and I'll see you soon," I said.

Sidney had grocery bags in her hand and was putting a few things in the refrigerator. "Hi. How's it going?" she pleasantly asked.

"Not so good," I admitted.

"Oh, what's wrong? You don't like the apartment?"

"No, no it's not that. It's fine."

Sidney walked into the living room, kicked off her shoes, and pulled off her shirt. "Talk to me. What's going on?"

"Leonardi won't talk to me. I moved in here to be with him. Since I've been here, he hasn't called me, and when I call him, he won't talk to me. He won't see me. He just hangs up the phone," I explained.

"Did you guys have a fight or something?" she asked as she pulled down her pants, rolled them off her feet, and threw them across the room onto the bed.

"No, that's just it. We never fought about anything. There was no fight. Leonardi introduced me to you and set it up for me to move in with you so he and I could be together. Leonardi and I... you know. I mean, I moved out of David's. Well, you know the story. You know David from years back," I rambled on.

Sidney slipped off her bra and panties. Naked, she walked across the living room towards her dresser near the bed. She bent over looking through the open drawer, but stopped and turned to talk with me, "Yeah, yeah? I haven't seen David in years, except for occasionally running into him at the salon when he started coming to get his haircut. He always seemed like a really nice guy," Sidney replied.

"Well, I was living with David for five years, and then I recently met Leonardi, and we had a very heavy thing going on. That's why I moved out of David's and moved here," I added.

"To be with Leonardi right? Yeah, I knew that much. Go on," she said.

Sidney finally, thank God, found a piece of clothing in the dresser drawer and slipped on a silky, red polyester kimono.

"Okay. I don't understand why Leonardi suddenly won't talk to me. He just hangs up the phone. I went over there, and he wouldn't even open the door."

"Did he say why?"

"That's just it. He won't say anything. He just told me to go away and he sounded so frightened," I replied. I explained, in detail, Leonardi's behavior to Sidney.

Sidney strolled to the kitchen to get a glass of coke with ice. She put a few shots of rum in it and stirred it with her finger. "That's strange. I don't know what to tell you." Sidney licked the beverage from her fingers.

"You see Leonardi at work every day. You've known him longer than I have. You must have some idea of what is going on?" I asked.

"Leonardi hasn't been at work hardly at all for the past week," Sidney replied.

"Isn't that odd?"

"No. I don't know. Not really… You say, 'he sounded frightened?'" Sidney asked.

"Yes, he sounded frightened. No, not just frightened, panicked. He didn't sound mad at me. I mean it didn't seem like he was angry at me for anything. He just shut me out, like he was hiding from someone or something. I got the sense that he was in serious trouble. I don't know how to explain it," I said.

"Do you know about Maria?" Sidney asked.

"Maria? Maria? Who's Maria?"

"She was a runway model in Milan that he fell in love with."

"Yeah, he mentioned her to me, but I assumed that she was someone he was seeing quite a while back, and that he had broken up with her some time ago. Was it more recent?" I asked. Sidney nodded.

"How recent?" I asked.

Sidney stood in the middle of the living room and stared out the window. She took another sip of her rum and coke, moved a lit cigarette up to her lips, and raised her chin high blowing the smoke up to the ceiling.

"I'm not sure. A year ago, more or less. I don't remember. But they were supposed to get married. She was living in Milan, though, with a very wealthy and powerful Italian Mafia guy. He wasn't going to let her go. He would have killed Leonardi or her, or both of them. They broke it off. It was too dangerous," Sidney explained.

"Have you ever met her? Do you know her?"

"Yeah, I know Maria. I know Maria very well, and I think Leonardi is still in love with her," Sidney smirked.

Sidney's insensitivity to my feelings made me shiver. Sidney continued to stare out the window into the distance. "I don't know. From what you've told me, it sounds like he may be with her right now. But I can't tell you that for sure. If I were you, I would forget about Leonardi for now," Sydney suggested.

"What are looking at?" I asked.

"I can see Leonardi's window from here. His building is right there. Straight ahead. And his light is on."

I looked out the window. "Which building?"

Sidney pointed with her cigarette, "Right there."

"That's five blocks away. We can't see anything in his window."

"No, but if you had a high-powered telescope or something, you could," she suggested.

"Well, that's not going to happen. I don't want to spy on him. I just want to know the truth. I want him to tell me what is going on," I replied.

"If you want my advice, since he's not willing to tell you anything right now, I would stay away from him. If that's what he's asking you to do, and if that's what he wants, you should do it," she insisted.

"I've decided to go to Europe for three or four weeks, so I was wondering if I could get someone to sublet my room here while I'm gone," I asked.

"Yeah, sure. Just make sure whomever you bring in is not a thief or anything," Sidney warned.

"No, no. I'll be careful. Thanks Sidney. I really appreciate it."

"No problem. I'm pretty tired, so I'm going to hit the hay," she yawned.

"Okay, goodnight."

CHAPTER THIRTEEN

ROOM FOR RENT

THE NEXT MORNING, I typed up an advertisement for the sublet on my Selectric typewriter. I ran down to a nearby copy store on Broadway, made some flyers, and pasted them all over the neighborhood. That evening, I got a call from a woman named Ann. She wanted to come over immediately to see the apartment, but it was already eleven at night, much too late, so I asked her to come by in the morning instead. She was very eager, and insisted on making our appointment as early as possible.

Ann, a short chubby woman in her late thirties, showed up wearing a cornflower, sleeveless, faded house dress. I offered her something to drink and she took a glass of water with ice. Her hands were shaking. She then sat on the couch hunched over a bit and with her palms nervously ironed out the creases of the dress fabric draped over her lap.

"Why do you need to move?" I asked.

"I'm divorcing my husband," she replied.

"Why do you need a place for only one month? Wouldn't you want to find a long-term rental?"

"Yes, but I need something as soon as possible. I'm not going to find anything long-term right away. I saw your ad in the grocery store and I thought one month here could give me some time away from him, you know," she confessed.

"Is there any domestic violence?" I asked concerned.

"No, no. We're just not getting along, and the sooner I get into my own space the better," she smiled nervously. Ann's story sounded suspicious, so I thanked her for her time and told her I would give her a call at the end of the week.

"I have more people to see," I said. Ann's face swelled up like a ripe tomato, and she began to sob.

"Please, I need this apartment. I need to get away from him. Please, help me," she begged, tears streaming down her face.

I didn't know what to do. I put my hand on her shoulder. "Oh, oh boy, what's wrong?" What happened?" I asked awkwardly.

"He drinks. He drinks a lot," she wept.

"I see. Is he hurting you?" I asked as I gave her some tissues.

"No, not physically, but he's so mean. I always feel like he's going to hit me, you know. If I can get some space for at least a month, I can think a bit, you know," she begged.

"How long have you two been married?"

"Only a couple of years. He's changed a lot. He's just not the same person I married. I need to get some distance, some space. If I can stay here for a month, then he won't be in my face all the time. I can breathe a little and get some perspective. Maybe I won't be so confused. I just started this new job, so it's important that I have a clear head," Ann explained. I felt badly for the woman, and I thought she was sincere.

"I'll tell you what. Write down your references that I can call, and I'll seriously consider you and give you a call before the end of the week," I offered.

"Only call me at a certain time when I will be there to pick up the phone. I don't want him to know. I'm home by six in the evening," she warned.

"You won't end up bringing him here, will you?" I said firmly.

"No, no. Absolutely not. I don't want him to find me. I'm breaking loose completely. There's no way in hell he's coming here," she bellowed.

"That's good. That's important. I need to know I can trust you on that," I said.

"You have my word. I'm a really quiet and clean person. I will take good care of the place while you're gone. I promise," she insisted.

"Okay, well, you have some good references here. I'll call them," I assured her.

"You can call my boss at this number, and here is the name of a woman I work with. I started the job there a week ago. And you can call my sister in Michigan."

"Okay, that sounds good. I can't promise you anything, but I will think about it. Ann, thank you for coming, and I'm sure everything will work out fine."

"God, bless you." She smiled as she took my hands in hers. "Thank you so much, and God bless you," she said again before turning to finally leave.

I was hoping that someone else would call me for the apartment. I had only ten days left until my flight for Europe. It was good that I got a call right away, but I felt that this woman needed professional help, and I might be getting in too deep by letting her stay here. I wanted to help her though. She seemed like she needed it. No one else called me for the sublet over the next two days. Then the phone rang. It was a woman in her thirties named Margie.

She sounded strange. She spoke in a monotone, slow, sing-song kind of voice. She told me that she was living with her husband and wanted her own space for a few weeks. A voice was talking at her loudly in the background, sounding like a three hundred pound gorilla. I asked her, "Who's that in the background?"

"Oh, that's my husband," Margie said.

"I don't have anything available for a married couple. I'm looking for a single woman to take the place for a month only," I explained.

"No, he's not moving in with me. I'm looking for a place for myself for a month."

"I don't understand. Why don't you stay where you are with your husband? Are you separating or something?" I asked.

"No, we're not separating. I just need some space to myself for a short time . . . Yeah, yeah, Stan shut up already! I'll take care of it in a minute . . . You see what I mean? He's always up my ass about something. I need some time and space to myself . . . Alright already! . . . Sorry about that."

"Do you work? What do you do for a living?" I asked.

"Yeah, I work," Margie snapped.

"Well, what do you do for a living?" I inquired again.

"I'm a magician."

"Oh, that's interesting. What kind of magician are you?"

"Well, actually I'm not a magician - magician, like the rabbit out-of-the-hat kind of magician. I'm a mind reader."

"A mind reader? That's what you do for a living? You read minds?"

"Sort of," she said.

"Do you have a job?"

"I just told you I'm a magician," she insisted.

"I mean do you get paid for your work, like The Amazing Kreskin or something."

"Yeah, sometimes," she moaned.

"What I'm trying to find out is whether you have a regular job," I explained.

"Well, not really. I don't have a regular job. I read minds," she quipped.

"Can you read my mind right now?"

"Well, uh, yeah. That's my gift. That's what I do," she said frustrated.

"What am I thinking right now?"

"Well, hell, I don't know," she snapped.

"I appreciate your call. The sublet has already been taken. But thank you." A moment later, the phone rang. I picked it up. It was Margie screaming at me into the receiver. "You are a very closed-minded, judgmental person! I don't want your space anyway! I couldn't live with someone as narrow-minded as you anyway! So fuck you!" Click, dial tone.

I guessed Ann was a better choice for a sublet, and probably the only choice in the time frame I had. I called her references and they sounded legitimate. I called Ann after six in the evening, and she was eager to come by that night to give me a month's rent. "God bless you, God bless you. You're an angel," she kept chanting before we hung up.

I felt good. I'm getting someone to pay the rent while I'm gone, and I'm also helping someone who needs it very badly. I'm relieving some suffering, including my own. Okay. Something positive just happened. That's good.

Sidney walked in that evening as Ann and I were sitting on the couch talking and going through two large brown bags of old clothes. "Sidney, I would like you to meet Ann. She's very interested in taking my space for a few weeks while I'm gone," I announced.

Ann immediately rose from the couch to greet Sidney. "Hello. So pleased to meet you. I'm a very quiet and clean person. I won't be in your way at all, Sidney. I promise. I work all day and at night I sit in bed and read. Oh, my, that's such a pretty dress you have on. I wish I was as young and thin as you are to wear something like that," Ann sighed.

"Thank you." Sidney smiled appreciatively.

Ann rambled on, "Oh and sorry for the mess here, we were just going through some old clothes that I don't wear any more. I thought Whitney here, and maybe you, might find something you could use. I hate to throw things out that are in such good condition. You may need to wash them first, but I have some very nice stuff here for the both of you."

"Would you excuse us a moment?" I asked Ann as I pulled Sidney gently into the bedroom.

"Oh, sure. Oh and Sidney! If you ever need me to shampoo the carpet, or wash the windows, do some grocery shopping for you, no problem," Ann eagerly offered.

"Great! Thanks!" Sidney said, surprised and pleased as she closed the bedroom door.

"Who did you find to sublet, Hazel the Maid?" Sidney laughed.

"You don't like her?" I asked concerned.

"No, no. She's great! I can have dinner parties, and she can serve the hors d'oeuvres. When is she moving in? How long is she staying?" Sidney asked pleased and excited.

"I told you I'll be gone for about four weeks," I said.

"Okay, well, if you want to stay there longer, I think you're covered. Have a nice trip," Sidney smiled.

The next day, I got a call for temporary office work that would last for the week before I left for my trip. It was an accounting firm with a lonely, sterile atmosphere. The rooms were painted gray and the old metal desks had yellowing Formica tops. Piles of boxes and open files cluttered the floor space. The people working there were like the florescent lighting, harsh. Managers with stern, pale faces walked around silently. The bookkeepers, typists and secretaries, most of them past the age of sixty, rarely got up from their desks, or looked up from their work to talk with one another. When they did get up, it was only to walk lethargically down the hall to get a cup of coffee, or visit the rest room. At lunchtime, they ate brown bag lunches of tuna fish or baloney sandwiches, and they never ventured out until it was time to go home.

I don't even know if they went home, because I left at five o'clock and they were still sitting there. When I returned in the morning they were already there. They gave me dirty looks as I put my jacket on and walked out the door to go to lunch or go home. I was paid by the hour and was only required to be there from nine to five.

I was restless and sad most of the day, still thinking about Leonardi, finding it difficult to accept that it was over, and wondering why. A gray-haired woman, donning cat eye glasses accented by silver chain and a pale yellow cardigan draped over her curved in shoulders, shuffled sluggishly past my desk. I thought I was going to fall into a coma just watching her snail her way to the copy machine. Life was a brilliant burst of music and color with Leonardi, and now I was in hell, a lifeless, colorless, expressionless void.

Was Leonardi with that woman Maria? Still, that would not explain why he was so paranoid and frightened. I could only speculate. I had no clue, no clarity, and no closure. I was so grateful for having the opportunity to escape this environment and be in Paris with David and Tom.

It was Friday, so I called Ann at her job before I left the accounting office. I wanted to touch base and check in to see if she was ready to move in.

"Ann no longer works here. We fired her," said a man's voice.

"What? When? Why?" I asked.

"That's confidential. Sorry, we can't give out any sensitive information," the voice replied. Click.

I called Ann at her home and a man with a gruff voice answered.

"Is Ann there?" I asked.

"Who is this!" the voice demanded.

"I'm the girl that Ann . . . is she there?"

"Who is this?" the voice demanded again.

"Ann is supposed to move into my apartment next week. I called her at her new job and she had been fired."

"You don't want Ann to move in with you. Wha'da ya crazy! She's a God damn alcoholic," the man yelled.

"Are you her husband?"

"Husband? She ain't got no husband! She's been crashin' on my couch for three months. She's a drunk!" he declared.

"How do I know you're telling the truth? She told me her husband was the alcoholic," I inquired.

"I told you she ain't got no husband! She got kids, but she lost custody of them, because she's a God damn drunk, yah hear me!"

"Is she there?"

"No, she ain't here. She's probably out somewhere drinkin' Southern Comfort. If you don't believe me you can call her social worker yourself," he insisted.

"If you hear from her can you--," Click. "Why do people hang up on me like that?" I asked myself.

I made my way quickly back to Sidney's apartment to see if Ann had called or left a message on my answering machine. She had, saying that she would try me again later. As I was taking off my jacket the phone rang. I caught it on the first ring.

"Hi, this is Ann. Listen is it possible that I can move in tonight? Something came up and I need a place tonight."

"Ann, you can't move in at all," I said.

"What do you mean? You said --."

"I changed my mind, sorry. Something came up for me too. My plans have changed," I explained.

"No, you can't do that. I gave you seven hundred dollars. You can't do that!" Ann insisted.

"I'll give the money back to you. Meet me tonight downstairs right around the corner from my building in front of Duane Read Drugstore on Broadway," I instructed.

"Why there?"

"Because there's a cash machine there. I spent twenty dollars of the seven hundred you gave me to buy eggs, milk, and bread this morning and a few other things. I only have six hundred and eighty dollars on me. I can get the rest in the cash machine near Duane Read," I explained.

"You spent my money?" She said accusingly.

"No, no, just twenty bucks. I have your money. I just have to get the other twenty bucks out of the cash machine."

"You better give me back *all* of my money!" She warned.

"I am going to give you back all your money. For God's sake, you think I want to steal twenty bucks?"

"All of it! I want all of it back!" She demanded.

"Yes all of it. Just meet me there at seven o'clock tonight."

"I can't be there at seven," Ann replied.

"Why not? Don't you want your money?"

"You better give me my money!" she demanded.

"I don't want your money! What time can you be there so I can give it back to you?" I asked again.

"Eight o'clock. I'll be there at eight o'clock. And give me back my clothes. I want my clothes!" she demanded.

"Yes, I will bring you the bags of clothes too. Just be there at eight p.m."

I withdrew Anne's twenty dollars from the cash machine and some pocket money for myself. I waited in front of Duane Read and within a few minutes, I saw Ann walking across the street from the north side of 72nd Street. A lanky man in his forties, dressed in a worn and dusty black suit was walking next to her. I thought, "Oh great. She doesn't trust me. She's bringing her posse."

"Where's my money?" Ann demanded.

"Let's go over here in the doorway?"

"Why? Just give me my money," Ann shouted.

"You need to count it? You don't want to stand out in the middle of the street and count it out in the open, do you? Someone might rob you," I explained.

"Is it all here?"

"Yes, of course, it's all there," I insisted.

The man in the suit was pacing close to Ann, listening in on our conversation. He looked around with a cracked smile on his face.

"Who is he?" I asked.

Ann turned around, looked at him and then looked at me. "I don't know who the hell he is."

"He was walking down the street with you, standing practically next to you, and acting like he knows you. He's standing here with us right now. You don't know this guy?" I whispered to Ann.

"No, I never saw him before in my life," Ann insisted.

The guy paced slowly around us, watching and listening to Ann and me. He unwrapped a stick of gum and dropped it into his mouth as he continued to eavesdrop. He surveyed the area to see if anyone else was watching.

"Excuse me sir, uumm, could you, like, get the fuck out of here?" I demanded.

"Hey man, I'm just waiting on a friend." He spread his arms out wide in front of him and backed up a few steps at the same time.

"Is he your friend?" I asked her again.

"No, I told you I never saw the guy in my life. Give me my money already!" she demanded.

I turned around to the guy who was now behind me. "She's not your friend, so get the fuck away from us. NOW!" I screamed.

Still chomping his gum with his mouth open, the man turned on his heel, with his arms gestured out again like a jitter bug dancer wearing a Zoot suit, "Hey, chill out man," he muttered. He strolled slowly away down the block, occasionally looking back.

"Please come over to the doorway and count your money," I pleaded.

Ann stood with her back to the street and counted the bills quickly. "Okay. It's all here. Are those my clothes?" she snapped.

"Yes!" I handed her a large plastic shopping bag.

"There's only one bag here. I had two bags?" She rummaged through the bag.

"All your clothes are there! I even washed them for Christ sakes!"

"I just want to make sure that they're all here. That's all," she snapped.

Ann defiantly marched away with her money and her large plastic bag of clothes in her arms. I wondered if she really did know the character who was hanging around so close to us. *Whatever*, I thought. It's just more speculation, a lot of speculation. It's hurting my brain. I clambered back up to Sidney's place.

With no one to sublet my room while I was in Europe, I was not going to have much money to live on when I came back. I was leaving in four days. When I got back from Europe, I could be homeless. If I stayed here in the States with no job, I could be homeless.

Sidney was sitting on the couch watching TV when I walked in. "Ann's not moving in. There was a change of plans," I blurted out as I fetched a carton from the refrigerator and poured myself a glass of orange juice.

"Oh, what happened?" she asked, disappointed and concerned.

"Nothing. Nothing. She just changed her mind, that's all," I said.

"Can you change it back for her?" Sidney asked.

"No, no. It won't work out believe me. Trust me on this one. Just let it go," I wearied.

"Are you still going to Europe?" Sidney inquired.

"I don't know who I am, what I'm doing, or where the hell I'm going," I stated bluntly as I exited into my bedroom and flopped face down on my bed couch.

Sidney looked in, "Just keep me posted, okay?"

"Okay," I muffled with my face in the pillow.

CHAPTER FOURTEEN

THE BLACK ROCK

LEONARDI'S BIRTHDAY IS in May. My birthday is in June. David and Tom had arranged it so that we would be in Venice on my birthday. But I didn't expect to be in Venice on my birthday. I didn't know where I would be or where would Leonardi be on his.

I didn't understand Leonardi's behavior or what had happened, but it did not change my feelings for him. I began to realize that love is unconditional. I just loved him. The thought of him made me happy, and I missed him. Maybe David loved me regardless of how I had hurt him, too. Maybe people just love each other, and there's nothing we can do about it. Maybe that's the truth about it all, that we love people no matter what.

I ordered a bouquet of large, bright, multi-colored, helium balloons to be delivered to Leonardi's apartment for his birthday accompanied by a card with a prayer of love and protection. If Leonardi was in any kind of trouble or danger, I wanted him to know that my heart was with him, and that I prayed for his safety.

I decided I had made my bed and now I was going to have to lie in it. I would have to tell David that because I had failed to find a roommate, it was now imperative that I find a permanent job right away and cancel my trip to Europe. I knew David was going to freak out about it again, so I decided to wait until the day before our flight to tell him. Hopefully he and Tom would get on the plane without me.

I was so far removed from any sense of normalcy or stability in my life that it was impossible for my brain to process the intense confusion, guilt, and deep sadness. I was so overwhelmed that I was unable to cry. I felt numb from the shock, but eventually I managed to finally fall asleep.

The next evening, Sidney told me that her boyfriend was flying in from Las Vegas to be with her for a few days. I had no problem with it, but I wondered to myself, why Sidney had never mentioned that she had a boyfriend until now, and a boyfriend who lives in Vegas? Leonardi never mentioned Sidney having a boyfriend either. It was strange, but then everything was strange now. He'll be arriving tomorrow night? *Whatever*, I thought.

It was about eight in the evening. I was sitting in my room playing one of my favorite Simon and Garfunkel songs, An American Tune, on my guitar--in an attempt to free my mind from all the events that had transpired since moving here. Sidney called me into the living room to introduce me to her boyfriend. Except for his dark, negative aura, I did not see the romantic connection between him and Sidney. He was much younger than her, about thirty-five, average height, and stocky with a gym work-out physique. His black jeans, t-shirt, and sneakers matched his black hair and dark eyes. The friend he brought with him looked a few years younger and had opposite features: blonde, curly hair, freckles, and blue eyes. They shared the same muscular arms, stocky build, street clothes, and mischievous personality. Both men were loud, excited, and jumping up and down like rambunctious, out-of-control children. I didn't know what to make of it. I found them to be strange. I hung around for a few minutes only to be hospitable.

Sidney's boyfriend had a large black crystal rock with him, and he claimed it had magical powers. He told Sidney to hold it and feel the rock's energy. Sidney held the rock and claimed that she felt some kind of strong vibration coming from it. Her boyfriend was jumping up and down in excitement, and his eyes were bulging out of his head. He had a deranged menacing laugh. His blonde-haired friend bounced in the air full of beguilement along with him, until all three of them were now leaping up and down flipping out over this rock.

Sidney's boyfriend offered me the rock to hold. I politely refused. They insisted, and I did so only to be courteous. I briefly cradled the flint like quartz in the palms of my hand and did not get a good feeling from it. In fact, I felt a kind of weird vibration emanating from it which scared me. Yet, I wasn't sure if I was uneasy from the energy of the black rock, or the two unsavory guys in the living room. Those people were not my cup of tea. I quickly returned the strange charcoal lump back to Sidney's boyfriend, and excused myself escaping back into my room to play my guitar.

I was in my room alone for only about fifteen or twenty minutes when suddenly Sidney came in with a knock on my door. "My boyfriend has to take me to the emergency room right now," she said hurriedly.

"What's wrong?" I asked.

"I don't know. I started bleeding from my uterus. I think it's my diaphragm. I have to go right away and have it checked out," she said.

"Sure, I hope you're alright." I agreed.

"I think I'll be fine. My boyfriend is going to take me right away. We're going to leave his friend here to hang out. Can you keep him company? We shouldn't be long."

"Yeah, but --"

"His friend isn't going to feel comfortable being in the emergency room with us. They had a long flight from Vegas and he's pretty tired. He'd rather hang out here until we get back. Just stay with him for a little while and keep him company for me. We shouldn't take long," Sydney assured me.

"Okay, just get to the hospital already," I urged.

We had an L-shaped couch in the living room, so I sat on the right side of the couch, and the blonde guy sat on the other side of the sectional to my left. He lounged back in the seat with his feet up on the coffee table, smiling contemptuously to himself.

"Can I offer you something to drink?" I asked.

"No, no. I'm fine," he smirked.

There was an awkward moment of silence.

"How long have you lived with Sidney?" he asked.

"Two weeks now. I just moved in."

"Yeah, yeah," he sighed, as he leaned his upper body and head against the back of the couch, still smirking and looking around. "So what did you think of that rock? Pretty cool, huh?" he said.

"Yeah, I've never seen anything like that before," I agreed. "What's it for exactly?" I asked nervously, not really wanting to know.

"It puts curses on people. It has a lot of negative energy. Couldn't you feel it?" He asked. A strange uncomfortable quiver went through my body.

"Yeah, I felt something," I said.

There was another moment of awkward silence. Suddenly he pulled out a large pocket knife from his pants pocket, flipped it open, and threw it in front of me on the coffee table. I looked down at the knife and my heart stopped. He continued smirking and talking like the actor Anthony Perkins in *Psycho*. "I feel really sorry for you," he stated. The evil energy emanating from his spirit which I silently presumed was now blatantly and undeniably there, lying on the table.

I stared down at the knife and then looked straight ahead at the front door with the five locks on it.

"I feel so very sorry for you," he said again, his eyes gleaming with malicious intent.

The apartment was in a very old building with thick walls, and the unit was high up on the tenth floor. The windows faced the back of the building overlooking an empty lot. I realized that no one would hear me scream, and I also realized that it would take too much time to run to the door and try to unlock the five locks quickly enough to escape. I could have grabbed the knife off the table to try and throw it out the window, but this guy looked very strong, and I assumed his reflexes were quick, even though he was lounging back in his chair.

He sat up casually and leaned forward looking at the knife and then at me. "I feel really very sorry for you," he said again.

If I grabbed the knife he would not only be able to grab it away from me, but the knife would have my fingerprints on it, which might allow him to set up my death as a suicide. All this was going on in my head within a split second.

"So so sorry," he lilted again venomously through his smirk.

It also rumbled through my mind that I did not want to die. I did not deserve to die. I loved Leonardi. That was not a crime. Why was I being punished in some way for loving Leonardi? I thought how ridiculous it was to lose my life for loving someone. How insane it would be that my love for Leonardi would cause my death. I refused to allow it to happen. I said a big "No" in my heart and mind. Something in me took over, something greater than my own small self. I could say it was my instincts that kicked in, but it was much more than that. It was like some invisible force field surrounded me, and I had an awareness and clarity about the situation that was beyond my normal five senses. There was something telling me that I would not get out of here with fear in my heart, or a struggle. Something outside of me, outside my normal frame of reference, but yet a part of me, put me on my toes in a way I had never experienced before. Then I gave the greatest performance of my life.

I laughed and giggled a little and sat down next to him on his side of the couch. I touched his knee lightly. "I hope you didn't get the impression that I didn't like you. I'm really just shy," I flirted.

He placed his arm around my shoulder and leaned me against the back of the couch with him. "Really?" he asked pleased.

"Yeah, I get shy around someone I am attracted to. When you first walked in I wanted to be more talkative, but I just get so shy."

"You don't have to be shy with me, babe," he said, his face very close to mine and his hot breath on my cheek.

I kissed him lightly on the mouth.

He seemed to have forgotten about the knife as we kissed each other here and there. He paused to look in my face for doubt or fear, but he saw none. I kept giggling and laughing and kissing him on different parts of his face. Within a few moments, when I believed that I had convinced him of my sincerity, I sat up, still touching him and asked, "Have you eaten anything?"

"No . . ."

"I'm starving. Are you hungry?" I asked.

"Yeah, actually I am," he agreed.

I squeezed his hand tight. "Let's get something to eat, have a few drinks, and then come back here. We can accomplish a lot more on a full stomach and a few margaritas," I said with enthusiasm, still holding him and kissing him.

"Okay. Yeah, that sounds good. Where do you want to go?" he asked eagerly.

"There's a really great bar and restaurant right here on the corner. We don't have to go far so we can come right back up here," I offered.

"Okay. Cool let's go," he agreed as he jumped up enthusiastically.

I don't remember what he did with the knife. I don't know if he left it on the table, or if he took it with him. All I could think was that if I could get us both out of the apartment, out of the building, and into the street, I had a good chance of escaping. I grabbed my keys and walked in front of him towards the door, praying that he was still buying my performance.

I locked all the locks on the way out, feeling like it was happening in slow motion. I practically skipped down the hallway, holding his hand and kissing him. He was happy and pleased. We got in the elevator and I knew I had to keep up my performance one hundred percent, but at the same time not overdo it too much and make him suspicious. An elevator ride with a stranger can be tense; an elevator ride with your murderer can feel like eternity. Keeping up the façade long enough to get to the lobby and finally outside the building was a very fine balancing act. Showing one second of doubt, nervousness, or fear could have jeopardized my chances of escape, and being even a hair too affectionate, could have looked like over-acting.

It was around nine thirty at night. The streets were still somewhat busy on Broadway and 72nd street, but not busy enough to see a way of getting help. People in New York City will either respond right away to a call for help, or they will look on curiously if a problem is not clear to them. The pedestrians tonight looked as if they were deeply lost in their own thoughts and their own little worlds as they walked down the streets. I didn't see anyone who was conscious of their immediate surroundings. I also noticed that there were a lot of women and elderly men, no one strong enough to take this guy on.

I didn't think that anyone would respond to my pleas in the street or in a store fast enough or without hesitation. I didn't see any police either, so

I led my perpetrator into a bar and grill restaurant. We held hands crossing the street and entered the dark, but noisy establishment. There were hardly any customers, but the music was blasting, so it seemed livelier than it actually was. The perpetrator found us a table near the back of the room. A waitress quickly strutted over to our table with menus and just as quickly disappeared. I looked at the menu for a moment or two. I asked my perpetrator to order me a burger deluxe and a margarita. "I'll be right back. I promised to call my sister," I said.

"Sure go ahead," he agreed, still smiling from ear to ear.

I hastened to the pay phone in front of the bar near the doorway. I leaned over the bar to ask the bartender for change. I was hoping that maybe the bartender would be an ally to help me, but he was very distracted, and the waitresses at the other end of the bar kept calling on him for their drinks. His partner at the other end of the bar kept waving him over for help. The bartender quickly got me the change, but was gone too fast for me to even know how to explain anything to him. It was too risky. I took the change and dialed the pay phone.

David's phone kept ringing. He wasn't home to pick it up. I left a message on his machine telling him that someone had pulled a knife on me at Sidney's apartment, that I had gotten away, and that I would take a cab, but I didn't have enough money on me. I asked him to please meet me downstairs on the street to help me pay the cab driver. I was praying that David would get home soon and get my message before I arrived at his apartment. I took a deep breath to make my escape.

I scurried back to the table and told my perpetrator, "Oh, I'm so sorry my sister was just admitted into the hospital. She's seriously ill. I have to go there right now. Bye. I'll see you tomorrow." I tried to sound reassuring.

My perpetrator sat at the table still grinning, but this time the grin looked frozen on his face. Perhaps he thought I had called the police, or that something had been said between me and the bartender. I could have handed the bartender a written note to call the police, for all the perpetrator knew. I don't know what my perpetrator was thinking, but he just sat there with that frozen grin on his face, "Sure okay," he said. I think he thought he was busted, and that he better be cool and try to make his own escape once I left.

I quickly left the bar and grill, praying I would find a cab ride immediately. As soon as I hit the curb, the first cab I saw pulled up beside me and I jumped in. "Please take me to Gramercy Park. And please hurry. Will five dollars get me there?" I asked.

The cab driver stopped his car at the light. "You only have five dollars? That's not going to be enough. I make my living on tips you know," he argued.

"Yes, but I can get the rest of the money at the other end. My friend is waiting for me at the other end to pay you," I explained.

"I can't do it. The ride is going to cost you more than five dollars. At least eight dollars and then I want a tip, you know. I need to make a living, ya know. You'll have to get out and walk."

"Please, someone just threatened me with a knife, and I have to get home. I'm in danger if I stay here. I'll have the rest of the money for you when I get there. Please," I begged.

"Who assaulted you?" he asked as he turned around.

"Some guy in my apartment. I don't know who he is."

"How did he get in there?" he asked.

"My roommate brought him in. Please keep driving," I pleaded.

"Was it your boyfriend? I don't want to get involved with this kind of thing," he warned.

"No, no, he wasn't my boyfriend. Please, I don't know the guy. Please drive faster," I pleaded.

The cab kept moving, but slowly as the driver questioned me. "How did he get into your apartment if he's not your boyfriend?" he asked as he raised his hands in the air and slammed them back down onto the steering wheel.

"I told you, my roommate brought him in. My friend is waiting at the address we're going to and he's going to pay the balance and give you a big tip. I promise. I'm telling the truth. Please, please drive faster," I begged.

Luckily, the avenue was clear of heavy traffic allowing the driver to pick up speed. "Where's your roommate?" the cabbie asked.

"I don't know. She left the apartment and left me in the apartment with him, claiming he was a friend of hers. Sir, please believe me," I begged.

"Why don't you go to the police station?"

"I can't. I have to be in Paris in less than 48 hours."

The cabbie stopped asking question and stepped on the gas, causing my body to fly a few inches up in the air, and down again against the back of the warm leather seat. I inhaled and exhaled a deep sigh of relief.

I was hoping David had gotten my message on his answering machine, and he would be at the other end waiting for me. If not, I would have to call the police. I still had the keys to David's apartment, so I could call the police from there.

When the cab hit Times Square, the traffic slowed us down, but once we got past Thirty-ninth Street the road was clear again and the driver slammed his foot on the gas again. When the driver turned off the avenue onto the quiet, tree-lined street, to my relief, I saw David standing near the curb waiting for me. The cab driver almost missed David and his building, until I yelled out, "Stop, stop. Right here!"

David saw the cab pass him and then stop short. He ran up to the cab and paid the fare and tip. I gave the cab driver my five dollars for an extra tip. "Thank you. I'm so grateful to you for helping me to get home safely," I said.

"Yeah, sure. You should call the police," the cab driver warned.

David and I walked into his building. "What is going on? I went to walk the dog, and when I came back I got your message. You scared the hell out of me."

"Sidney brought these two guys into the house, and one of them threatened me with a knife."

"Where was Sidney?" asked David.

"She left me alone with this guy. I'll explain it to you when we get in the house."

Once we both settled on the couch in the apartment, I told David what had happened, and how I escaped. "We need to call the police, don't we?" I asked.

David thought for a moment. "If we go to the police, then we're going to have to stay in the country to be available for questioning, filing charges, and an investigation. We can't file a charge after the fact when we come back four weeks later from Europe. We have to do it tonight, but if we file a charge, we can't make our flight the day after tomorrow. You don't have any witnesses? David asked.

"No, she left the apartment with her so-called boyfriend, and left me alone with this guy. I don't even know his name. No one saw anything but me," I explained.

"Did anyone see you in the restaurant with him?" David asked.

"Yeah, but we were there maybe five minutes or so, and we looked like a happy couple. If anyone had noticed us at all, they wouldn't know who he was anymore than I did," I said.

"We don't know his name or who he is, and if we file a charge, with no proof, they most likely will not be able to convict him even if they find him. There were no signs of struggle, and you have no bruises or anything. You have no witnesses to his threatening you with the knife back at the apartment. Even if they find him, they'll have to drop the charges, because there's no evidence. No struggle, no breaking and entering. It's just your word against his. This guy will run free anyway, and we'll be out of a trip to Europe. I'm guessing that by now he's probably already on his way out of town," David explained.

"Maybe we should just leave for Paris, but what if he tries to come after me again? I mean, who is he? Why did he want to hurt me? Why did Sidney leave me in the apartment with him? What is going on?" I asked in confusion.

"Where is Leonardi? Does he know about this?" David asked.

"No, it just all happened. Leonardi refuses to talk to me ever since I moved into Sidney's apartment, and he won't tell me why? We never had an argument or disagreement or anything. He cut off communication with me as soon as I moved into Sidney's place, and he would not give me any reason for it. He told me it was over and he can't see me anymore, but he would not tell me why. He didn't sound angry, but he seemed anxious and frightened when he said it."

"Everything you're telling me sounds really screwy," David said.

"I know! I don't understand any of it! I almost got murdered tonight, and I don't even know why?" I cried.

"Maybe they were just trying to scare you out of the apartment?" David suggested.

"Scare me out of the apartment? Why would anyone want to do that?" I asked.

"Maybe Sidney decided that she didn't want you there anymore. I don't know," David said.

"That's not normal David. When you want someone to leave, you tell them. You talk to them. You sit down with them and tell them it's not working out, and make some kind of arrangement in a civilized way. You don't set them up to be murdered. You don't set me up in an isolated apartment with a man twice my size and strength, with five locks on the door and no one to hear me scream, and no way to get away. He had a large knife, and he threatened me with it! Come on! That's not how the average person asks someone to move out," I clamored.

"I'm just saying it's a possibility. I don't know," he said.

"That's not a possibility. That's a stupid possibility!" I screamed.

"Either way, it appears to me that the best thing to do is to not do anything, just leave town as planned. We have no proof to convict him. No witnesses, nothing. They may not even be able to catch the guy. Like I said, he probably ran to the airport by now and is on a flight back to Vegas or wherever he came from," David insisted.

"What about my stuff? I can't live at Sidney's anymore. How do I get my clothes and everything out of her apartment? I'm afraid to go back there."

"Don't worry about that. Whoever these guys are, they're going to assume you called the cops and leave town or hide. I'll go back with you to the apartment early tomorrow morning. We'll move your things back in here and then catch our flight the next morning."

"We're going to go back into the apartment? What if he's there?" I cried.

"He's not going to be there. He would have to assume you called the police, and they would be looking for him, so he won't be there. He'll be on the run and hiding. Believe me, that guy is not going to hang around waiting to get caught. Let's get some sleep," David said reassuringly.

David and I woke up at about six a.m. and got to Sidney's apartment just before seven. I wondered if Sidney knew anything, and if she had something to do with what had happened. After all, a boyfriend suddenly showed up and he had a friend and then she suddenly had to go to the hospital. I felt that she knew something.

She wasn't home when we got there. I hid behind David shivering, as we snuck around the apartment to see if anyone was at home or hiding, but no one was there. I still had empty boxes lying on the floor in the corner of my room from moving in. David and I stuffed everything into the boxes, my suitcase, and a laundry bag, and within twenty minutes we had it all ready to go in the hallway near the elevator.

We piled everything into a big yellow taxi and moved all my things back into his apartment, dumping everything in the middle of the living room. I emptied out my clothes from the suitcase and laundry bags, and set aside the clothes to pack for our flight the following morning. Everything was left askew. I would deal with it when we returned from Europe. Tom had some writing deadlines, and had already left for London on a flight the day before, to meet with his publisher. He would join us at the hotel in Paris a day later.

The following morning, while David was out picking up more travelers checks, I got on the phone to speak with Leonardi. He was not at his apartment, so I called the salon. He came to the phone, not knowing that it was me.

"Someone pulled a knife on me at Sidney's apartment last night. One of Sidney's friends tried to kill me last night with a knife, Leonardi," I stated angrily.

"What do you mean?" Leonardi sounded shocked.

"Just what I said. One of Sidney's friends tried to kill me last night. Sidney brought two strange guys into the apartment, and she left me alone in the apartment with one of them, claiming that her boyfriend was taking her to the emergency room because she was bleeding internally from her diaphragm. She left the other guy in the apartment with me, and he threatened me with a knife. I got out of apartment. I escaped," I said.

Leonardi never interrupted me nor did he hang up. He listened, and then he sounded frightened and concerned for me, but he did not offer any information or any clues as to why all this had come about.

"Oh, Whitney I'm so sorry. That sounds awful. Are you all right?" He asked.

"Do you know if Sidney had anything to do with this? Why would she bring these guys into the apartment? If you know anything, you need to tell me."

"Whitney, this is the first I've heard of this. I don't know anything. I'm in shock hearing this right now. Where are you?" he inquired.

"I'm back at David's house. We moved my stuff out of Sidney's this morning. Sidney wasn't there when we showed up. Can you explain to me what's going on, and why I almost got killed last night?"

"Sidney didn't come into work today. Whitney, I would never hurt you like that. I don't know what to say. I just don't understand . . . I'll try to get some information from Sidney when I see her, okay?" he offered.

Somehow I believed Leonardi, because he did sound shocked and concerned, and he wasn't hanging up on me. But at the same time, I didn't know what to think.

"I'm leaving for Paris in the morning, and I'll be gone quite awhile. So find out what you can, and I'll talk to you when I get back," I said.

"Yeah, sure. Jesus, I'm so sorry. I thank God you're all right. Please give me a call when you get back from your trip, okay?" Leonardi asked.

"Yeah, okay," I agreed.

"Relax and enjoy yourself while you're there. I wish you a safe and happy trip. I'll question Sidney about all this," Leonardi promised.

"Yeah, okay. Bye," I said.

When I hung up the phone, I didn't know what to think. Leonardi sounded shocked and concerned, and was as in the dark about what had happened to me last night as I was. But he still didn't explain his bizarre behavior towards me in cutting off our relationship as soon as I moved into Sidney's house. I was still so shaken up from last night, it did not occur to me to ask him again why he had cut me off.

I couldn't wait to get out of New York. I did not believe for a moment that Leonardi would do anything to physically hurt me or anyone. And he sounded so sincere in being surprised and shocked by my fate. Although I knew he would never do anything to hurt me, I wondered if he knew more about why this had happened to me, and was not telling me in order to protect someone, or keep himself out of trouble by keeping quiet. More speculation was frying my brain.

I was now eager to get out of the country to escape all this craziness, rather than sticking around trying to figure it out. I was an innocent, twenty-four-year-old girl, with no job and very little money. Whatever was going on was going on with people who were not only much older than me, but who had a lot more information and a lot more resources than I did. The whole situation was just too big for me. I wanted to be out of New York as soon as possible, to get some distance from it all, if that was possible.

CHAPTER FIFTEEN

NEXT STOP PARIS

AS WE LEFT David's apartment for the airport, he asked, "Do you have your wings?"

"Right here," I glistened as I adjusted the airline wings on the lapel of my short bolero jacket.

"Okay, *Let's Go Europe!*" David shouted.

The media warned of more possible terrorist hijackings on European flights--but after what I had been through at Sidney's apartment, flying was a piece of cake. I was relieved to be with friends, and safely on a plane heading out of the country. I felt safer in the air than on land. I clicked on my walkman to listen to "Heaven", by the Psychedelic Furs for take-off. It was euphoric. I loved being so high up in the clear blue sky. Despite all that had gone down over the last few weeks, David was also in high spirits and enjoying the flight.

We landed in France on time. Driving from the airport along the highway, the view outside the taxi window was overcast and rainy. My heart sank. I thought to myself, this is France? Yuk. It looked worse than the gray factory landscape of Long Island City near Astoria, Queens where I grew up.

Yet, as soon as we entered the heart of Paris, it was like entering a magical kingdom of absolute wonder. It looked just like it did in all the movies: cobble stone streets, the Seine, artists on the river painting pictures for tourists, the beautiful old architecture, the quaint little outdoor cafes and bistros. My eyes lit up in awe.

"See, I knew you were going to love this," David smiled with excitement.

We checked into a run-down pension called the Eugene Hotel. We had a small room with a simple wooden dresser, a ceramic bidet, and a mouse trap under an old, squeaky brass bed. We shared the bathroom with the other guests on the floor. We didn't care, because it was within our budget of ten dollars per night, and included a breakfast of coffee and croissants.

Once we settled into our modest accommodations, we ventured out into the foggy streets of Paris and headed straight for the famous Michelin Cafe down the street. We ordered café au lait and looked out the window to watch the rain. Pedestrians, many in trench coats, some carrying umbrellas--splashed by on their way to their destinations. I spotted a drenched couple in the middle of the street, huddled under a limp newspaper, embraced in a passionate kiss. We were in Paris!

That evening, the heavy, black, antique phone in our room rang. It sounded like one of those old-fashioned phones from a Doris Day film. I picked it up. The receiver was so much larger in comparison to my small hands; it made me feel like *Alice in Wonderland*. "Bonjour," I said knowing it must be Tom.

"Hi, I'm here in Paris," Tom sniffed.

"It's Tom. He's here," I said to David.

David took the phone, and I sat on the bed next to him listening in on the conversation.

"I just checked into my room, but I have a really bad cold. I'm going to retire early and meet you in the morning at the Michelin Café. Is seven a good time?" Tom asked.

"Yeah, seven is good. How was your trip to London?" David inquired.

"I don't remember most of it. I just remember getting a check from the editor for some articles I wrote, which was a relief. Other than that, everything was hazy. I was pumped up with Nyquil and cold capsules most of the time," Tom explained.

"Wow, you really sound stuffed up," said David.

"It was worse. I'm actually starting to feel a little better, but I need the rest," Tom sniffled.

The next morning, David and I arrived at the Michelin Café to meet Tom. He was already there, snuggled up near a window, nursing his cold with a cup of hot tea. It was still damp and rainy outside, but no one cared.

"Bonjour," Tom greeted us.

We smiled and laughed at each other because we had never seen each other out of context like this in a foreign setting. It was usually the three of us in a New York City diner, and now it was the three of us in a famous, quaint café in Paris. We loved it. Tom had lived in London for many years a while back, and visited London many times, but he had never been to France or Italy.

By the time we finished breakfast, the sun was breaking through and we were off for a long day of sightseeing.

To meet our hectic itinerary, we toured Paris those three days from seven in the morning until midnight. We probably covered more sites in three days than most people get to see in a lifetime. We rarely stopped to eat during the day, and our diet consisted of mainly Jambon sandwiches (ham and cheese) purchased from a street cart.

We paid a visit to the usual tourists' spots: the Tower of Notre Dame, a few castles, the Louvre, a boat ride down the Seine, and then finally, the famous Parisian cemetery of Pere Lachaise. I had been studying the dance style and choreography of Isadora Duncan for a few years, so I wanted to visit her grave. I thought I might feel her spirit, but I didn't feel much of anything. The grave was nothing spectacular. She had been cremated and her ashes were placed in a small compartment inside a long marble wall.

Jim Morrison's grave was also here and was much more interesting. His grave stone was covered in graffiti. It was decorated by visitors' flowers, condoms, wine glasses, beer bottles, and rolled joints. It was rumored that young couples would come to the cemetery at night, get high, and have sex on his tombstone. We learned that MTV music host Martha Quinn and her film crew had just been at the gravesite a few days earlier to film a quick segment for MTV.

I was enjoying Paris, but turning down some cobblestone streets, I felt an eerie déjà vu, like I had been here before. This feeling was overwhelming at times. Paris was a city I felt sure I had experienced before, perhaps in another lifetime.   I don't believe in reincarnation. I always thought it would be a cruel fate to have to keep coming back to this world over and over again to experience the ups and downs and uncertainty of human existence. Instead, I hoped to be lifted out of this world into a permanent heavenly place full of unending peace, freedom, joy, and love. Did heaven actually exist, and how could I get there?

For some strange reason I felt that Leonardi was in Paris. I didn't see him or hear his voice, nor did I even see anyone that looked remotely like him, but I knew he was there. I could feel him. I didn't glance around the streets or look through crowds to try to find him.   Leonardi had abandoned me for reasons I didn't know.   I had almost been killed for reasons I didn't know either. I hoped not to run into him in Paris.

I had another strange experience when Tom, David, and I walked up the Champs Elyse one hot sunny afternoon. Many women from India or Bangladesh, dressed in brightly colored saris, were kneeling on the ground holding woven straw baskets, begging for money from the pedestrians passing by. There was such a desperate anguish in the way they begged that I could feel their hopeless despair cut deeply into my heart. I also realized that they probably repeated these cries for help day after day receiving little or no empathetic or compassionate response from the well-to-do around them.

Most of the middle class and the rich citizens would either ignore these women or scoff at them in disgust. It was clear that these women did not have the necessary education or skills to infiltrate themselves into the middle-class Parisian lifestyle, but their colorful saris, and gold bangles reflected an esteemed history and rich culture. Looking upon these souls, I was stirred inside by the extraordinary beauty in their faces; a divine presence emanating from their being. Yet, the Parisian citizens didn't seem to have any interest in initiating any kind of social program that would lift these immigrant women up out of their misery, and off the street, and put them on equal terms with everyone else.

They were treated like undesirable objects, not dignified human beings with value. The more disdain the pedestrians showed to the beggars, the more exaggerated the beggars' agony and sense of desperation became, until a pedestrian's action often resulted in a merciless kick forcing the beggar to crawl timidly away, back onto the curb. It was an oxymoron to see an educated, well fed and well dressed individual act so barbaric. The entire situation felt so unnecessary and so heartbreaking it was unbearable to watch.

I don't believe these women came into the world to play the part of beggars. Rather they came here to live a dignified life, and the role of beggar was thrust upon them by the unloving hearts of others who thought of themselves as different and better. I thought, 'If there was a God, he would never create a world such as this. God would never give so much to one, yet deny another.'

My heart had been opened by my experience with Leonardi. My spiritual understanding was opening up as well from being in a foreign country, and I now understood for certain that the many billionaires in the world could alleviate the suffering of many but they simply won't. *It is the non-recognition of the great value of another human being that renders him homeless.*

Later that evening, back at our shabby hotel, I lay in bed feeling reflective and pondering what this life was all about. How long will God allow the iniquity of humanity to continue? Does he see it? Does he care? I was so exhausted from our daily excursions, I was unable to stay awake and think much more about it. Instead, I fell into a deep and restful sleep.

I woke up the next morning full of zest and vigor, and enjoyed a hearty breakfast at a local quaint café with David and Tom while we giddily planned our day's itinerary to see more of Paris. We were the perfect traveling companions because we collaborated on everything. We had the energy and enthusiasm to carry out our heavy tour schedule. We laughed so hard and had so much fun that the nightmare back in New York seemed like a distant memory.

After our three days in Paris, we hopped on the Eurail to Blois, a town noted for its chocolate factory. It was a quaint village with the smell of sweet chocolate in the air. We spent the afternoon perched on a hilltop overlooking the small town eating Jambon sandwiches. The little stone houses below were crowded together. Their crooked rooftops and chimneys made me think that Mary Poppins was going to fly down from the sky any minute with her suitcase and umbrella. The sweet smell of chocolate, at first pleasing, was so strong that it actually made us feel nauseous, so we planned to leave Blois early the next day.

Many of the stores and restaurants in the village of Blois were closed due to a French holiday, The Ascension, which falls on a Thursday, 40 days after Easter, and celebrates Jesus' ascent into heaven. As we strolled down the narrow cobble stone streets, I wondered about Jesus' life on earth. Who was he really? Why did he leave and is he actually coming back? If so, when?

We finally stumbled upon a restaurant that was open and specialized in duck. We were not too excited about eating duck, but nothing else was around, and we were hungry.

The restaurant was cozy and rustic, but expensive. The establishment raised and slaughtered their own ducks, which explained why this was the only item on their menu.

During our meal, David began to get very hostile and angry with me, raising his voice and bringing up my affair with Leonardi. The duck tasted very gamey, and I couldn't get it down without gagging. David slammed his wine glass on the table.

"You better eat that duck!"

Tom and I realized that David was a bit drunk from the four glasses of wine he had before and during the meal. David was not a drinker.

People from the other tables turned around to look at us.

I guessed, like with the lobster incident in California, if I didn't like the food in the restaurant, David would get very upset. I realized that it probably upset him more than the affair I had had with Leonardi.

I didn't respond to David. I sat there quietly and hoped that it would blow over. Tom looked at David. I looked at Tom and then at David. Tom looked at me, and David looked at Tom. Finally, I looked down into my lap. I didn't want to discuss my affair with Leonardi now or *ever* while on our trip. I refused.

After we silently concluded that it was the alcohol talking, Tom took the wine glass away from him and replaced it with a glass of water.

David suddenly composed himself. "Alright forget it. Let's just not talk about it. The duck is a bit gamey. You're right. It's gamey," he said as he took his glass back, and slugged down some more wine.

David never got drunk again, and he never brought up my affair, not even in jest.

The following morning, in the old-world, country style pension, my eyes opened to the dead silence of dawn. I pulled the covers up to my chin to warm myself from the unusually chilly morning. Out of the peace came the solitary click clack of high heels marching down a cobblestone street outside, the tempo of her shoes, serious, humorless, and Gestapo. The sound grew louder as it passed under my open window. I imagined it to be a middle-aged French woman, wearing a trench coat and a silk scarf. The posture of her chin raised and stoic, leading her to another hum-drum day at the job, her senses completely unaware of the sweet smell of chocolate in the Blois Village air. With each step she took, I heard the pounding pain hidden in her chest for the longing of a kiss, the kind of kiss from someone that mirrored her inner, child-like joy. The cold modulation of her heels could be heard moving further away now. I was curious to see if my image of her was true. I ran to the window sticking my head out into the cold crisp air. The yellow orange horizon peaked above the rooftops, and the remaining night cast a purple shadow over the quaint Mary Poppins town. I could still hear the marching heals clomping down and echoing on the pavement, but I could not see anyone. She must have disappeared turning down a narrow street corner.

By noon, we arrived in Buene, a medieval city which lies in the heart of the Burgundian vineyards, and is one of the most beautiful places in

Burgundy, France. Besides being a famous city of wine and incomparable art treasures, it also possesses the hospital, Hotel Dieu, an institution which catered to the poor and sick, offering food and shelter in addition to medical care during the Middle Ages.

We found the Hospital Hotel Dieu to be a magnificent building made of mosaic tile with a grand courtyard, a marvel of Burgandian-Flemish art. The tour guide spoke with great enthusiasm about its history but from the onset of the excursion I became queasy.

In the main hall there was a church altar. Rather than rows of pews, there were rows of single beds with bright, crimson blankets over crisp, white sheets. A heavily polished, brass bedpan sat at the foot of each bed. All the beds were lined against both walls opposite each other. The guide spoke about Bubonic Plague, and how all the people in the surrounding village came here to be treated, but often died here as well. I could feel the lingering history of unimaginable horror and suffering.

When the tour guide brought our attention to the many gruesome paintings of people dying and falling to hell, I felt the suffering and death so strongly that I had to leave the building and wait outside in the courtyard while David and Tom continued on with the tour. Even as I sat outside in the courtyard, I felt uneasy. If there was a God that created this world, why would he create a world of incredible beauty and yet allow such unbearable horrors and suffering? I remembered the opulence and beauty of Paris. Yet, at the same time there were desperate immigrant beggars along the Champs Elysees living in hell. This city of Buene was also magical, but yet tainted by the terrifying history of this building. I was relieved to finally leave the property.

By early evening, my spirits were lifted and my soul rejuvenated when we splurged on one of the more expensive, local restaurants located in an old crypt with an historic wine cellar. Both the food and cast-iron lantern lit atmosphere were magnificent.

After two weeks in France, we got back on the Eurail and made our way through the Swiss Alps and into Italy. At the Italian border everything changed. The trains ran slowly or they didn't run at all. The clientele transitioned into mostly old fat Italian women in long black dresses, and cigar-smoking Italian men with tire-bellies popping out of their sleeveless t-shirts.

I noticed the signs on the train warning passengers not to stick their heads out the window. Perhaps it was because the long metal poles along the tracks were so close that one's head would be taken off if one did stick their head out of the window. More signs told passengers not to throw their garbage out the window. "Why do people in Italy need a sign for that?" I thought to myself.

Our next stop was Verona, home of William Shakespeare's *Romeo and Juliet*, but I was too excited to care. We were on our way to visit Gabriel DeNunzio's Vitorale and Museum on Lake Garda, which was an exceedingly significant visit for me and inspired by my dear friend Candido Martinelli. It was Candido who first inspired me to act, write, and dance.

....

In the summer of 1979, when I was nineteen years old, I had been sending my modeling pictures to agencies in the hopes of getting representation. I stopped by the Ford agency, but they rejected me. I tried getting an appointment with Wilhelmina, but I couldn't. Finally, I got a call from an agency called Chelsea Models, which was located in a high-tech loft in Manhattan on West 23rd Street. I met the owner of the agency, Simon Keller.

Simon was an attractive man in his late thirties, who always dressed in safari clothes. He said he liked my look, but I needed to lose some weight. He was right about that. Actually, I looked normally thin for the average person, but for modeling, I was too chubby.

He asked me to lose at least ten pounds, which I easily did. On the weekends, I roller skated at Busby's from eleven p.m. to about four in the morning. I loved skating around for hours and hours listening to the disco music, especially the song by SOS, "Baby Take Your Time", going backwards, and forwards, turning, and swaying to the rhythmic beat.

Shortly after, Simon set me up on a "go see," where an agency sends a model out on an interview with a photographer for test shots. The first photographer I met for a "go see" was Candido Martinelli.

It was a sweltering summer day. I wore a cheap maroon terry cloth dress that I had bought in Alexander's Department Store when I had worked there part-time after school. Looking back, I now realize how hideously ugly the dress was, but at the time I thought it was fine.

When I got out of the subway station, I found myself on the Lower West Side of Manhattan in a desolate area with nothing but factories. After walking up and down and back and forth a few times, I finally found the address. I walked into what appeared to be a factory that had been turned into a huge photography loft. A lanky, thin, effeminate man with an angular face answered the door. I read the name from a small sheet of paper. "I am here to see Candido Martinelli."

"Candido is very busy right now. He's in the middle of shooting a job," the man said sternly.

"But the agency, Chelsea Models, said to come here today and meet with him at eleven a.m.," I explained.

"Just leave your portfolio. He'll take a look at it, and you can come back tomorrow to pick it up," he snapped.

"I don't have a portfolio."

"You don't have a portfolio? You can't model without a portfolio," he replied, looking at me strangely.

"I know. That's why I'm here. The modeling agency sent me here to meet Candido so that he can take pictures of me. He's expecting me," I explained eagerly.

The man looked like he was ready to chase me out, but instead he paused. "Wait here," he instructed.

A short man in his late thirties with blonde hair, pale blue eyes, and a long blonde beard strutted out to the entrance area. He was of average weight, but he looked soft, pudgy and pasty, rather than muscular.

"Candido?" I inquired.

In a heavy Italian accent, he said, "Si, yes, I'm Candido. Are you the girl Simon Keller sent?" he asked as he put out his hand.

"Yes, yes. Simon said you might have a modeling job for me."

"Yes, yes. Show me your book," he smiled.

"I don't have a book," I said squinting one eye.

"You don't have a book. Ummm . . .," Candido stepped back. "Let me look at you. You know who you look like? Sophia Loren."

"Sofia Loren?" I said squinting one eye again.

"Yes, you do. Honestly," he smiled.

"Nobody ever told me I looked like Sofia Loren!"

"It's true. Step back and let me look at you. You are beautiful, like Sofia Loren. Yes, yes! I want to take some photographs of you. I cannot give you a job right now. We need to take some test shots so we can see how photogenic you are. But we can take some, and you can use them for your portfolio," he explained.

"Great! That would be great," I agreed.

"Here is my card. Call me Wednesday of next week, and we can talk. I have to go now and finish my work. You call me, okay?" Candido instructed.

"Yes, yes, I will. Thank you Candido."

Before disappearing down the subway steps to head back home, I looked at my reflection in the window of a mannequin factory. All the white painted mannequins were naked and faceless. Did I look like Sophia Loren, or did all Italian men from the old country think *all* women looked like Sophia Loren? He obviously loved Sophia Loren, and he thought I looked like her, so why argue with that, I thought to myself as I disappeared down the steps into the subway.

The following week, Candido picked me up early Saturday morning in front of my apartment building in Queens. He arrived in a little, red convertible with the top down, a European sports car. I don't remember the make of the car--only that it had a stick shift, he had the top down, and he drove it really, really fast.

First, we traveled to his old apartment in Forest Hills, where he picked up some extra boxes to bring to his new apartment in Brooklyn Heights. We talked and got acquainted during the car ride. In Brooklyn Heights he lived only a few blocks away from the Promenade waterfront with its beautiful view of Manhattan. I loved Brooklyn Heights, with its charming historical brownstone buildings and tree-lined streets named after Shakespearean characters like Horatio and Beatrice. Candido lived on Henry Street in a brownstone walk-up.

His apartment was cozy with two rooms and a tiny kitchenette. It was furnished with eclectic pieces of elaborately carved wood furniture. The walls were lined with bookcases filled with literature on art, film, photography, and cooking. His black and white photographs hung on the walls - landscapes of his small hometown in Lucca, Italy, along with a few photographs of abstract nudes. Candido introduced me to his chubby and old, but affectionate orange cat with no teeth, Tiger.

We settled into his apartment. He turned on opera music, and cooked us a homemade Italian meal with all fresh ingredients including fresh basil. He picked the basil from clay pots on his windowsill, which sat next to a few marijuana plants.

While cooking, he poured us both a glass of Italian red wine, and lit a roach from a clean astray. I shared a toast with him on the wine, but I refused the marijuana. "No thanks. It makes me paranoid," I said.

"It's much better than cigarettes. You should not smoke," he warned.

During lunch, we brain stormed together about the types of photos he would like to take of me. He took a quick Polaroid, and flopped it in the air to dry. He looked at it pleased, and handed it to me. "See. You do look like Sofia Loren," he insisted. I looked at the Polaroid.

"If you say so," I agreed. "You're the photographer," I smiled.

After lunch, he served espresso along with Italian biscotti. After that, we drank more wine. I loved Candido's company. He spoke five different languages: English, Italian, French, Spanish and even German. He had lived around the world in at least five different countries. He was warm, honest, open, inspiring, and very talented. He and his partner, Bill, had written a screenplay about a famous Italian named Gabrielle D'Annuzio. I had no idea who Gabrielle D'Annuzio was, but Candido briefly told me he was one of the most colorful and controversial personalities of the Great War.

Gabrielle D'Annuzio, the Pescara-born literary innovator moved to Rome in 1881, and quickly became a distinguished poet, novelist, dramatist, and librettist. He was also considered a great lover and womanizer. Two of the most famous women he involved himself with were Eleanor Duse (a great actress) and Isadora Duncan (a renowned dancer). I learned how Eleanor Duse brought natural techniques of acting onto the stage for the first time, as opposed to the artificial theatrical style of her predecessor, Sarah Bernhardt. The dancer, Isadora Duncan, was the first to introduce a new kind of natural dance movement onto the stage, which was also very controversial in her time, and the foundation of what we now call modern dance. Candido opened a whole new world for me, and I loved learning about these eccentric people in history.

Candido suggested that I be an actress in his movie. I told him I was flattered, but I really did not know anything about acting. Candido replied, "You'll learn. You would be perfect for one of the smaller parts we have written. There is a young Italian girl who is a lover of one of the young American soldiers. You can play her. I want to give you a copy of the screenplay, and you can take it home with you and read it," he insisted.

"Are you serious?" I asked delighted.

"Yes, please. I want you to read it, and tell me what you think," he encouraged.

I rushed home that evening, anxious to read the manuscript in the black leather cover with the title *D'Annunzio* printed in gold lettering.

I met Candido the following weekend for a fashion shoot on the beach, and we later traveled back to his apartment for dinner and listened to Puccini and some Bob Dylan. Candido was very European, but he was also a product of the sixties and loved smoking weed and listening to Dylan.

"Uugh, I hate Dylan." I complained as I bobbed around the room doing bad Dylan imitations. "Everybody Must Get Stoned," I mocked. Candido called me a silly child who did not understand good music.

While discussing his screenplay, Candido explained some of the screenplay formats to me, and he lent me some books about Gabriel D'Annuzio, as well as the autobiographies of both Eleanor Duse and Isadora

Duncan. Candido told me that his writing partner, Bill, was friends with Robert DeNiro, and that they were trying to get Martin Scorsese to produce and direct his movie. I was astounded, but I never doubted him, because he was so enthusiastic and sincerely excited. We talked and talked, until I voyaged back home in the late evening on the R train.

Reading Eleanor Duse's and Isadora Duncan's autobiographies turned my world upside down with inspiration. It lit a flame inside me to become an actress. What moved me and impressed me so much about these artists was their purpose. They had a spiritual goal and the inspiration for their art was connected and intertwined with the Divine. Popularity or fame was just a means to an end, a sort of tool to have the financial means to continue their pursuit. The goal was never popularity or fame; the goal was to understand and share the sacred.

"I have sometimes been asked whether I consider love higher than art, and I have replied that I cannot separate them, for the artist is the only lover, he alone has pure vision of beauty, and love is the vision of the soul when it is permitted to gaze upon immortal beauty," *My Life* by Isadora Duncan.

Isadora Duncan also wrote about life as being eternal, and I could understand why, because I had the same suspicions about life being eternal when my first boyfriend, my first true love, passed away from drug addiction.

I was seventeen years old, and after he died, he came to me in a dream to tell me that he was not dead, but in another place much more beautiful and free than where he had been before. Although it was a comforting realization to have, the validity of it was not mirrored while I was awake. The experience got lost in my day-to-day existence until I read Isadora's passage about the loss of her very young children:

"Was it that I was really in a state of clairvoyance, and that I knew that death does not exist – that those two little cold images of wax were not my children, but merely their cast-off garments? That the souls of my children lived in radiance, and lived forever," *My Life,* Isadora Duncan

When I met Candido for the third time, I told him that I very much wanted to be in his movie, but I would need to take acting classes. If I was going to be in a film of this caliber, I wanted to be a truly good actress, not just a novice.

I met with Candido in Brooklyn Heights almost every weekend. He often took me to a restaurant in Brooklyn Heights, or he whipped up a fresh Italian meal at home. After lunch or dinner we would stroll along the Promenade, look over the river towards the Manhattan skyline and talk about everything and anything. Sometimes, we would sit on a bench in comfortable silence. Sometimes, in the evening, we took bubble baths together by candlelight. Candido and I were not intimate, and I was grateful that he never made any advances toward me. Maybe he thought I was too young. He had recently been treated for cancer, which was in remission, but I think he was still taking medication. I didn't know if it was the illness or the medication that kept him docile sexually. He never discussed any details with me about his cancer treatments past or present.

My friendship with Candido was special and unique. He was kind and generous, and he openly shared his knowledge and passion for art. He inspired me to do more with my life and to be more. He was sincere about wanting me to be in his film, and he was excited when I told him that perhaps I should take acting classes, which is what I ended up doing from then on. I instinctively knew that the young people in my neighborhood were only living up to the low expectations society held for them and they were taught to maintain those low expectations for themselves. Candido reflected the beliefs I had about my possibilities. He saw my potential and encouraged it. He gave me a better reflection of myself. I was truly blessed to be befriended by this man named Candido Martinelli.

....

The ferry ride up Lake Garda into Lake Cuomo to visit D'Annuzio's Vitoriale was incredibly beautiful. The sky was neon blue. The lake glistened like a turquoise crystal gem reflecting many shades of blue and green. Lush and majestic mountains laced around the large body of water. David and I would point out to each other the refined Italian Villas owned by the wealthy citizens of Lake Cuomo sprinkled in among the landscape, and the yachts anchored in their backyards.

D'Annuzio's home was elaborate, eclectic and ostentatious in its décor with what was considered cheap and inexpensive art work during his time. He had collected pieces of art from his travels all over the world, mostly from Asia. Even his bathroom walls were covered with an array of porcelain plates. I felt sorry for the person who had to clean that place. He also had his own outdoor amphitheater and a museum where his motorcars were on display and private airplanes hung. I posed on the red velvet bench seats in the very vestibule where Eleanora Duse and Isadora Duncan had waited to be received by him. I had not felt Isadora's presence at her gravesite back at the cemetery in Paris, but I felt her spirit in the vestibule.

We then ventured into D'Annuzio's art studio located on the upper level of his home. D'Annunzio believed that art was sacred and that the studio where he wrote was Holy ground. The doorway to this room was so small and low that one had no choice but to kneel in order to enter; he had purposely designed it that way. I was forced to kneel in humility and reverence before entering the place where he created his art. I greatly admired, appreciated and respected his attitude towards art.

Once inside, on his writing desk, among his many treasures, was the dried pomegranate; the same pomegranate that he gave to Eleanora Duse, or did she give it to him? I don't remember now, but I do remember them exchanging a pomegranate. I picked it up and held it in my hand. I was in awe as I held this pomegranate that they had both held and exchanged. It was a mind blowing experience not only to be in his house and museum, but to be able to pick up this magnificent fruit. It was dry, hollow and mostly brown, but when I held it in the palm of my hand, these historical figures came alive and seemed to be standing in the room with me. The tour guide of the museum quickly asked me to put it down and to not touch anything else.

After touring through his home, the museum, and the gardens, I sat on the steps of his outdoor amphitheatre surrounded by tall cypress trees and the view of beautiful Lake Garda and the surrounding mountains. The sun was hot and beat down a melancholy feeling onto me. *Will I ever be an actress?*

I walked down the white, granite steps of the amphitheater to the center circle of the stage, and into a sun that was so sizzling hot I could melt. With great passion that bellowed up from the depths of my soul, I recited Shakespeare – sounding verse out onto the empty seats surrounding me.

> "What truth, what light through my mind's window breaks? It is the east, and the Holy Spirit is the sun. Arise my friend, dissolve the ego moon who is already sick and pale with grief. That thou the truth are far more greater than he. Oh, it is the Christ Child. Yes, it is my love. And if I knew what I was, the brightness of my mind would shame the stars as daylight does a lamp. My Mind in Heaven would through the unseen regions stream so bright, the world would sing and knoweth not the night."

As I took my bow, I imagined the amphitheater filled with people clapping and standing to their feet with great joy and enthusiasm, "Bravo! Bravo! Bravo!" The great actress, Eleanor Duse, along with Isadora Duncan, and Gabrielle D'Annunzio were also clapping and standing to their feet in exhilaration.

An Australian tourist, dressed in white with a bright, orange backpack over her shoulder, stood up and applauded my performance. Bravo! Bravo! Bravo! She shouted as she pulled off her sun hat and waved it in the air.

I smiled back and gave another dramatic bow to her. David was in the distance now calling to me to hurry on so we could catch the next ferry back to Verona. The tourist and I waved goodbye to each other as I disappeared up the amphitheater steps into the distance.

Back in Verona, David and I met up with Tom that evening for pizza at an outdoor café. He said he was enjoying his solo tour of Verona, and did not mind spending an extra day there alone while David and I took a short day trip to Milan to visit some modeling agencies to show them my portfolio.

Milan was the home of the Italian stock exchange and most of the country's important corporations. Milan had a very different feeling from any other European city that we visited. It was industrial, fast-paced, and hectic. One could feel the high-levels of anxiety, impatience, and stress emanating from its local population of mostly ambitious business people.

Milan is also recognized as the world's fashion and design capital, and the Milanese pride themselves on an expensive, name-brand lifestyle. I noticed there was a lot of wealth in Milan and high esteem for the quality of objects, but not quality of life. The average person in Milan looked genuinely stressed, unhappy, grumpy, and fearful. The foggy and rainy weather made it feel unbearably sad and lonely. The narrow treeless streets felt lifeless and foreboding.

David and I took cabs around the town, stopping at quite a few agencies. Some were mildly interested, but when I told them I was only there for a few days on vacation, and then returning to New York, no one twisted my arm to stay for test shots or modeling assignments. I was not disappointed with their lack of enthusiasm because I hated Milan and could not imagine myself living and working there.

Zucchero Management, the last modeling agency on our list of 'go sees,' was owned by a woman named Teresa. She wanted to arrange within the next week or two to have me test with a photographer from Venice. She asked me to stay for a few more weeks in Milan. My heart actually sank, because I could not wait to get out of that city. Instead, David and I agreed to return to Milan for an extra week after we completed our trip to Rome.

David and I returned to Verona to meet with Tom for dinner, and the next day we did some sightseeing before hoping back on the Eurail for our next stop, Florence.

The artwork in Florence was breathtaking, and we were sky-rocketed out of the earth's atmosphere by the best gelato ice cream we had ever tasted. We rented a clean and simple room in a small pension in Florence, but it was booked solid, so Tom had to share a room with us for one night. We kept laughing about the proprietor who ran the pension, because he did not look like the average local Italian. He was a tall and skinny man who resembled Frank Zappa with his black hair in a mullet haircut, spiked up like one of the musicians from A Flock of Seagulls. He looked very out of place living in Florence. He was soft spoken, and friendly. We always referred to him as "Our Little Frank Zappa."

He told us that if we needed anything, to ring the miniature gold bell on the night table. We rang the little gold bell to order tea for Tom, and then espresso and biscotti for me and David. Our Little Frank Zappa gingerly tiptoed in with a tray of refreshments. We loved the home-style hospitality.

We romped around Florence for three days, and then took short day trips to small towns like San Giorigiami, in Tuscany. The warm gold light reflected on the cottage roof tops, mountains, and wheat fields in the late Tuscan afternoon sun were in shades of gold I had never seen in the United States. Florence and its countryside definitely have a unique lighting different from the rest of the world. Back at the pension, we delighted in ringing the little bell, and we loved 'Our Little Frank Zappa', and found it hard to say goodbye to him as we headed off to romantic and beautiful Venice.

We had planned our itinerary so that I would be in Venice on my birthday. Venice was everything I had hoped for and more. Because there were no cars, only gondolas and a few water taxis to get around the city, it felt like we had traveled back in time.

All the pensions in Venice were full, so the three of us had to share one room on our first night there. The room was long and wide, but because it was on the first floor and close to the canals, everything, including the beds, were damp due to flooding during the past winter months. The three single wooden beds in the room were also tiny. Our feet hung off the edge, resting on top of the end posts. Throughout the night David coughed, Tom sneezed, and I snored.

The next morning we demanded dry beds that we could actually fit in. The proprietor, a buxom, but jolly Italian woman, eagerly granted our wishes. Tom got his own room on the second floor, and David and I checked into one across the hall from him. Our room was spacious and beautiful with a grand piano and fine oil paintings. Rustic wooden shutters opened to a romantic view of a narrow alleyway, the canal, and a nearby pedestrian bridge.

Placed on an elegant table near one of the windows was a vase of purple roses with yellow tints. I gasped as I moved towards them to touch the soft petals. They were the same roses I had written about back in New York City over a year ago.

> *"…. just as the light from the windows slides around the wall onto this vase of violet roses with yellow tints… I've never seen roses like that before, except in old oil paintings. So full, so round and open, with brown framing the edges of the petals, like antique lace. They sit there in the sun as if they've always been there. Not young budding flowers, but not old. Just in full maturity that would never change. They would stay just as they are, bent over a bit, but never growing older, never withering away.*
>
> *Oh, but it's so hopeless to hold onto. It goes away as if it never happened. Like a dream. Like you're waking up from a beautiful dream…*
>
> *Then I go to…Venice! Why? Because… Venice is sinking! It's sinking at two and a half centimeters per year. I hear people are moving up to the second floor the water level is so high. In twenty years, Venice won't be there. I have to go to Venice.*

At nighttime in Venice, we often heard cats growling and screaming in the alley. Day and night, cats were everywhere, and often mating. Even in broad daylight we spotted groups of stray cats mating in threesomes, a wild, frenzied orgy.

David and I bought authentic, hand-made Venetian masks at a local artisan's shop. At sixty-five dollars per mask, they were the most expensive souvenirs to purchase, but we had to have them. We spent most of our money in Venice buying souvenirs. We splurged on gold engraved leather bound writing books and phone books that were too beautiful to pass up.

In the evening, we celebrated my birthday by having dinner at a crowded, outdoor cafe in St. Marco's Square. Afterwards, we took a romantic gondola ride through the dark and eerie canals.

In the days that followed, we walked the neighborhoods of Venice that were far removed from the center of the city. Tom was so good at using maps that we were able to find our way through alleys and over bridges that most tourists never came upon. Off- the-beaten track, we found courtyards where young boys played soccer and old, Italian women washed their clothes by hand in a tin basin and hung them on a line to dry. We ate in the neighborhood restaurants where the wine was homemade, and just one glass made us drunk. Venice was amazing.

We headed off to Rome for three days, a big city with a lot to see. I especially enjoyed the Coliseum, the Roman Ruins, and the Vatican took my breath away. Its architecture was magnificent, and the marble sculptures and paintings in the Vatican were jaw dropping. I had never seen such splendor and beauty in one place, nor have I ever seen such wealth displayed in one place. It saddened me that the Catholic Church would embroider itself in such pomp and circumstance while so many people in the world suffered from poverty and hunger. Also, what was it with the silly red and purple robes and towering hats that the Pope and clergy wore? Since I was a child it had always appeared to me to be nothing but a big masquerade party.

I never had any trust or respect for people who flaunted power and material wealth, and made themselves more important than most of the population by hording and coveting much more than they needed while so many went without. I remember my childhood teachings of Jesus. Though an all powerful king, he was a humble servant of his people who loved humanity more than his title and used his power to uplift, heal, and bless.

On our final day in Rome we bid Tom a pleasant and safe trip back to New York City. David and I were heading back to Milan, to re-visit the Zucchero modeling agency for test shots. I did not want to return to that dreadful place, but David insisted that I give Milan a chance, and no harm could come from just checking it out for a few days to see what it has to offer.

We hopped on the Eurail, expecting our non-stop journey to take no more than four hours, but halfway through our ride the Italian Rail Road decided to go on strike. We waited it out, and seven hours later our train started moving again. We spent twelve grueling hours on the train headed for Milan. By the time we ended up at the Milan train station at three in the morning, we were hungry and tired. We were also smelly and dirty. The weather had turned hot and muggy during the trip, and the trains had no air conditioning. David spent over an hour at the public phone trying to get us into a room for the rest of the night, but with no luck. All the hotels were full. So we ended up sleeping on our luggage.

Finally, at around eight a.m., David located a hotel with an available room. We hopped in a cab and got there in about ten minutes. The hotel was small, old, and a bit shabby, but clean. As we were checking in at the front desk, we noticed that there was a lot of activity. Young, tall, attractive women roamed around the hotel. David asked the elderly man at the front desk what type of hotel it was.

"What do you a mean? It is hotel," he said in broken English.

"No, I mean, we see a lot of very young girls here," David said.

"So! Si, we have woman here, so? I don't a understand?" he replied.

"We see all girls here. No men? Only le donna, umm, no le uomo?" David said.

"Oh, ah yes. Le donna, molti donna. Fashione model. Molti fashione model e qui."

"Oh, si! Models?" David understood now.

"Si, si," he replied as he handed us our room key.

"This is a hotel for models? I guess we came to the right place," I said to David as we walked up stairs to our room.

Once in the room, we crashed on the bed for the rest of the day. When we both woke up, we took showers in the bath down the hall, and then wandered into the hotel's restaurant directly downstairs from our room.

The dining room was filled with models. David and I found seats at one of the long bench tables next to two attractive young girls accompanied by a young man with dark olive skin. Both girls had English accents, and the young man had an Indian accent. They immediately began a conversation with us. We learned that the two girls were models from England and the young man was originally from Bangladesh, a student in college, and here on vacation.

The young man, Babu, sporting tan trousers, a bright green golf shirt, and wire rimmed glasses, had a gentle and easy-going personality, and a dry sense of humor.

Lynn Stony was a street-wise, tomboy girl. Tall, skinny, and flat chested, she fancied herself in black cigarette jeans and short black boots emoting the rough-and-tumble attitude of a trashy punk rock band member. She kept her cigarette pack rolled up in her t-shirt sleeve like a gang member out of *West Side Story*. She wore no make-up on a flawless canvas of clear white skin, strong cheekbones, and big black eyes. The only color she carried was her plump, ruby-red lips. Her black, stringy hair was tied back, yet the strands often fell in front of her eyes as she chain smoked.

Amanda was the opposite of Lynn with her wavy, strawberry blonde hair, freckled face, and full figure. She was passive, gentle, and shy.

We hung out in the restaurant for a few hours, eating, drinking, smoking, talking and laughing. Then we all trotted back upstairs to the hotel and spent some time in Lynn and Amanda's room looking through each others' modeling portfolios.

Lynn was incredibly photogenic. Her photos projected a woman of feminine and sophisticated qualities but also one who was tough, edgy, and mysterious. Lynn said that she had acquired a lot of work in London, but needed to come to Milan and build up her portfolio to give her more marketability back home. Amanda was a bit shorter, and her full-figure was not really suited for modeling, but she was a pretty girl just the same.

I loved Lynn. Lynn would say in her working-class, Manchester accent, which sounded musically similar to the Beatles, as she nursed on her cigarette. "I don't come from a broken home. My home is shattered! I don't know who my father is. He left us a long time ago, and I probably have brothers and sisters somewhere who I've never even met."

Lynn made everyone laugh because she was so honest and down-to-earth. Her modeling pictures portrayed a woman who was sophisticated and privileged but Lynn was none of those things, and she was not embarrassed about it. She didn't try to hide the fact that she was from the streets and knew how to, not only survive, but get around. Lynn was fearless.

"My boyfriend in London lives a sheltered life in college. When he graduates, I'm going to have to show him how to travel and get around the world. He doesn't have a clue," she gloated.

The next day David and I headed downtown to the Zucchero Management modeling agency. On the way to the agency, everywhere along the streets, were models and photographers working at scenic locations throughout the city taking photos. It appeared that Milan was all about modeling and fashion and about nothing else.

The agency set me up with a photographer for test shots within the next few days, and I did not enjoy the shoot. The photographer did not speak much English, and I found him obnoxious, and difficult to work with. At the end of the day, I called the agency to find out how long it would take to book me for a job. Teresa told me there might not be anything for weeks or even months. If I wanted to work at all, I would have to stay in Milan and be patient. David had to return to New York by the end of the week because of his work, but he suggested I consider staying in Milan for as long as I could on my own to give modeling here a chance. The thought of being in Milan alone without David was scary.

I found the local people, even the office workers and business people on the subway and in the cafes, rude to one another. The few that did appear friendly came off as phony and dishonest, like shysters who wanted to get you involved in a scam that would leave you high and dry.

That evening, when we met up with Lynn, Amanda, and Babu for dinner, we were attacked by a group of local men. Even though we traveled in a group, grown men grabbed our behinds or tried to grab our breasts. They didn't care that David and Babu were walking with us. This also happened one other time in broad daylight. We were shocked and surprised at the behavior, and did not understand why the Italian men in Milan believed that they had the right to grab us. We yelled at them and pulled away. David and Babu swung their arms at the men, but the men only walked away laughing. It was bizarre. I hated Milan and could not wait to leave. We all hated Milan and couldn't wait to leave. David agreed. He would not feel comfortable leaving me there alone.

On our last day in Milan, David and I visited the famous Duomo, a church with an extremely ornate and gaudy exterior, but the was interior sparse, empty, and disappointing.

We then grabbed a bite to eat for lunch at a coffee bar. I observed the working-class businessmen in cheap, crumpled suits standing at the counter hurriedly gulping down their espresso. Their bodies looked haggard, their faces stressed and tired. Some looked around the room with suspicion. One man opened his brief case to pack up some documents. His hands were clenched tight and rigid, his right arm locked to his side shielding his chest. I remembered the women in saris begging on the streets of Paris having opposite gestures - their necks extended, their chests expanded, their arms stretched out, their palms open and fingers spread wide, but their bodies also haggard and their faces stressed.

On the way back to the hotel, David and I passed by a posh restaurant with an outdoor garden café where wealthy executives in high-priced suits and gold watches sat tall and confident. They shared exquisite lunches with their clients and colleagues, and their hands neither extended nor clutched--simple natural gestures ensued. Their faces seemed relaxed and self assured, and they exuded an air of confidence. Others dressed in casual attire appeared to be on holiday. They posed gracefully while passing the time. A chic, manicured woman looked out onto the open square, the upward curl of her closed smile pointing to her *Dolce and Gabbana* sunglasses. Her left arm lay loosely on her crossed leg. Her right elbow rested on the back of the chair as her refined hand hung limp. She was not there so much to enjoy the moment but to be seen rather than to see.

David and I spent our last evening hanging out with our new kindred spirits, Babu, Amanda, and Lynn at a local restaurant to share more great food and good conversation. To stretch out our final moments together, after dinner we strolled around town eventually coming upon a local pub-- their open doors sucking us into the sensual exploding vibrations of "Space Age Love Song" by A Flock of Seagulls.

We spent the rest of the evening getting plastered on imported beers and vodka *Menta Verde*. Lynn kept daring to grab the handsome Milanese bartender's butt simply because we girls were giggling over how cute it was. David and Babu rolled their eyes at each other with a discontented sense of rejection. When Lynn actually grasped for the bartenders behind, we all howled and laughed with a mixture of surprise and fear. Her reach would always just miss him by an inch as he motioned away to mix a drink or ring up the cash register, oblivious to her exploits. More and more patrons trickled in during the night until the joint was packed and everyone was shoulder-to-shoulder. We partied until the wee hours of the morning expressing with giddy enthusiasm an occasional Italian phrase here and there: Per favore, Si, magnifico, Mi scusi, dove il bagno?, Prego, Molto bene, Ciao amico, Buona Notte!

David and I agreed the best reason for being in Milan was getting to meet this unusual fun and down-to-earth trio from England. We were going to miss them the most. Arriverderci!

CHAPTER SIXTEEN

NEW YORK CITY BLUES

DAVID AND I trudged into our New York apartment with our luggage. The furniture and clothes we had moved from Sidney's apartment the day before we left for Paris sat waiting in the middle of the living room. Neither one of us could deal with the mess, so we escaped to the coffee shop for a bite to eat.

The next day David got up early and left the house for work. I got up shortly after, hobbled out into the living room, and found the sunlight from the window shining down on my furniture and clothes. I didn't know what to do. Should I unpack all my belongings and put everything back where it originally was, or should I just leave everything where it is until David decided whether or not I could stay with him? If I couldn't stay, where would I go? I didn't have a job, and I didn't have any money, nor did I have another place to go. I stepped around the pile and dawdled into the bathroom to take a shower.

Just as I got out of the shower, the phone rang. It was Leonardi.

"Hi. How did you know I was home from Europe?" I asked.

"I didn't know for sure. I just felt that you might be back, so I took a chance. Is David there with you?" he whispered.

"No, he left early. I think he went to work but I'm not sure."

"I was in Paris. I left about a day after you did," Leonardi admitted.

"Yeah, I know you were," I replied.

"You knew. How? Did you see me or something?"

"No, I just felt it. That's all."

"I never got to thank you for that bouquet of balloons you sent me for my birthday and the lovely card. It was the most beautiful gift I ever received. There was a very dramatic thunderstorm that afternoon. I opened up my window, and let the balloons drift out into the glowing sky," Leonardi marveled.

'Is that what he had done to me?' I thought. 'Released me, unshielded and unprotected, into a raging storm?'

"Leonardi did you ever ask Sidney what she knew about that guy she left me with that night, who pulled the knife on me? Did she tell you anything? Did you get any information from her?" I questioned.

"No. I asked her, but she claimed she was in the hospital emergency room that night and most of the next morning and had no idea or knowledge of what happened. When she finally got home she said, you and your belongings were gone, and the bedroom was empty. She says that's all she knows. I think she's telling the truth. I'm so sorry you went through that. I really am."

"Leonardi what about the guy she left me in the apartment with? Did you ask her who he was?

"She says she didn't know him at all. That he was just a friend of her boyfriend, whom she had never met until that night," Leonardi replied.

"What did her boyfriend know about him? Her boyfriend seemed a bit wacky himself. I don't know, Leonardi. She has to know more," I responded.

"I really don't think she does. I think she's telling the truth. Did you at least report it to the police?"

"No, I didn't because David and I were scheduled for a flight to Paris the next day. There were no witnesses, no break in, or evidence of a struggle, and probably no way of finding him. We thought it would be a useless endeavor where the police wouldn't even catch him let alone be able to convict him of anything. It would have only forced us to cancel our trip," I explained.

"That makes sense. Listen, I just want you to know. I'm truly sorry about what happened. I thank God that you are safe and okay. Really. I am so grateful you are okay." Leonardi sounded sincere.

"Thanks," I replied.

"That bouquet of balloons you sent me was so beautiful. I wish you were there to see them fly away into the dark stormy sky," Leonardi marveled again.

A sudden migraine came on, and I felt like my head was going to split in half. "I gotta go. Thanks for calling," I mumbled and hung up.

I migrated into the living room, sat on the couch, and stared at my belongings in the middle of the room. Who set up the knife attack on me? Because it was clearly a set-up. Was it Maria, Leonardi's ex-girl friend? Was Sidney involved? Why was Leonardi suddenly afraid to be with me as soon as I had moved in with Sidney? It was all speculation, and I had no answers. Thinking about it made me sick with confusion. I buried my thoughts.

How could I have been so stupid! Why had I believed that Leonardi really loved me or cared for me? And what made me even more furious was the fact that I still loved him. I sat on the couch looking at my disheveled life, askew in the middle of the floor. I couldn't even cry. I felt numb, angry, and confused all over again.

David phoned me from the office later in the afternoon. "What am I going to do with my stuff?" I asked.

"What do you mean?"

"My stuff in the middle of the living room? What am I going to do with it?" I snapped.

David laughed. "Put it back where it was before, spaghetti head."

"You want me to put everything back where it was before?" I asked.

"Well, yeah. You're not going to keep it in the middle of the living room are you? I mean how are we going to see the TV set? I want to watch Letterman tonight?" he reasoned.

"Okay, right. I never thought of that, okay," I agreed.

"Tom called and wanted to know if he could come by tonight to bring over his photos from our trip. I got ours developed today also," David added.

"Yeah, sure. That'll be fun. I better clear out the living room then," I agreed.

"Okay, so we'll order pizza, and have a photo party. See you later," David replied.

I put everything back in its place, but I felt like, good grief! Did nothing ever really happen here or what? How come everyone acts like nothing happened and it's the same life as usual, except for me? I'm not the same person anymore, or am I? Leonardi left me, and won't tell me why. David's back at work, and I'm back here with no job, no money and nowhere to go anyway, so what the heck. We'll order pizza!'

Over the next few weeks, after our return from Europe, David was friendly and amiable, but he seemed distant, and maybe I was just as distant with him. My mind was obsessed with the thought of Leonardi, mostly because I needed closure. He had still not given me an explanation as to why he had suddenly cut me off. If I continued to try to find out, maybe my life would get threatened again. No one seemed to know anything. And if there was someone who knew something, they were not going to talk. I had to let it all go, but I didn't know how, because there were too many unanswered questions.

Under different circumstances, maybe David and I would have gone to see the Bob Geldof Live Aid concert. Instead, we sat at home and watched it on TV. Madonna's performance was electrifying, but I wondered if it was really true that she had to sleep with sleazy night club owners to get her career moving? I don't really know, but if that's the case, I may never have a film career. Watching the male performers, I pondered the fact that they don't have to sleep with anyone unless they want to. Men seem to have more freedom in society to be themselves without those kinds of conditions or even rumors placed upon them.

As I stared at the TV, set I wondered how all these musical performers managed to establish a career doing what loved, and making more than enough money for ten life times while still helping starving people in Africa. I mean, why would a billionaire residing in Los Angeles, or even

Ohio, prefer to own over one hundred antique cars worth $100,000 each when he knew a family in Pittsburg was living on food stamps, and kids were ducking down behind kitchen windows to dodge flying bullets. I don't want to deprive people of the fruits of their labor, but isn't one or two Mercedes enough. Why do these people have to own a whole fleet of cars, and why do they need to own the entire world? Why are they so insecure and so selfish? And why are they so looked up to by society strictly because of their wealth? There are people that have more than enough money to rebuild an entire city let alone a town or a community that needs it? Why don't they do it? Common sense and politics don't mesh I guess, and I knew nothing about politics.

As I watched the performers, I realized if I did become rich and famous through my art, my wealth could be used to pull my brother out of the old neighborhood of drugs and crime. I'd stick him on a farm in the middle of nowhere so he could plant crops and learn how to ride horses. I'd hire a detox-psychologist/motivational coach to help turn his life around while my brother was still young enough to break free from the life of bondage he was living. That was worth more than a fleet of private jets or antique cars. Thinking about all this stuff made me feel confused and inadequate, and I felt a migraine headache coming on, so I dropped the thought and decided to focus on just enjoying the concert.

I admired the sexy musical philanthropist, Bob Geldof, and the cute bass player from Duran Duran. David got jealous. David and I only had sex twice during the five years I lived with him, but it didn't seem to bother him that much. But once he knew I was willing to sleep with my hairdresser, he felt more rejected by my lack of interest in sleeping with him. I was not a sexual person. It was the joy of life, and a joyful state of being that drove me toward Leonardi not sex.

I told David the truth; I did love him, but the physical attraction was not there. It never had been. I wished we had been sexually compatible, but we weren't. My feelings for Leonardi had very little to do with sex anyway; it had more to do with 'a state of being'.

I had lived in a hostile environment as a teenager, where drugs and crime were everywhere. I had been an artist growing up in an environment that lacked inspiration and culture. Sex was not on the list of things to want, feel, or desire. I always focused on developing my talents in the arts as a way of escaping. Luckily, New York City was only a few train stops away. The arts, rather than making love and making babies, were my ticket out of Queens.

"Are you still in love with him?" David asked.

"I don't know. I only spent two nights with him, and that was back in April. I moved into Sidney's place in May. Then Leonardi cut me off for no reason at all. My life was threatened and the next morning I was back at your place. The morning after that I was in Paris followed by a trip to Italy. Now it's the middle of June. I don't know what I feel anymore. My brain is fried. I'm confused," I said.

"Well, maybe you should sleep on the couch until you figure out where you are going to go, and how you are going to get there," David suggested.

So I slept on the couch. David went to the office every day, and I made phone calls, sent out resumes, and went on job interviews which were few and far between. Nothing was materializing for me, and the hostility and tension from not finding work along with David's impatience with me got worse each day.

I sometimes cried myself to sleep. Maybe David was in the bedroom doing the same thing. I didn't know. I hardly ever saw him after that. He went to work and afterwards went out with Tom or his other friends. When he was around, he treated me like a roommate rather than his best friend.

....

It was now August. After another job interview, I exited the dark office building squinting my eyes to adjust to the midday sun. I strolled over to a park for a moment to reflect. The job interview had not gone well at all.

Claire, an attractive woman in her late thirties, highly polished in a professional designer business suit, interviewed me with her *Invasion of the Body Snatchers* politeness. She told me it was a high-pressure job and that the hours were from seven in the morning until seven at night. It was a secretarial position. Why were the hours so long? What was so high pressure about it?

"You'll be working for three guys who work on the trading floor," she said.

"We're on Park and 27ᵗʰ Street. Isn't the trading floor downtown on Wall Street? I asked.

"Yes, but we have our own trading floor here, so there's no need for them to be downtown," she replied.

"What happened to the secretary before me? I asked.

"She left. She couldn't handle it. So I'm warning you up front. There's a lot of pressure."

"What kind of pressure?" I asked.

"These guys are stock brokers," she replied.

I looked at her like, 'Yeah, so and?'

"I have to be honest with you. These guys are hard workers and under a lot of stress. I don't know how to say this. They are extremely rude, vulgar, and crass," she said as she examined my reaction.

"To who?" I asked.

"To everybody," she jumped in.

"Toward the girl that left?" I asked.

Claire nodded. "Yes."

"Why, exactly, did the last girl leave?"

"They call people names; there are a lot of loud obscenities. They may even pinch your behind, or grab your breast. But that's the way the environment is on trading floors. It's just the nature of the beast. It's not something I can change, so I need to hire someone who can handle it. Someone who has a thick skin. It's not something you need to take personally," Claire explained.

I pictured beer-bellied, middle-aged men in pin stripe suits, drinking scotch, smoking cigars, and laughing and cajoling like pigs in a strip club. I had often seen men like this in restaurants down on Wall Street, during lunch time, on the few occasions I did temp work there.

"Can you handle it?" she asked as she tried to read my face.

"Absolutely not," I stated.

"You can't handle it?"

"That's what I said, but I appreciate your honesty," I replied.

"It pays $45,000 a year, plus a $10,000 bonus at the end of the year, and full health coverage starting on the first day," she added.

"That's nice. I can't do it," I replied

"You don't have a thick skin?" she asked in a condescending tone.

"No, I guess I don't," I quipped.

"If we made you a better offer would you consider it? I can talk to my boss, and see if we can go to $55,000 plus a bonus?"

"Hadn't I made myself clear?" I thought. I couldn't work from seven in the morning until seven at night while being treated like a cheap cocktail waitress in a strip club, not for any amount of money. If that's what I had been aiming for, I would have dropped out of high school and become a stripper; fewer hours, and more money.' "This is not the place for me," I said firmly.

"Here take my card. I see from your resume that you've been out of work for a while, and perhaps you might want to sleep on it."

I took the card, and looked at it and then at her intently. "I'm not going to change my mind," I stated.

"I appreciate your honesty," she said as she held out her hand to shake mine goodbye.

I ripped up the card and threw it down on her desk in front of her and left.

A cloud moved over me swiftly as I sat on the park bench, and watched some children in the distance share mellifluous giggles while hanging from a set of monkey bars.

My thoughts were colliding, 'You would think I was in the music business, where there was supposedly nothing but sex, drugs and rock-n-roll. I was interviewing for an office job. Good grief!

In any business these days, there was much accommodation for unethical behavior for those who played dirty, and it was demanded of everyone else to suck it up or look the other way. Maybe there was no such thing as a normal job with normal people. If there was, maybe I didn't fit in anyway. Was there any compassion left for me? Who was going to protect me?'

A humongous dining needle with golf-ball size eyes, scooped down towards me like a jet liner. I jumped off the park bench and ran outside onto the side walk.

'Besides, I don't perceive life the same way accountants do, or stockbrokers, for that matter. A yellow plate sitting on a kitchen table is not a yellow plate, it's the sun. And it's not just the sun. It's a proud sun, an enthusiastic sun, a pale waning sun, or a royal sun, but it's not just a sun and it's never just a plate for eating food,' my mind rumbled.

Regaining my composure, I lit a cigarette, and waited for the intrusive bug to fly away in the distance as my mind continued its rant.

'You just can't take a tropical fish, and drop it into a heap of wet cement and say, 'Swim, damn it, swim!' Since seventy percent of the earth is covered in water, I'd much rather take my chances jumping out of an air plane without a parachute and hoping I'd land back in the ocean, than hang around for any more of this nonsense. If there's that much water awaiting me below, then I'm going to take my chances and jump. Give me liberty or give me death!', my mind screamed.

The dining needle finally out of sight, I resumed my place on another park bench. My thoughts confirmed themselves, 'No, I was not going to sleep on it. There was nothing to sleep on.' I crunched out my cigarette on the black tar floor with my uncomfortable, skin-pinching dress shoes.

As I leaned my back against the park bench, a tall, lanky but good looking, young man sat next to me to strike up a casual conversation. His name was Justin and he was a working musician who played guitar and wrote his own songs. His looks reminded me of the independent film director, Jim Jurmusch. Justin wore all black: black jeans, black t-shirt, black, urban cowboy boots with silver spurs. He had high cheekbones, full lips, and his dark chestnut hair accentuated his intensely bright green eyes. He was strikingly handsome, but that's not why I let him talk to me. Maybe it was the thick, old-fashioned, hardcover book that he held in his hand that gave his presence a gentle, humble, and unassuming quality. He seemed sincere, and comforting to sit with. He popped out a gold lighter from his denim vest pocket and lit my cigarette. Then he lit his own as it dangled out from his blowfish-sized lips.

"What are you reading?" I asked.

"Kafka. Do you know Kafka?"

"No," I nodded.

Justin opened his book and read me a passage:

> "Human nature, ever changing and as unstable as the dust, can endure no restraint. If it binds itself it soon begins to tear madly at its bonds, rendering everything asunder, the wall, its bonds, its very self." Franz Kafka

"I can relate to that," I sighed.

"Ah, yes, Kafka. The most important and influential writer of the twentieth century. You never heard of Kafka?"

"I've heard the name. I never read his work," I admitted.

"You deprived little girl." And he read some more:

> "We are as forlorn as children lost in the wood. When you stand in front of me and look at me, what do you know of the griefs that are in me and what do I know of yours. And if I were to cast myself down before you and tell you, what more would you know about me that you know about hell when someone tells you it is hot and dreadful? For that reason alone we human beings ought to stand before one another as reverently, as reflectively as lovingly, as we would before the entrance to hell." Franz Kafka.

Justin lived in Hoboken, New Jersey, a place I had only heard of and never been. We chatted about music and films. He mentioned that he had just broken up with his girlfriend a few months ago. She had found someone else and moved out on him overnight. The story sounded familiar, but I never mentioned my own story or situation.

"Would you like to come down to a club in the West Village and listen to me play music?" He offered.

"Yeah, I would," I agreed.

We exchanged phone numbers.

Since David was now going out at night, and left me alone most of the time, I decided to go to the small bar in the Village to watch Justin perform. He was an amazingly gifted musician. He finger picked a twelve-string acoustic guitar, implementing hammer-ons and slides, with precision and clarity. He performed a rough and tumble interpretation of the song, "King of the Road", by Roger Miller, which impressed me. The original songs that he sang were quite good too. We hung out together and talked over a few drinks, and then I went home. He asked me if he could see me again sometime soon, and take me out to a movie or something.

We met again and he took me downtown in the Village to see the independent film, *Brother from Another Planet*, by John Sayles. I had already seen the film with David last year, but I didn't tell Justin. I thought it was an okay movie, so I didn't mind seeing it again. After the film he took me to a quiet pub for a bite to eat, and I told him about my living situation, and how I was working on finding a job so I could move out of David's apartment. Justin seemed to understand and was agreeable. He still wanted to see me again and just hang out.

He took me out to dinner and to a few clubs downtown to hear other local bands. We never kissed or got physically involved. He often put his arms around my shoulder, or reached for my hand as we walked down the street. He seemed like a regular guy, and an easy person to be with.

Justin invited me over to his house in Hoboken to listen to some of his recordings, and he gave me a few guitar lessons. I felt comfortable and safe with Justin. David wasn't being communicative with me. He was distant and cold and I felt guilty and ashamed for still living there.

Finally, I confided with Justin that living with David was quite difficult, and I was frustrated as to what to do. Justin suggested I live with him in Hoboken. I believed it was premature, but then I did not see many options. I couldn't move back to Queens. I felt the best solution was to find a job, have my own money, and get my own apartment, but I didn't see where or how or when that solution was going to come about. I declined Justin's offer, but thanked him.

A few nights later, David and I had a terrible fight. David and I had rarely ever fought as far as yelling and screaming matches. That night, though, I had never seen him so hostile and angry. It scared me. I left the apartment and called Justin, and he offered to let me stay at his place.

So, I found myself in Hoboken, New Jersey. By late evening Justin and I were cuddled under the bed covers, the candlelight swaying to the soft, slow sound of Beethoven's "Moonlight Sonata". Justin read more Kafka to me:

"To die would mean nothing else than to surrender a nothing to the nothing, but that would be impossible to conceive, for how could a person, even only a nothing, consciously surrender himself to the nothing and not merely to an empty nothing but rather to a roaring nothing whose nothingness consists only in its incomprehensibility." Franz Kafka.

We made love. I really did not want to have sex with Justin. I just wanted good company, but friendship with the opposite sex always seems to revolve around the pressures of having sex with them. I could not deal with the idea of Justin feeling rejected, and having him angry at me, too.

When I woke up Justin was already in the kitchen making us breakfast. We had scrambled eggs, bacon, French toast, and fresh coffee. He put his arms around me, kissed me, and told me that I looked very sexy in his shirt.

"You can move in with me you know. I want you to. Would you?" he asked.

"Are you sure? Do you want me to? Really?"

"Of course I do. Look, you can't stay where you are any more, and I like you. I like you very much. So why not? There's plenty of room here for two," he reassured.

"I still don't have a job yet."

"You'll find a job. Come on move in. We can make beautiful music together," he insisted.

"Just give me a few days to think about it," I asked.

"Okay, but you're more welcome here than you are there with David."

"Yeah, I know. God. It just seems crazy," I nodded.

"Yeah, well, life can be like that," Justin smiled.

We kissed each other for a long time and then finished breakfast.

I thought Justin was very handsome and sweet, and I was very fond of him, but not in love with him. I was still in love with Leonardi. Leonardi did not seem to be anything but a dream and a memory that would never appear in my life again, and if I thought about him I felt sad, then confused, and then angry.

I felt so guilty for cheating on David with Leonardi, and I felt that no one liked me anymore, least of all David. But here was a man, Justin, who did like me. So I seriously thought about packing my bags and moving out of David's place to live with Justin.

The next day David left the house again and did not come home at all that night. When he finally came home, he didn't say anything. Then he left again. Either David was having an affair, or he was keeping himself out of his own apartment and away from me, hoping that I would disappear. Perhaps it was a bit of both. I packed my things to leave.

"What are you doing?" David asked.

David startled me. I didn't hear him come in.

"I'm moving out. That's what you want, isn't it?"

"Where are you going?" he snapped.

"I'm moving to Hoboken."

"Hoboken? Where in Hoboken? With who? How?"

"I'm moving in with a friend," I replied.

"A friend?"

"Yeah, a friend. He lives in Hoboken, New Jersey," I replied.

"He? Who is *he*? What's his name?" David asked.

"His name is Justin, okay? Why? What's the difference?"

"So you're moving in with another guy?" he snapped.

"First of all, I'm not moving in with another guy. I never moved in with Leonardi. I slept with Leonardi. I never lived with the man," I snapped back.

"And this guy, Justin? Are you sleeping with him?"

"What's it to you? You want me to move out. I want to move out. You want me out, and I found a place to stay. It's that simple, okay?"

David stood staring at me.

"Why do you have to know all the details? What do you care? You don't care about me anymore, and I understand why you don't. Regardless, I need to do something about my life too, you know," I barked.

"So living with some guy in Hoboken is doing something about your life?"

"Look, what do you want me to do? Move back to Queens with my parents?"

"No, no. Of course not. I don't want you to do that for God sake," he agreed.

"I just don't know what you expect me to do. I can't stay here. It's not fair to you, and it's not very comfortable for me either. Just what do you expect me to do?" I pleaded.

"Who is this guy?" David asked.

"He's just a friend, alright?"

"I don't believe you," David pointed his finger accusingly.

"You know what? I don't care. You have no reason to trust or believe anything I say anymore after I was with Leonardi. I don't even expect you to be civil to me. Nor do I expect you to allow me to stay here anymore. You know I need to go, and *I* know I need to go. You've made it hard for me to live here, and now you are making it hard for me to leave," I complained.

"*You* made it hard for you to live here," David retorted.

"Alright. I did. You're right. I made it hard for me to live here. I slept with Leonardi. I fell in love with Leonardi. I made it hard. I did it. So there! That's it. It's *all* my fault! Do you want me to sleep in the living room on your couch for the rest of my life, while you go out with your friends and leave me here to sit in the dark by myself and feel guilty about what I did for the rest of my life? Is that what you want?" I yelled.

"No. I just thought you would find a job and get your own apartment instead of shacking up with some guy," David softened.

"In the past five years that I've lived with you, have I ever had a steady job?"

"No, but that's your fault," he snapped.

"Yeah, that's right, it's *my* fault. I'm responsible for the recession, the Vietnam War, and I shot J.R. Ewing. It's all *my* fault! When I have a job, I can type 100 words per minute, take steno at 130 words per minute. I show up for work on time, do a good job, have a cheery disposition, and I get bullied and harassed for turning my head left or right or for sneezing. I don't know what that's about. I don't know how to overcome stuff like that. I don't know how to fix that either," I frantically retorted.

"The job at MWR with Tony was working out for you until you got your picture in the paper."

"Yes, exactly! Until I got my picture in the paper! Don't you get it? I have to play small in life, because if I'm myself, too many people get *soooo* upset about it."

"Maybe you should wait until you find a permanent job," David suggested.

"That office job with Tony was over eight months ago. What if it takes another eight months for me to find a job? Do you want me here sleeping on your couch for another eight months?" I reasoned.

"No, I thought you would find a job first before moving out."

"I thought so, too. I thought I could do that since I left school, but I can't seem to make it work. I can't stay here. So I have to go. I have to go."

"You're right. Go," David flatly agreed.

I walked out of the apartment with my small suitcase feeling like I had just lost my best friend, but there didn't seem to be any other option.

I moved into Justin's three-room, railroad flat in an old tenement building in Hoboken. The kitchen was huge and painted an ugly dark brown with yellow trim. The walls had the old wooden paneling running along the bottom half of the wall, and the ceiling still had the tin tiles from the late 1800's. A love seat was placed under the three windows in the kitchen. The sight of the claw foot, antique bathtub in the kitchen, next to an old black furnace made me cringe. It was not my taste in décor, but it felt cozy and poetic.

It was a step down from David's apartment, but there was someone there waiting for me who enjoyed my company and wanted to spend time with me.

Justin and I went out to dinner and came back to his apartment and made love. He woke up early for work because he had a day job at a printing house on the Lower West Side in Manhattan. I got up later. That night, Justin swaggered into his apartment late and indubitably drunk. He started yelling and screaming, flinging his arms at me, and knocking things off the kitchen table with his fist. I had no idea until that moment, Justin was an alcoholic.

I had seen him drink maybe two beers when we were out together over the few weeks we had known each other. He occasionally had a shot of scotch at the bar, but until that night I was unaware that he was a serious and abusive alcoholic. I was mortified and extremely frightened. I didn't know who this person was. He was no one I had ever known or met before. He was verbally abusive, angry, and threatening. I stood in the corner, backed up against the wall crying. My body slid down the wall, and I huddled on my knees, hiding my face in my chest, my hands over my head begging for him to stop. Justin marched into the living room and then into the kitchen again only to rush out of the house slamming the door behind him. I didn't know what to do. Should I call the police? Should I leave? Where would I go?

I sat up in bed alone most of the night wondering what I should do. I was too scared and paralyzed to do anything. A few hours later, just before the sun came up, I heard Justin's key in the door. I jumped under the covers and pretended I was asleep. He crawled into bed with me, put his arms around me and kissed me on the head. I continued to pretend I was fast asleep until I actually did fall asleep.

The next day was Saturday, and Justin's day off. I let him get up first to shower, hoping that he would leave the house before I woke up, but he didn't. He made us both breakfast, and woke me up to join him in the kitchen. He hugged me and told me how sorry he was about last night. I was quiet for a moment as I ate my eggs and drank some coffee.

"You never told me you were an alcoholic. I had no idea. I never saw you drunk before. Why didn't you tell me?" I firmly demanded.

"I was afraid. And I'm not an alcoholic. I mean, I am. My father was, but I think I have it under control. I mean . . . I know I didn't have it under control last night, but I usually do. I'm sorry," he said.

"Justin, sorry is not good enough. Are you going to AA or anything?' I asked.

"No. I don't need AA," he mumbled.

"Justin, you need AA," I snapped.

"Who are you to tell me what I need. *You* tell me you're looking for a job, and you turn off the alarm in the morning and go back to sleep. That's not looking for a job. Who are you to tell me what I need?" he yelled.

He put on his coat and slammed the front door in the kitchen behind him as he exited the apartment.

It was true; I did turn off the alarm at seven in the morning, rolled over and fell back to sleep. I did so because all the temp agencies that I had signed up with didn't have any work for me. If they had, they would have called me the night before. Why jump in the shower at 7:30 a.m., get all dressed up in uncomfortable business clothes, and hot sticky stockings, and call all the agencies at 9 a.m., only to find out that they didn't have anywhere to send me. It seemed pointless. I preferred to get another few hours of sleep, and then call the agencies in the late morning, and late afternoon. I knew they had no work for me regardless of what time I called them.

The lack of work was depressing, and made me want to roll over and go back to sleep. It wasn't just the lack of employment that made me depressed, but I was lethargic and deeply saddened about everything that had transpired over the past year. I needed Justin like I needed a hole in my head. I needed a compassionate, skilled therapist to talk to, rather than another man to live with. Therapy required money, money required a job. Therapy also required health insurance, health insurance required a job. But if I had a steady job in a normal environment, and my own apartment, I wouldn't need a therapist.

Here I was, living with an abusive alcoholic who was in denial about his condition. If I had known he was an alcoholic, I would have never brought my suitcase here. In fact, I would never have talked to him again. I had enough problems of my own. I needed someone stronger than me, not weaker.

I was in the worst pickle I could ever be in. I had no job and no money, and now I was not in David's apartment either. I was with an alcoholic; living in his home.

I packed my bags and moved back with my parents. That was a pretty desperate and toxic decision, but I didn't have much of a choice. So I jumped on the train and headed back to their two-bedroom apartment in Astoria, Queens, New York, a lower-middle class, urban, working class neighborhood, a few train stops out of Manhattan. I went from the fire into the frying pan, but, hey, what else do young, talented women with no job opportunities and no money do? Boyfriend, or parents? What else was this so-called liberated society offering me; a woman with skills, talents, and brains? I was angry again at the so-called crap the media brain-washed people into believing: That if women had talent, intelligence, education and skills, and applied themselves, they could support themselves and live on their own and make their own decisions. Yeah, right--perhaps if she came from a rich and affluent family.

I could see that the world is a rat race, and the big fat rats get to eat all the cheese. As an office worker you were just a tool to make someone else wealthy, while they paid you only $10 an hour, and then they taxed you on it, which did not come close to paying for living expenses, let alone a life. It forced women to look for a boyfriend or a husband to pay all or half the bills. If you weren't famous in the arts you were broke. With art it is either feast or famine.

Too many women have to work at jobs they hate, or work with people who don't match their value system, and live with men simply to cover expenses? Their decisions are based on survival, not choice. This probably accounts for why most women buy a lot of crap that they don't need to fill up the emptiness of their daily routine. I never understood why women liked to shop all the time; it's such a stupid waste of time not to mention a waste of hard-earned money.

Maybe one day women will wake up to the fact that models in magazines don't really look like that? There is a well-paid, make-up artist and hair stylist who fuss over them all day. Clothes are pinned and tucked back with clothespins and safety pins. The model's breasts are taped together for cleavage. There is special lightening, and sometimes even airbrushed images to create a fantasy, not reality. Most models don't live in front of the glamorous backdrop of Monte Carlo. On their days off, most models are relieved to walk around the house with no make-up and wearing only a bathrobe and slippers, just like any other woman.

I knew of too many models, fresh off the farms of Nebraska, who shacked up with rich, crusty old' men in order to survive the deep, economic hurtle of New York City. There again, decisions not based on one's inner compass for authentic friendship and love, but based on economic survival.

CHAPTER SEVENTEEN

LIVING IN QUEENS, AGAIN

I MOVED BACK into my old room, which had become my brother's room, but he was in jail again for something related to drugs. When I had moved out at age nineteen into Manhattan, I shut myself off to what was going on with my brother, Robert. For one reason, my parents yelled at me for giving advice about getting him into therapy or counseling. It appeared to me, at the time, that my parents were using judgment, blame, and guilt to motivate my brother into sobriety, which only made him want to escape into drugs more.

I tried to explain to my parents that he was not going to gain self-esteem and self-worth by giving up drugs. It was the other way around; he would quit drugs by first recognizing his worth. They didn't want my advice and they didn't want me to interfere. They got angry at my suggestions and input, but maybe because they wanted to protect me from the stressful, dark realties of police stations, courts, and prisons. I don't know. I could never quite figure it out.   As for my brother, I concluded that maybe the many people addicted to drugs, alcohol or anything to the extreme were people who have a more difficult time coping with the oppressive, judgmental slaughterhouse of this world we occupy.

This toxic situation with my brother carried on and escalated over the years while I was gone. He was in and out of the slammer often for drugs and drug related crimes. I didn't know the specifics, because my parents refused to tell me, so I stopped asking.

I did not understand it at the time, but my parents were too frightened, frustrated, and ill-prepared to handle my brother. The outside help, or so-called expert advice they sought, wasn't helping much. I suspect there were some genuinely helpful social workers and drug programs willing and able to help my brother, but I felt that the justice system was also designed to keep him locked in a cycle of self-annihilation.

My brother's obstacles began at birth. He had a severe case of Attention Deficit Disorder, something that had no label at that time. He could never keep up in school, his attention span was zero, and he was extremely hyperactive. The problem was never addressed properly. His behavior as a young child was attributed to laziness, stupidity, and this 'bad boy' always getting into trouble.

I had no grievance with my brother, as I could see that he took drugs to numb the pain of being seen as inadequate by others. In truth, when he was sober, he was a very-easy going, good-natured, and considerate person. I understood his frustrating boredom of growing up in a lower-middle class neighborhood where there was little money and resources, no positive stimulation, and a lot of pressure by one's peers to get high. Also, his inability to keep up with the rest of the kids in class due to his Attention Deficit Disorder and Hyperactivity made him all the more susceptible to feelings of worthlessness resulting in the need to escape those feelings through drugs once he hit the confusing hormonal changes of puberty.

Decades later, I learned that he was often framed by other thugs in the neighborhood, and arrested for things he was innocent of doing. I am not saying my brother was any angel as I heard he had committed a considerable amount of petty thefts to secure drug money, but he was not always the guilty party. Perhaps the justice system, prison system and the lawyers would profit financially by my brother staying stuck in the system, rather than by his ability to overcome his environment and addictions. His lifestyle was a serious matter in which I had no expertise and in which I felt powerless.

My parents appeared to be overwhelmed emotionally by my brother's life and his behavior. Their anger and frustration made the house always feel tense and frightening. I knew that my parents loved my brother, because they did the best they could. They bailed him out of jail, took him to the hospital, and drove him to court. They filled out all the necessary papers for court, for welfare, and for lawyers. My mother cooked for him, washed his clothes, and ironed them. My mother would jump in front of a train for him. My father would take a bullet for him. Yet, they would never ever talk to him in a way that would make him feel valuable or empowered. That was the irony of the situation. They had trouble letting us exist innocently in the moment. They were so full of anxiety and fear about the near and far future, no one could just relax in the moment and just 'be' at peace. My father had an illness of being a narcissistic bully. Therefore both spouse and children were subject to the toxic emotional environment mandated by the head of the house.

I could remember even since I was a small child that my father always came home frustrated and angry. He would take it out on my mother, criticizing, interrogating, and marginalizing her. My mother became frustrated and angry with everyone in the house because she was at a loss as to how to please her husband and alleviate the torment of his anxiety and struggles. Maybe his struggles were financial. I don't know. I was too young to know anything. When things were quiet in the house it was only the silence of apathy and indifference -- the air was filled with the fear of the next outbursts of rage which would inevitably come. No one knew when, where, or how, but it would come. I felt sad and helpless in not knowing how to make my parents happy. I was just a child. I felt powerless and alone. I usually played quietly while in the house, losing myself with Barbie dolls, drawing, and reading books.

I was fortunate though to end up in a Catholic grammar school where the nuns and teachers were kind, patient, gentle, thoughtful, encouraging, and joyful. I loved going to school, had lots of friends, and was considered the talented school artist. I was very outgoing in school and wrote short plays and gathered my fellow students together to perform the stories I wrote in front of the class. In fifth grade, I once walked around the neighborhood stopping people on the street, asking them what they thought about "pollution". I would tape record their responses and present my project into social science whole class. I wasn't afraid of people, and I wasn't shy. I was only quiet around my parents because they would either say, "Don't bother me now, can't you see I'm busy watching TV, or shut up and leave me alone." They were receptive when things were going well for them and they were happy, but they were rarely happy.

As I got older, I suspected that my parents also fell into the same trap most parents find themselves in – unless one's kids grow up to be self-sufficient, independent human beings in society, then the world would judge them as bad parents. None of us would be worthy until "the world" considered us worthy, and no parents were considered worthy by "the world" until their kids were socially acceptable in every way.

The outwardly successful families often manage to hide from others much of their dysfunctional histories throughout their adult life from others through the façade of a decent job, high income level, and social status. If they have a big house and a manicured lawn, then they must be A-okay, but this is just not true.

I never became a drug user, but I had experimented with drugs and alcohol a few times as a teenager because that's what was going on in the neighborhood. Fortunately for me, the experience only left me feeling physically ill, and actually gave me a feeling of low self-esteem that I did not like. Being high made me feel out of control, and I am the type of person who does not like feeling out of control.

When my first boyfriend was seduced into drug use, and a few years later died from drugs, I made the choice that I would not become the product of my environment. An inner energy kicked in that forced me get off my butt and start doing something more with my life. This was why I was so adamant about going to college, why I was so adamant about dropping out of college after my first year, and why I was so adamant about getting a job and enrolling myself in drama school.

As I was sharing the exciting anticipation of enrolling in school with the rest of the kids at school, to my rude awakening, I found out my father was not going to allow me to attend college. He said I was not smart enough or worth it. I knew the truth at the time; he could not afford it. In the 1970's New York City was bankrupt, and there were very few jobs. My father had been out of work for a few years, and we lived on very little money, so it would have been impossible for him to afford to send me to college. Being emotionally immature, he hid his shame by shaming me and telling me a lie--that I was too stupid to be worthy of a higher education.

I told him not to worry about the money. His lack of income over the past two years had made me eligible for a government grant. In my persistence, he resentfully signed the necessary documents that would enroll me in college. He did not like the idea that I would be hanging out on campus or in the library reading books rather than being an adult who could bring home a paycheck.

I was a B plus student but studying was a difficult task. When I sat in the kitchen to study for a few hours after dinner, my father would scream, yell, and bang pots and pans to disturb me. My father took great pleasure in antagonizing me as a way to relieve his frustrations. It hurt me to see him in such pain, and to see my brother destroy his life, but I was too young and too scared to know what to do. I reasoned that if I could just focus on working towards doing the things necessary that would save my life I could come back and save them.

In an attempt to keep myself in school, I would visit a school psychologist on campus to help me get through the rough times at home. It didn't change what was happening at home, so my emotional state only got worse. Also, I found community college to be a very dry and stale environment. No one seemed to be excited about being there. Everyone walked around campus like a zombie. The curriculum was geared toward getting people jobs, not careers. Nothing interesting or innovative was going on, and teachers only fed information for students to regurgitate back on paper. There were no lively discussions or talks. Students were trained to blindly accept everything they were told and to not question anything. Also, most kids in this city college came from the same home environment I came from where there was stress and tension in the home due to either financial struggles, alcohol and drugs, or both. They walked around campus with either an outer aura of toughness or the opposite disposition of quiet and withdrawn desperation.

One night, as I lay in bed in the dark, I literally experienced a light going out in me, like I was a dimming lamp whose bulb was burning out. I knew I would die in that house; that I was dying. At that moment, a boyish figure, perhaps an angel, made of golden light glided out of the closet in my bedroom, and touched my right hand as it hung over the side of the bed. I knew it was not a dream. The boy made of golden light came to save me, to give me strength and hope, to temporarily sustain me until I found a way out of there. I left college, got a job as an administrative secretary, and enrolled myself in acting school at night.

In drama, dance, and music class I finally found a place where I could be happy. I spent all my spare time studying plays, and rehearsing scenes and monologues, and practicing my guitar and dancing. The act of practicing art, any art, allowed me to be in the moment and experience myself and all emotions, both my own and the characters I played, without judgment. Artistic expression was my own unique path for seeking God. I loved the arts, and I felt at home there. I had peers and friends in my classes who shared my love and enthusiasm for what we were doing.

When I started, my teeth were crooked, my clothes were shoddy, I wore thick glasses, and I had a heavy New York accent. I knew nothing about the business of modeling or the craft of acting, but that all changed, not over night, but over a few years. "I" was a major project in the making; a solid piece of marble that needed to be chiseled upon throughout the coming months and next few years in order for the young ingénue to emerge. I knew it was a huge endeavor to take on, but I was high-over the heavens excited about the challenge. It gave me a purpose, and a hope in a better future. I think God puts big dreams in our hearts so that we have a reason to go on, a reason to believe we can one day climb out of a negative situation and toxic environment.

I did not realize I had a heavy New York accent until my first experience in a scene study class. Most of the students who were from different parts of the country did not understand a word I was saying. For example, I pronounced the phrase "did you eat?" as "didgheet?". The instructor suggested speech classes. I took the pain-staking speech classes for two years. It was agonizing. I had to learn how to talk all over again. I had to exaggerate all of my syllables in order to lose the accent so much that during the first year I sounded pretentious. My family and friends thought I was trying to be a sophisticated English woman from London. They accused me of trying to be something I wasn't.

Eventually, my speech balanced out into normal Standard English, and although it did not guarantee me an acting job, people outside my neighborhood understood me better. I was able to communicate intelligent ideas without appearing uneducated, and it helped me get better paying jobs, than I would have with the New York accent. Physically, I already had an inner grace of movement from being a gymnast and social dancer, but studying the classical dance of Isadora Duncan gave me an extra dose of freedom of movement on stage.

My day job was a lot more challenging. I worked as a secretary for a scientist who specialized in Cryobiology, the study of blood. The office and the adjacent laboratory were straight out of the 1950s. The office was dark with old wooden book shelves and pine green leather chairs. The laboratory contained freezers, various sizes of glass test tubes, and a centrifuge--all sitting on long white counter tops under blinding florescent lights. The scientist, Dr. Balastop, was in his early sixties. He was fat and bald, except for the ring of gray hair around the bottom of his head that matched the color of his fading lab coat.

I took dictation filled with difficult and obscure scientific terminology each morning in his office for about two hours. I had no medical or scientific background, but for some reason I was able to transcribe everything accurately at the end of the day in letters and manuscripts. I enjoyed trying to figure out what I had written in Greg shorthand. Ga, ga, blu, bla, blah, cia, ma, -- comma - wa, gu, wa – paragraph – lik cha, pa, semi colon – And to conclude our findings, oodu, cra, bia, mu, la pu cha – period. The more obscure and incomprehensible it was, the better I liked transcribing it.

The other work I had to do for the rest of the day was boring. Thick manuscripts arrived everyday from scientists all over the world, and I had to rubber-stamp the date of its arrival on each page before handing it over to Dr. Balastop for review.

The other difficult task I had was to keep Dr. Peabody out of Dr. Balastop's office. Dr. Peabody was a plump woman in her early fifties. She was shaped like a ripe fig with a little head, little hands, and little feet. She was always waving a dainty handkerchief while in a state of frantic anxiety. My boss, Dr. Balastop, had offered to lend Dr. Peabody an ear for her woes concerning her marital problems, but after a while, Dr. Balastop got tired of the everyday drama, so he would hide in his back office when he saw her coming down the hallway. "Sorry, he's not here. You must have just missed him," I informed her.

"Oh, but I'm sure I must have seen him come this way," she insisted.

"No, he's not back yet, but I'll let him know you were here," I promised.

"Oh, this is terrible. I really need to talk to him. I've been all over the building looking for him. Please tell Dr. Balastop to call me," she whined waving her hanky. After a moment or so, Dr. Balastop would quietly emerge from his office to my front office.

Is she gone?" he'd ask.

"Yes, I think so," I said.

Dr. Balastop would then peak his head out the front door cautiously and scurry down the hall to sneak a late lunch in the cafeteria downstairs.

Most of Dr. Balastop's time was spent in the adjacent laboratory, and once a month he would travel to Sterling Forest in Upstate New York where he kept experimental monkeys. He brought back monkey blood and monkey parts to analyze in the laboratory. Once or twice he gave me the task of delivering monkey brains in a jar to the Medical Examiner's office on First Avenue.

It was a pretty gory and unsettling scene. The lobby had a museum of human body parts and organs floating in tanks of clear liquid. I didn't stop to observe. I dropped off the monkey brains at the front desk and left.

The good ol' Dr. Balastop, I discovered, had a crush on me, and started chasing me around the laboratory and around my desk. I looked for advice from Howie. Howie was a short, Jewish guy with a large out of date, neatly trimmed afro. He worked as a lab technician on the second floor, and he often invited himself to join me whenever he saw me eating lunch in the cafeteria. I usually tried to avoid Howie and eat lunch at my desk or in the park across the street, but since I had a problem with Dr. Balastop, and Howie was the only other person I knew in the building, I thought to ask him for some advice.

Howie seemed more intrigued with my predicament then concerned, which I found more unsettling. Howie tried to calm me down by saying we should change the subject.

"What do you like to do? He asked.

"I like art. I paint and draw," I said.

"Me too! I just finished a self portrait. I can bring it into work tomorrow and show it to you. I'd like your opinion on it," he said.

The next day at lunch time, I met Howie in the cafeteria where he secretly unveiled his self-portrait; a Cubism/Picasso style painting of his erect penis. I threw my tuna fish sandwich at him and marched away.

"Hey, it's the human body! It's art. Nothing wrong with that," he yelled.

I went to see the Personnel Manager, Rudy, in the Human Resources Department. Rudy was a thin black man; an energetic, enthusiastic guy with a big Cheshire cat smile. He dressed more like a pimp than a personnel manager. He wore a lot of chunky, gold jewelry, and flashy business suits with bell bottom flared pants. His wide-lapel jacket was accented by a blood-red silk handkerchief, and over-sized, gold cuff links adorned his sleeves.

Rudy said he would talk to someone about my problem with Dr. Balastop, but he didn't seem too concerned. I thought Rudy might just as well have broken out into the song "Just My Imagination (running away with me)", by The Temptations. I could even imagine Rudy performing the choreography: snapping fingers, swiveling side to side, arms moving up and down touching each elbow, while his spry legs smoothly pushed my concerns under the rug with the electric-slide step.

I visited Rudy a few times to complain about Dr. Balastop, until finally Rudy admitted to me that there was nothing he could do about it because Dr. Balastop had clout and seniority. Plus, the accusation would cause a scandal and a lawsuit. He said that the board of directors would protect Dr. Balastop's reputation at all cost, and Rudy could lose his job trying to back me up. The company expected him as the personnel manager to avoid scandals and lawsuits. I explained to Rudy that I didn't want to sue anyone. I just wanted this dirty old man to keep his hands off of me. All Rudy could advise me to do was to stay until I found another job. It was my first direct experience where people with money, position, and title were protected regardless of their behavior.

I stomped back to the office, and slumped into my chair in exhausted disgust. "And these little brown paper bags, I don't know why I save them. Every morning when I finish my coffee at my desk, I neatly fold the little brown paper bag it came in. They're just piled up in a corner on my desk. Isn't that sick? I don't know why I do it. I don't even need little brown paper bags!" So I quit.

I found a part-time job working for a professor at a graduate university. I decided I would work there until I could find a full-time position. My new boss was chipper and easy-going, and I had no problem with him. Instead, I ended up getting stalked by a thirty-two-year old graduate student who followed me around the building trying to convert me to Communism. I had no knowledge of, nor any interest in politics, so it baffled me why this man singled me out for recruitment. I was only at the job for six months because a research program was cut off from government funding. My stalker problem became history.

Eventually, I found a full-time job at an advertising agency in the penthouse of the Chrysler building, working as a secretary for the Marketing Director. The Marketing Director was a shy, quiet and patient man and we worked well together. The TV producer, a middle-aged divorcee was hell on wheels, though. Half of the time, she was in the studio at another location directing commercials, but when she marched back to the office, she was on the phone yelling and screaming at her ex-husband, her lawyers, and her rebellious teenage daughter, as well as all her co-workers. She threw the heavy desk phone at me a few times for not being able to keep her whiny, bratty, and spoiled daughter on the other line. The CEOs put up with her behavior toward subordinates because their well-paying clients were happy with her advertising work.

My only escape was acting, dance, and music classes, the only places where I could be myself. Between the TV producer's continual outbursts, the emotional violence at home, the crowded, and dirty, rush-hour subway ride to and from work, I couldn't find any mental equilibrium or peace outside of my artistic endeavors. I was so wired from stress and fear all the time, that one day at lunch, while eating a piece of steak too fast, I started to choke. Not being able to breathe or talk, I stood up from the table clutching and pulling off the table cloth, and then pushing nearby chairs and tables over as I pointed to my throat. People sat staring at me with their mouths open. A young man, who recognized me from high school, ran over and gave me the Heimlich maneuver. The piece of steak popped out of my mouth and flew across the room. I was so grateful to him for saving my life.

After experiencing a few more extremely unpleasant outbursts from the TV Producer over the next few weeks, I quit my job. Shortly after, I met David in one of my acting classes, and soon after that we moved in together. At the time, it was the only positive solution available to me of getting out of Queens without money and a job.

....

Ironically, five years later, here I was back where I started. Twenty-five years old and back in Queens living with my parents, who treated me and talked to me the same way they always had. I notice that even my brother's room still looked exactly the same. It was cluttered and small with cheap, oversized furniture, old electronic equipment, and a few Kiss posters on the walls. My brother was doing time in jail, as usual. I had his room and a bunk bed to sleep in for now, at least for three months until the prison system let him loose. I shuttered at the large Kiss poster with its image of Gene Simon's angry eyes and long devilish tongue mocking my return.

My father screamed and yelled all day and all night when he was home. He banged pots and pans in the kitchen, and constantly instigated arguments and confrontations with me over the stupidest things.

"Why don't you drink soda, at the dinner table, like the rest of us? Why do you drink water? What's wrong with soda? What's wrong with you?" he threatened.

"Nothing. I just prefer water." I said.

"Well, there's something wrong with that. When are you going to get a job? Any prospects? Money doesn't grow on trees you know," he snapped.

"Your father's right," my mother added.

The phone rang. My father banged his fist on the table and cursed.

"Goddamn it! Every time we sit down to eat, that God damn phone rings. It's probably the other idiot. Your brother calling from jail and asking me to send him more money and cigarettes. Pass me the phone!"

That's exactly who it was, my brother calling from jail, asking my father to send him more money and more cigarettes.

I would lie on the bottom bunk at night hearing the TV blasting in the front living room, and listening to my father curse with disgust and resentment at the TV set. I didn't think I was going to survive there. I had to find a way out again and quick. I hoped one of the agencies would call me for a permanent job, and call me very soon.

David and I were still talking. I think he knew how toxic being back at my parents' house was. I had only lived with Justin for three nights and four days, so David realized that I had not left him for another man again; I was only looking for a safe place to be.

Justin's house was not safe. My parents' house was not a healthy place to be, but living with David again was not sound for David or me either. It was a ridiculous set of choices because there was no good choice.

Where could I have a career, a safe place to work, and make enough money to match my talents and skills in order to live on my own? The media constantly portrayed this reality as the norm, but it was a lie. At the time, I didn't know it was a lie, so I blamed myself.

David and I talked on the phone once or twice a day. We were on good terms again, and David wanted me to continue to attend an auditioning workshop called The Audition Lab. The Audition Lab was not an acting school, but rather a place where seasoned actors auditioned monologues or did cold readings for professional casting directors.

David and I had been going there for almost a year now, and I hated the place. It was run by a seedy, creepy looking guy named Edgar Wolf. Even his name sounded like the deformed Egor who lived in the bell tower, or a troll in a bottomless dungeon of hell. Edgar had a huge, bald head shaped like an overgrown melon that had been injected with hormones. His sleazy, glazed eyes seemed to drip with gory pornographic images absorbed into his irises as if he had stayed up all night in his dark and dirty apartment, leafing through *Hustler*, or spending time at peep shows and strip clubs. The sight of him made me physically ill.

He wore the same puke green, probably unwashed knit trousers every day. The pants had stains near the crotch and on his backside. He changed his shirt sometimes from a gray, short-sleeved polyester/cotton to the only other one he owned, which was yellow/white.

The actors in the workshop were nice, but I couldn't understand why they put up with this guy. He was physically revolting, often condescending, and sexually degrading to the women in the group. No one seemed to object, and the same people came back again and again. I suspected that they suffered more from the circumstances of being poor and obscure, than they did from being manipulated and humiliated by Edgar Wolf. I told David, after the first few weeks, that I didn't like it and that there must be another workshop. David insisted that Edgar managed to get important casting directors and agents to come see us audition, and that I should stick it out and give it a chance.

I couldn't stand Edgar. He didn't like me either, and he was always condescending in his remarks about my auditions. Even when I gave a good performance, he would nit-pick at something.

I still didn't understand why the agents, casting directors, or even the other actors in the group tolerated him. It made me feel guilty for being so "thinned skinned" as David called it. It took me twenty years to realize that being "thinned skinned" in these situations was a good thing. It was an intuitive alarm in my gut that protected me. Most women have it, yet we are taught to ignore it. I was constantly taught to doubt it or distrust this 'gut' feeling, by people who viewed these 'gut' feelings as judgmental and paranoid rather than healthy discrimination.

I often made the decision to leave the workshop, and every time I tried, David and I got into an argument. I would end up feeling guilty about giving up an opportunity to be discovered. Eventually, I gave up trying to leave and stayed in the group. Besides, what if David was right? What if an important casting agent came in one week, discovered me, helped me land an acting job that solved my financial woes, and finally put me on the map for financial independence and the freedom to have the life I had worked so hard for? Was I sabotaging that opportunity because I was "thin skinned?"

At this point, the only time I was able to give myself an excuse to hang out with David and be away from the old neighborhood was when I met David at The Audition Lab. Acting was still our common ground, and it connected us. David was my friend and my one supporter. I missed being around him. I knew after we did our monologues and cold readings and I put up with Edgar's crude sexual innuendos, David and I could hang out in a coffee shop and just talk.

One week, we had a commercial/film director named Michael as a guest. He was a fun guy with an easy-going disposition who worked well with actors. He talked to us with appreciation and respect, and worked with the group in a collaborative and joyful manner. I wanted to audition for Michael because I could see that he liked actors. He was casting a commercial where he needed a female to play an angel, and he was there that night hoping he could find someone to fill the role. After many actors had performed their monologues and cold readings, I saw that the class was almost over, and I might not get a chance to audition.

During the last ten minutes of the workshop, rather than watch more cold readings or monologues, Michael directed a group of actors to go on stage to improvise a scene together. None of us knew anything about improvisation. We were trained as scripted actors, but we were up for the challenge.

Michael picked five actors to go on stage, but I was not one of them. I continued to sit in the audience, disappointed again that I was not going to get a chance to audition for him. I thought it might be just as well since I had no experience in improv.

The setup of the scene required one spindly, nerdy looking actor, wearing thick black glasses, to stand at the edge of the stage, and threaten to jump out the window of an office building. The remaining actors were supposed to try to stop him. There was no script, no direction, just total improvisation. Michael, as an afterthought, directed me and another young actress onto the stage to be extras, background office girls, not participating, but observing the office drama. I was disappointed that I had such a passive role but, because it was my first experience with improv, it gave me an opportunity to observe and learn.

I stood upstage at an imaginary file cabinet. The scene seemed to go on forever because the nerdy actor, who kept threatening to commit suicide by jumping out the window, was not believable, and the other five actors who were supposed to convince him not to jump were not believable either. The acting was tense and pretentious. It was painful to see everyone doing so poorly since I knew they were all so talented. The whole scene was torture for the audience, the actors themselves, and for me.

The nerdy actor stood, leaning over the edge of the stage.

"I'm going to jump!" he threatened.

"No. Don't jump!" they shouted.

"I'm going to do it," he threatened.

"No, don't do it, please," they pleaded.

"Here I go," he warned.

"Somebody, do something. He's going to jump," one woman shouted.

"I'm doing it. I'm gonna do it. Here I go," he warned again.

"No, don't jump!" they screamed.

"I'm jumping. I'm gonna jump," he said.

Finally, I stopped leafing through my imaginary file, and yelled with a pissed-off and disgusted look on my face, "Would you just jump already!"

The whole room burst out laughing hysterically, the director, the audience, the actors, even Edgar.

If there is an elephant in the room, rather than pretend it is not there, call it out, and it disappears. Many people often make the assumption that actors pretend, actors make believe, actors fake things, actors are good liars and good sales people, but the truth is that actors are most effective when they seek and express the truth in every moment and in every situation.

There was also a sense of worship for me in the craft of acting, because it demanded "the truth" of each moment, which is effortless when I can get out of my own way. Get out of the way of my own preconceived ideas about what I should feel, or how I should behave. It is not that I am most happy when I am doing a particular thing and in a particular way. I am most happy when I am effortless. There is no "I" that must do something or be other than what "I am" in any given moment. Judgment about how I feel in any given moment will give me false direction. Come to ground zero willingly.

The key is to have the "ideal" be freedom. Inner freedom, outer freedom – it doesn't matter, the "ideal" is freedom. Yet what is true "freedom"? That was yet to be unveiled to me and would be revealed to me simply because this was the question I kept asking, and this was the purpose for which I gave my art and my life.

My inner freedom was not generating much outer freedom. Michael offered the part of the angel to the other girl, Betsey, who also played an extra in the improv scene. She didn't say anything or do anything on stage to give Michael a reason to cast her. She was not more or less attractive than me. I had to chalk it up to her just being the "right type" for the part of the angel. Often this acting business was about "type" and not always talent and I think that's where the idea of having a "thick skin" comes into play. Since being in the workshop, everyone seemed to be getting work but me. Again, I told David that I needed to leave The Audition Lab. It wasn't working for me. I wasn't getting any jobs from it. David tried to reason with me, and convinced me to stay for the last four weeks of the workshop, since it had cost $300.

"Why throw that money away? Finish up the series of sessions, and decide later on whether or not you should go back and continue," David pleaded.

I thought that was a reasonable request and a reasonable plan. I just couldn't understand why David treated me like a spoiled brat and an ungrateful child whenever I expressed how much I hated being in that workshop and hated being around Edgar. I couldn't understand why David would make me feel wrong for feeling that way. David was convinced that someone extremely influential and powerful was going to come into that class and discover me, but I felt that even if that were true, Edgar would sabotage it for me somehow, some way. It was a gut feeling I had and it wouldn't go away.

CHAPTER EIGHTEEN

NO EXIT

THE NEXT DAY was another uneventful day at one of my temp jobs. No one was bullying me at this office, probably because there were no people around to bully me. On my first day, the manager, a pleasant middle-aged woman, directed me down a long, dark, empty hallway. The hall ceilings were hidden under wooden scaffolding covered in wide, clear plastic sheets cascading to the floor. Our walk down this hall seemed to go on for miles. Finally, it led to a large, gray room with no windows. It was totally empty except for a metal desk.

The desk held a console phone with lots of extension buttons, a pencil holder filled with shiny new pencils and two yellow legal pads. A huge white clock with big black numbers on its face surveyed the room from behind me. There were absolutely no people in this part of the building, and there was absolutely nothing for me to do but answer the phone. But the phone never rang. "Even if it did ring, who would it be for? And who would I transfer the call to?" I thought.

I was only there five days, but on each of those days, I sat there waiting for a warm body to come by and give me an assignment. No one ever came. For Satre, in his play *No Exit,* hell was other people, but this was also hell; spending long days in a colorless, empty, lifeless, soulless environment, in which the only sound was the deep and heavy tick tock of a massive clock that moved at the pace of eternity. I tried to rationalize that the job wasn't so bad, because there was no one around to harass me, but it made me feel like I did not exist at all.

At lunchtime, I walked up bright and busy sunny 42nd Street toward Madison Avenue to search out a place to eat. The commercial/film director, Michael, was walking down the street towards me. I was embarrassed to be caught in my stuffy office suit and hoped he wouldn't recognize me. I wanted to ask him why he hadn't hire me for the part of the angel, but one doesn't ask people in the business such questions. It's nothing personal, it's just business. Plus, it makes an actor look desperate and unprofessional.

Though it was true I lived a desperate existence, that's not why I wanted to ask him why he hired Betsy over me. I was curious to know if Edgar had bad mouthed me and kept me from working. I waved hello and Michael waved back as and we passed each other on the street. Nothing was said and we never saw each other again.

After having a slice of pizza and a Coke at Zaro's Pizzeria, I returned to the sterile, gray, lifeless office for the rest of the afternoon and listened to the hypnopompic eternity of a clock. Tick-tock, tick-tock, tick-tock, tick-tock...

When I returned home to my parents' after work, my father was making dinner. Over the past year, while I was going through my own drama with Leonardi, my father had lost his job managing a prestigious restaurant on the Upper West Side. It was a job he had enthusiastically performed during the five years I had been living away from home. He didn't own the place, but he had been the boss. He was very good at his job because he knew the restaurant business inside out. He loved it. He had made good money there for the first time in his life, and he was respected and appreciated by his patrons.

My father showed up one morning for work only to find the place boarded up, no warning or explanation. He was devastated. His devastation soon turned into rage and constant anxiety. He lost his sense of purpose and did not know how to contribute anymore. Those past five years at that restaurant had been good to him, rewarding financially and psychologically, and now it was all gone. Shortly after, my father learned the owner of the establishment, a wealthy entrepreneur, who owned many businesses, abruptly closed it over night because he was caught up in some tax issues with the IRS.

My father took his job loss out on everyone in the house. I came home to pots and pans being banged around in the kitchen and the evening news blasting on the TV in the living room. He cursed while chopping carrots and tomatoes like he was cutting off someone's head and limbs. He yelled constantly at my mother for being late for dinner. My mother had no control over the fact that the R train was not running, and that she was stuck in a subway tunnel for over an hour. She had no control over the transit system, but for some reason my father insisted that she did.

She would yell back at him, "Now, you know what it feels like, wise guy! All the times I was waiting for you to come home for dinner while you were out at the club with the guys playing cards. Meanwhile your steak is getting cold. You God damn son of a bitch. I worked all day! I don't need this shit! Fuck... shit," she screamed gnashing her teeth.

My father continued banging the pots and pans on the stove and in the sink. My mother wandered into the bedroom to put down her handbag and take off her jacket. She slipped off her shoes, and massaged her feet to relieve the soreness from standing all day in a department store. She tried to rub out that one impatient and nasty customer she dealt with during the day, the one who insisted on being shown the perfect pair of hosiery or they would drop dead.

My mother had told me similar stories many times. They wanted sheer to the waist, or seamless or toeless, or seamless and toeless, and were they control top, and did they have a matte or shiny finish?

"And why don't you have them in taupe? This is beige not taupe," the shrunken, sour grape in the Chanel suit complained.

"We only have beige and coffee left in your size in this brand, ma'am. The taupe is all sold out," my mother replied.

"This can't be. I have a dinner engagement tonight at Sardi's. I must have the taupe. I only wear taupe," the old lady whined.

"I have taupe in this brand, but it's not control top," my mother offers.

"Oh, well I certainly can't wear pantyhose without a control top," the customer complained.

"Okay, here's another brand with a control top and a taupe, but it's matte, not shiny," my mother offered.

"Oh, no that won't do! I need a shiny taupe with a control top. Look, these are not toeless. How can I wear my sandals with toes?" the old woman whined.

"Ah, here we go. Size C, taupe, shiny, control top, and toeless," my mother replied as she hands her the package. Can you excuse me a moment? It's very busy today and there are five other customers calling for my attention," my mother explained.

"But this is not my brand. I don't like this brand! Can't you go down in the stock room and see if you have my brand in taupe?" the old lady insists.

"Ma'am, we just restocked what we have left this morning, and so I know that they must be on order, and have not arrived yet. I'll be back with you in a minute," my mother assured her.

"I can't wear these. They're not even my brand. This is not my shade of taupe. Can I speak to a manager please? You're not being very helpful at all. I should report you," the customer snapped.

My mother thought to herself, 'You're a fat, shriveled up old prune. Who the hell is going to be looking at your legs anyway?' "Sheila, when you finish ringing up that sale, can you call Luwanda, the manager, on the house phone, and ask her to come to Hosiery?"

My mother was not very concerned about being reported. Just the week before, the Personnel Department gave her five gold stars for congeniality and a twenty-five cent raise for selling the most stockings. It was unbelievable to me, that a middle age adult with a ten-year seniority would receive only a twenty-five cent raise in the mid 1980's, but that's department store retail. It's pretty much like grammar school; they give out stars and shiny pennies, not a living wage.

My mother was a notably attractive woman in her youth with a sense of humor, and she said if she could have had life her way, she would have been a movie star like her idol, Betty Grable, or a song and dance star like Mitzie Gannor, shaking her booty in a low cut, shiny dress of silver-tinsel and tassels tussling to and fro.

She also had an undeveloped talent for storytelling and filmmaking. In the late 50's she made short silent movies with her eight millimeter home movie camera, and cast her older brothers in them as well as herself. She stayed up all hours of the night slicing, dicing, and editing it herself. One film she made was titled "The Eviction." She made it all in fun, but it turned out to be timeless, creative, and extremely funny.

In his younger days, my father was a tall, handsome and suave Dean Martin type with black wavy hair and a thin mustache. He wore tasteful suits adorned by a pack of Lucky Strikes in his breast pocket as he proudly posed in front of his 1954 hunter green Chrysler. He had good manners, fine taste in food, and he was an excellent dancer. Both my parents were good dancers, and I believe they met one night and became enamored with one another while tearing up the floor at a Manhattan night spot doing the Cha Cha, the Fox Trot, and the Rumba.

My mother had been the sexy blonde: creative and entertaining, while my father was the handsome, debonair, more serious and moody intellectual who knew every answer to Alex Trebek's *Jeopardy* questions. He said if he could have had life his way, he would have aspired to become an orchestra conductor like Zubin Mehta.

I told him I thought he should have become a criminal lawyer because he constantly used big words in his vocabulary and was always interrogating family members.

"The reason I am inferring that you absconded with the last dish of chocolate pudding in the refrigerator is under the stipulation that your mother and I were not home during the time in question. If it wasn't you, where were you on the night that the perpetrator took it upon themselves to engage in the covert and presumptuous act of gratifying themselves with the last chocolate pudding? And with no deliberation on their part that perhaps I would be looking forward to indulging in this confectionary treat myself which would have been quite complimentary with my evening coffee," he stated with a courtroom Spencer-Tracey-*Inherit-the-Wind* intensity.

I stood there with my mouth open.

"I ate the last chocolate pudding," my mother stated flatly as she walked out of the kitchen to put away the bundle of laundry she had just tugged off the clothes line.

"Aaah! The truth comes out!" He stuck his index finger high in the air with enthusiastic triumph.

It was obvious that I inherited my love of the stage from both my mother and father. When I was happy and light-hearted, people often said I looked like my mother, and when I was pouty or upset, they said I resembled my father. I had inherited the two opposing harlequin faces of theater: comedy and tragedy.

After massaging her feet some more, and placing them in the comfortable haven of fuzzy pink slippers, my mother returned to the kitchen determined to have her dinner in peace.

"I just don't understand it," my father expounded as if he was in sheer physical pain, "Why can't they let you leave earlier if the trains aren't running?"

"Did your boss ever let you leave earlier because the trains weren't running? Idiot. Besides how the hell is anyone at work supposed to know the trains aren't running on time? You're an idiot, you know that? Pass me the God damn peas, will ya!" she snapped.

"Niency!!!!! It's time to eat!! Niency!!!! Time ta eat!!!" My father shouted through the apartment like he was dying of a fresh bullet wound to his chest.

"I'm coming!" I yelled back.

"Niency!!! My mother screamed.

"I'm coming! I'm coming!" I hollered back.

"It's time ta eat!!!!!" My father yelled again.

"No, don't sit here. Sit over there." My mother snapped at me, not looking up from her plate.

I moved over to the chair near the window. I leaned over to get myself a glass of water from the sink.

"What the hell are you doing? I just poured you a glass of Coke with ice?" my father growled.

"I don't drink soda. I always drink water at the dinner table. I tell you that every time, but it's like ...never mind," I said.

"Never mind what!" he yelled.

"I'm having water, like I always do, okay?" I said.

"We all drink soda. Why can't you drink the soda! What's wrong with the soda?" he reprimanded.

"Nothing's wrong with the soda. I just want water. What? Soda makes me thirsty. I want water, that's all," I explained.

He gave me his usual angry look of crucifixion and utter contempt. Everyone tried to finish their dinner as quickly as they could to get out from under his radar. Yet, somehow my father always managed to leave the table first and escape back into his living room chair to watch the news with the volume blasting leaving everyone else in the kitchen feeling badly for no reason at all.

My mother washed the dishes, and I dried. The tension in the air was more painful than a splinter. The atmosphere was exactly as it was when I moved out over five years ago. Nothing had changed. My parents were still angry, hostile, and bitter. My brother was still on drugs and in and out of jail. Right now, he was in, but he would be out in a few months. The real hell would begin once he got out and came back home. You would think that my parents would have wanted to know what went on in my life during the five years I was gone, but they didn't ask me nor did they care to know.

I resided in my brother's room, and sat on the bottom bunk. I could hear the phone ring in the kitchen. My mother answered.

"Yeah hold on . . . Nieeency!!! The phone!!" my mother yelled.

"I'm coming!!" I yelled back. Great, now everyone who called here was going to ask me who the hell 'Nancy' was, or rather, who the hell 'Niency' was, and then I would have to explain. It was nobody's business.

I stomped into the kitchen feeling like a rebellious teenager again, but I didn't complain about the 'Nancy' crap. I knew it was my parents' way of antagonizing me by marginalizing me, my talents, and accomplishments. Throughout my life they had always insisted on defining me based on their false perceptions regardless of the evidence to the contrary to justify their negative viewpoint.   I had changed my name to Whitney when I was about nineteen years old.

....

In 1979, I was doing modeling shots for my portfolio with a fashion photographer named Eric out in the Hamptons for the weekend.   Eric informed me that we would be staying in an elegant country mansion near the ocean owned by the wealthy parents of some rich kids who were using the house for the summer.

When we got there, I realized he wasn't kidding.   After briefly meeting the young hosts, Margot and Nathan, I was escorted by a housekeeper to my own room with a working fireplace and an expansive bay window view of wheat fields and ocean.   Eric and I were some of the first guests to arrive so he gave me a quick tour of the mansion.   Eric explained to me that Margot and Nathan's grandfather was a wealthy banker, and their father became the owner of a fast-food eatery that spread throughout most of the East Coast in the late 1950s.

The children, now fresh out of college, were recipients of all the accumulated wealth.   Being born into a life-style of swimming pools, tennis courts, equestrian lessons, ski trips to Aspen in the winter, and summer vacations on the French Rivera, Margot and Nathan were used to being around rich and famous people.   During the summer months, these young adults often invited their friends over for small weekend gatherings, which consisted of up-and-coming writers and artists, and the already established celebrities in the fashion and entertainment industry.

The guests we met during our stay were extremely nice, and we had a good time.   Even the outdoor fashion shoot on the beach was enjoyable despite the windy, wet, and rainy day.   I did not find anyone pretentious at all.   In fact, Margot thoughtfully offered to lend me one of her swimsuits when she learned that I didn't have an extra suit to change into for the photo session by the pool.

At the end of the day, I took a private walk down a long and straight dirt road towards the beach, passing solitary homes among open fields of tall, gold colored weeds.   The air was moist and misty.   The wind was cool yet warm and building up to the clear warning of a big storm. I wore my old worn comfortable jeans and Eric's Yale sweatshirt. I enjoy the feeling of my bare feet against the sandy dirt road. An occasional car zoomed by me in the opposite direction. Then a girl in white shorts rode towards me on her antique, red bike cycle. A long French bread peeked out of the grocery bag in the front basket hanging from the handle bars. She waves and tips up her sun visor with one hand. "Do you have the time?" she inquired. I shrugged my shoulders.

"Three, three-thirty...sorry, I don't know," I replied. She smiles and moves on.

The road ahead of me seems like a million miles long and the beach is nowhere in sight, but I enjoy the beauty of the scenery along the way, and the feeling of a soft peace and a quiet sense of freedom.

Finally arriving at the edge of the beach, the sand under my feet, the winds now wild, I could see the white-capped ocean rumbling. Tall dramatic waves crashed violently against the shore. The place was deserted except for hundreds of white seagulls gliding across a charcoal sky and the lonesome figure of a teenage boy sitting atop a sand dune playing guitar and singing loudly, passionately, and skillfully towards the teal-colored sea.-- the wind in his face, his long brown hair flying back like the wings of an eagle. I felt I had walked into the private magical spirit of another soul. I absorbed the richness for a long moment, then quietly left feeling deeply blessed.

When I arrived back at the house, I took a long hot shower in my own private and luxurious bathroom. I then wrapped the thick, soft towel around my torso and stepped out into the bedroom resting my body down on the fluffy white bear-skin rug. I watched the warm, cracking fireplace while listening to the rancorous wind outside. I thought, "I must admit-- having wealth is quite complimentary to my nature. I rather enjoy this."

A knock on the door, it was Eric. "Dinner will be served at six."

"What time is it now?" I yelled out to the closed door.

"It's five. What are you doing?" Eric asked.

"I'm basking in the opulence of wealth," I replied.

Eric chuckled. "Dinner in an hour; don't be late," he warned.

When I floated downstairs for dinner, I was surprised to see so many people mulling about. Small groups were scattered around the room-- some lounging on the stuffed sofas, and some were standing near the fireplace sipping white wine, eating hor d'oeuvres, smoking cigarettes, and chatting. One of the guests, a writer for *Rolling Stone Magazine*, was outside on the canopied deck grilling a huge shark he had caught that afternoon.

Most of the people were already seated at the long rustic dining table, canopied under a flagrant crystal chandelier, munching on appetizers. No one in the house appeared unusual or eccentric. They looked like regular people dressed in jeans, t-shirts, sweatshirts, and sneakers.

Nathan handed me a plate and escorted me to all the various appetizers available on the table. I listened to the group's lively discussion regarding art and celebrity as I placed stuffed artichokes, smoked salmon, black olives, fresh tomato covered in mozzarella cheese, and slices of pink roast beef on my dish.

Margot introduced me to everyone as she motioned me over to sit next to her. "Nancy came with our dear friend Eric. She's a model and aspiring actress," Margot announced. The guests raised their wine glasses enthusiastically and yelled out, "Welcome, welcome! One man replied, "An actress? To be an actress you'll need to change your name. Anyone have any suggestions?"

Some of the guests at the table explained to me that being an actress meant that I was a commodity and in order to be successful I had to be packaged and marketed correctly. They were very enthusiastic about helping me select a stage name to assist me in my career.

While the main course of shark, stuffed mushrooms, honey-glazed sweet potatoes and fried asparagus smothered in garlic sauce were being served, everyone was throwing out suggestions. "I like the name Brook? No, Casey! That would be a good name for you. How about Levy? Do you like the name Levy?" Another woman asked me. I had a confused look on my face as I thought to myself these names sounded so waspy and contrived. Eric silenced the debate with, "We'll call you Whitney."

I thought Whitney wasn't much better than Brook, Casey *or* Levy. In the fashion business, though, during the late 70's and early 80's models and actors hid their ethnic origins and tried to look waspy and All-American like Christie Brinkley or Brooke Shields. All-American fashion designers such as Ralph Lauren were in vogue. Very few people realized that most people in show business changed their last names and often their first names as well, such as Judy Garland, who was born Frances Ethel Gumm. Cary Grant was born with the name Archibald Leach. Ralph Lauren was born in Brooklyn with the worst name, Ralf Lipschitz, not the kind of name that could be successful selling high-end designer clothing.

Everyone insisted that Whitney was a good name for me. Throughout the evening and during the rest four-day weekend, everyone called me Whitney. When new people came by the house, I was introduced as Whitney. It was fun to hear them call me Whitney. The best part about being there was that people listened when I talked as if they were truly interested in what I had to say. I felt included and valued.

The name Whitney felt right for me, and people in the acting and modeling business loved it, too. I hated the name Nancy. I hated the name, not so much because of the way it sounded or even looked on paper; I hated the way my parents and some of my relatives pronounced it. It was always said with a tone of condescending judgment. They pronounced it with a closed nasally tone. Sometimes their noses even crinkled when they said, "Niency," as if they were smelling a bad odor in the room and I was the bad odor.

Only Candido could say my name, Nancy, in a normal, respectful way with his Italian accent. He pronounced the "A" in my name fully, with his lips and mouth open so that all the air flowed with no obstruction, and one could hear the up-beat note of Nancy, as if I had value. I chose to change it permanently to Whitney--because of the way the vowels and consonants were arranged, the name Whitney couldn't be manipulated into any negative slur and no one could contort their face in disgust when they said it.

David knew my birth name, but by the time he met me, my name was already Whitney. He hated the name Nancy also. He and his friends always knew me as Whitney. Everyone I ever met or associated with from then on, even people at my office jobs, knew me as and called me Whitney, except my parents. They insisted on calling me what they had named me, Niency.

....

I picked up the phone. It was Darcy, one of the actresses from The Audition Lab.

"Who the hell is Niency?" Darcey asked.

"That's my cousin. They were calling my cousin who is here visiting. What's up? I asked.

"Oh. I was just wondering how you were doing?" I called you at David's, and he told me you had moved back with your parents. What happened?"

"It's a long story. I really don't want to talk about it now."

"Okay . . . If there is anything I can do. Whenever you're ready to talk, let me know okay? I think David loves you and cares about you a lot, and I'm sure you two can work it out."

"Yeah, okay, thanks Darcey. We'll keep in touch."

"We can hang out and have lunch or something?" Darcy suggested.

"Sound great, thanks," I agreed.

When I first met Darcey in Edgar's workshop at The Audition Lab, I was flattered by her kindness and thought she was a nice person. She admired my physical appearance and told me that she thought I was beautiful. She also said I was very talented, and I appreciated the recognition. I liked Darcey, but I began to feel uncomfortable around her.

She didn't just like me and want to hang out with me; she was in awe of me. She didn't just admire me, she worshipped me. Even Tom thought that there was something abnormal about the way she behaved. He pointed this out to me after the four of us hung out one night at the coffee shop. She kept insisting that I was one day going to be this big movie star, which one would think I'd appreciate considering my parents didn't think I'd amount to anything. The problem with Darcey was that she tried to emulate me, in every way. She always tried to talk, walk, and dress like me. She also became very jealous and possessive when I didn't give her my full attention and focused on someone other than her. Tom insisted that she was obsessed with me, and there was a possessive jealousy behind all that adulation.

The thought crossed my mind: What if I did become a movie star? Did fans behave like that? Would I have to worry about people becoming obsessed with me, not just other women, but men too? Would women look through *People* magazine to copy what I was wearing, read what I was reading, see what I was eating or not eating, and try to find out who I was dating or divorcing? Would men stalk me, and would photographers camp outside my front door every time I took out the garbage or drove to the grocery store?

I suddenly realized how much I valued my privacy, and that I was, in fact, a very quiet and private person. If I couldn't handle one obsessed fan like Darcey in my personal life, how was I going to be able to handle a bunch of anonymous movie viewers or obnoxious paparazzi and gossip magazines?

As much as I loved acting, the idea of being famous and having strangers prying into my personal life, or putting me up on a pedestal only to knock me off, made me cringe. At the same time, I didn't feel comfortable working in an office as a secretary earning peanuts and being called 'Niency' either. It was clear to me that my path in life was not one of an office worker, but of an artist and a performer. Yet, like any profession, an artist must be financially successful in order to pay their bills, take care of family, and the material necessities of life. What was not clear was how to do so without the trappings of fame that the financially successful artist must contend with.

Darcey and David insisted I was "somebody" and my parents insisted I was "nobody". Neither side of the argument made sense anymore. I was not a "nobody" and I was not a "somebody". No side of the argument was worth defending, because I am not more "important" than anyone else, but I'm not "unimportant" either. I just am. Besides, it's not even about "me". What it's all about, I don't know. But it's not about "me". It suddenly dawned on me that I didn't want to be anything at all; I just wanted to "be." I didn't know exactly what that meant, but a light bulb went on in my head. *Who was I without any concepts at all? Who was I? Who am I?*

"Niency!" Get off the phone! Your father needs to use the phone!"

So powerful is this question *"Who am I?"* it seems like something doesn't want me to find out.

"Darcey, I gotta go," and I hung up the phone..

The next morning I left the apartment early to keep out of my father's hair and avoid any kind of confrontation with him. The day was cloudy but humid and hot. I strolled around the neighborhood through the sticky air, but there was nothing to see and nothing to do. Turning down a treeless street lined with mostly factories and a few houses, I ran into a deranged, drugged out acquaintance from the neighborhood whom I had known briefly back in high school.

He was an Irish guy, his blonde hair now long and greasy, his skin still covered in freckles. Wearing soiled army & navy clothes, he looked like a soldier who had just crawled out from under the mud. He did a wheelie with his worn, rusted bicycle on the pavement in front of me, stopping me in my tracks.

"Ah, Niency, is that you?" He smiled revealing brown and black rotted teeth, some missing. I looked at him, recognizing his face, but not remembering his name.

"It's Dillon, man. How ya doin?" he asked.

"Hi." I said.

"Man, I thought you moved out of the neighborhood a long time ago. I heard from Maria Mancini that you moved away and became some fashion model or something," he exclaimed.

"Yeah, I was living in Manhattan. I'm just staying with my parents for a short time visiting," I replied.

"Yeah, man, me too. I'm staying with my old man. He's a nasty, drunken son-of-bitch, but he always was. Well, you remember me and my brother, Kevin, ran the Tavern up there on 38th Avenue past the train station with my Pop. Closed the place down after my brother died," he declared.

"Sorry. He died, huh?" I mumbled.

"Yeah, well, you know the usual shit, drugs. He jumped in front of one of those moving freight trains down over there in Long Island City. When ya take acid man, you gotta know how to handle yourself. My brother was one crazy motherfucka, always takin' acid and runnin' off by himself doing some crazy shit. I always make sure I have a babysitter whenever I take that stuff, ya know what I mean?" he bellowed.

"Nice seeing you. I gotta run."

Dillon pushed the wheel of his bicycle in front of me to keep me from leaving. "Hey, fuck man; I haven't seen you in fuckin years. What have you been doin' wit' yourself?" His blue eyes were fierce with anger for snubbing him.

"Nothing; I'm just heading out. I have a job interview. I don't want to be late, that's all," I reasoned.

"Fuckin' job interview, man? Like, fuck that. My Pop is always trying to get me to get one of those fuckin' things, man. No fuckin' way. He threw me out of the house again a few days ago. He's always throwin' me out of the fuckin' house to get a job. I'm like 31 years old, man, doesn't he know by now, that I'm gonna do what I'm fuckin' gonna do, shit. Shit, you don't need no fuckin' job, man. Check this out, man," he said, as he pulled out a plastic bag of hash from the inside breast pocket of his army vest, and held it in his calloused dirty finger nailed hands. "This is how I make my money. I'm taking a trip up to Maine this weekend, and hangin' out at this hippy commune wit' people, and just selling this shit, man. I'm smoking this shit, man, and having a good time, man. Fuck, what's wrong wit' you, man?" he asked?

"I'm not into drugs. Not my thing."

"Not your thing? You gonna work for one of those nasty, fucked up corporations. Their fuckin' Nazis, man. Their fuckin' communist man, the fuckin' government is all in on it, too. They just screw people, man," he proclaimed.

"Bye, I gotta go," I said as I moved past him and the wheel of his bike.

Dillon yelled out to me as I walked down the block. "They're gonna fuck you, screw you, man. Nazis. They're fuckin' Nazis. The government, too. Nazis all of them," he roared.

Dillon whizzed himself around, and his bike passed me in the street while he continued yelling out, "You'll see, they are gonna fuck you up. All of you, man. They are gonna fuck all of you. Corporations, jobs, man, all fucked up!" He turned and disappeared around the corner onto the main avenue.

As I escaped from view into the air-conditioned newsstand to buy a pack of cigarettes, I thought to myself that the most disturbing thing about my encounter with Dillon, aside from the fact that he was a character from hell, was that he was partially right, at least in my experience. There was always some kind of economic recession going on, in one form or another, which would cause people to lose their jobs. Also, none of my office jobs paid well enough to afford me to live on my own, nor was I ever there long enough to get a raise or a promotion. If down-sizing due to some Wall Street volatility didn't do me in, then I usually got sexually harassed or bullied, and then laid off within the first six month for the stupidest things like dropping a rubber band on the carpet, or not getting the operator on the phone fast enough for my boss find out what cross street The Wonton Wok Restaurant on Sixth Avenue was located.

I tried being the best possible person I could be, but that never seemed to be enough, and there was no room for mistakes, which was exhausting, because, as wonderful as I sometimes was, I was still so hopelessly imperfect.

As an actor I could play characters who were neurotic, funny, vulnerable, honest or even psychotic and I was applauded for it. If I could find an agent, I would be paid for it, and paid well. Without that, I did not know where I belonged. I didn't know where I could breathe.

Was it my parents fault? I picked up the new issue of *Self* magazine from the rack, and flipped through an article written by one of those so-called "expert" psychologists who claims one shouldn't blame one's parents for their miserable life. I had to agree, simply because judging my parents also made me feel guilty. I felt guilty for dropping the rubber band on the floor and losing my job for it. The last thing I needed was more guilt about blaming my parents for what was not working in my life. I wanted to escape the guilt, give up the guilt but I couldn't figure out 'of what' I was so really guilty.

I picked up another woman's magazine and flipped through it to an article, "How to Tantalize Your Live in Lover into Proposing". "A bit too late for that," I thought. I felt guilty for leaving David, but David never wanted to marry me anyway. Nothing personal, David was determined to never marry anybody. He didn't believe in the institution. I threw the magazine back in the rack.

I pulled out a thick, high fashion magazine, flipped it open to an editorial of, "This Season's Hair-Do's and Hair <u>Don'ts</u>". There was a photo of Leonardi styling an Oscar-Nominated actress's long tresses. Ugh, I wished that I had never met him, because it landed me in hell. Seeing his photo, though I realized I still missed him, and I felt guilty about that. My inner voice whispered, *"You are the love that you feel. God is love."*

"Well, screw you. I want to be loved back. What am I chopped liver!" My thoughts barked back.

I learned years later that Leonardi was a womanizer and had always been. I did not know it at the time because I had only spent a few days with him, and was unable to see past his show biz facade. I was too young and naïve. My heart for him was innocent and sincere which left me vulnerable. I truly loved him, but he didn't love me.

Leonardi loves women. He sinks his teeth into each female like an assorted box of chocolates, putting each one unfinished back into its wrapper in search of the one with the Marciano cherry. No wants to be a confectionary sweet that was considered not good enough to consume completely, and left with their creamy insides oozing out onto an open cardboard box. But this is precisely what a womanizer will do to his conquests. This is what Leonardi had done to me.

The young actress in the photo with him was quite beautiful. I wasn't jealous of her, but it made me realize that if Leonardi did love me, and saw me as a person of value, he would have introduced me to all his successful Fashion Avenue and Hollywood friends as the well-trained, talented actor that I truly was, and I would have had a career just by association. This is how it really works in Tinsel Town. An ingénue gets invited to the right parties, and is introduced to the right people who have the power and influence to give an unknown artist a break. Maybe Leonardi didn't see me clearly at all. Maybe he just put me in the category of a female groupie. Maybe it didn't matter, since I did not want Leonardi to perceive me solely as a product to market around town anyway.

The statuesque actress in the photograph looked serene and composed, but only a few weeks ago, she was once again on the front page of the news for drunk driving and cocaine possession. It seemed to me the constant scandals gave her more notoriety and afforded her more opportunities than her talent. Like kids in lower-class neighborhoods, were celebrities pressured into going against their own sense of inner well being in order to be accepted by their peers? And why did it increase box office sales?

I placed the magazine back on the rack backwards and upside down. Before stepping back outside into the thick hot air to head home, I peeked my head out of the front door to make sure Dillon was nowhere in sight.

Walking home I thought to myself, I did not want to be the worthless "nobody" that my neighborhood environment reflected, and I did not want to be the worthless "somebody" that Hollywood insisted actors be, where couture figures with shallow faces stand by the pool sipping champagne feeling a sense of self-importance above the common man, yet all the while trying to fill up the empty spaces with gratuitous sex and lines of white powder. All I wanted to do was practice my craft, enjoy my work, share and collaborate, and support myself. I loved art. The art of acting was a form of reflection and prayer for me which the show business environment could so easily defile.

I climbed the steps to my parents' apartment. The heat was getting to me. As I stopped to rest on the landing, I came to the conclusion that perhaps I did not have the biological and chemical make-up of a person who was comfortable navigating the shark infested waters of Hollywood in order to have a film career. I didn't have a thick skin, and I wasn't all that interesting.

I laughed to myself, thinking of my headlines, "Famous, young film star drops rubber band on the floor and helps herself to home-made cookies in the reception area. Production shuts down during investigation."

A news reporter pushes a microphone in my face and asks, "Were they chocolate chip cookies or macaroons?" My defense lawyer sporting dark sunglasses, shields me from the mob as he raises his right palm in the air, "No comment" and quickly escorts me past more frenzied paparazzi before we disappear into the refuge of a courthouse.

After dinner, while cleaning up, I accidentally dropped a pot onto the floor while drying it. It slipped out of my hand and banged on the floor. My father jumped out of his living room chair and into the air, the TV remote flying out of his hand.

"Jesus Christ, what the fuck was that!!!" He screamed, as he stomped into the kitchen doorway.

"I just dropped the pot. Sorry," I sighed.

"I can't get any fuckin' peace in this house. God damn it!!" he screamed, as he banged his fist against the closet door in the hallway.

I retired to my brother's bedroom for the rest of the evening. My heart was beating faster and faster. I was having another one of my anxiety attacks. I didn't know what it was. I had no label for it. I never told anyone about them, because it would have only made them angry.

I propped up my pillow on the lower bunk, closed my eyes and tried to breathe slowly in and out, but my heart kept pumping faster and faster, and then tears welled up in my eyes because I was so scared. I was petrified. I sobbed quietly for a few hours and then fell asleep. I woke up in the late evening when everyone was asleep, and sat in the kitchen helping myself to a cup of tea, making sure I didn't make the slightest noise so as not to wake anyone up. I sat in the kitchen until two in the morning, sipping tea and smoking cigarettes in a numb state of mind, thinking, but not thinking, and then I headed back to bed.

CHAPTER NINETEEN

THE DREAM

AT ABOUT FIVE in the morning, I had a terrible nightmare that felt so unbelievably real, that I woke up finding the bed soaked with sweat. I laid on the mattress paralyzed with fear before I realized it was only a dream. But was it? It seemed so real.

In the dream, I found myself in Milan, Italy. I entered a small studio basement apartment. I held a small, brown suitcase in my left hand. Standing by a window to greet me as I entered the apartment, was a beautiful Eastern European woman who appeared to be about thirty-eight years old with long, wavy golden hair. She was very feminine, slender, but full-figured and womanly, with a Venus like quality. As soon as I entered, she professed in a Russian Accent, "Hello. My name is Kundera, and you are an actress."

No sooner had she uttered these words to me, than a group of men in army, guerrilla uniforms, appearing to be terrorists, burst into the apartment, chopping up a group of people that suddenly emerged out of nowhere. The terrorists used their guns to beat the victims over the head, sliced them up, and dismembered them into little pieces. I crawled under a small, square kitchen table, hiding my head, and kneeling over with my face to the floor in the fetal position. I was in shock. I couldn't move. The troops finally marched out, leaving the carnage behind. Blood, arms, legs, and heads were everywhere. I realized that I was still alive. I looked out the window to ascertain how I could get a hand-written letter delivered to my parents to let them know I was alright.

As I looked out the front window, I saw Justin from Hoboken at the edge of the town with a black Labrador retriever by his side. A vast brown, dry desert stretched for miles into the distant horizon behind them. Justin stood strong and silent at the edge of the city bordering the desert. He threw hand grenades towards the apartment I was occupying, as if to finish off the few remaining buildings. There were fires everywhere, and the whole town was in ruins.

I had never had a dream as terrifying as this one in my entire life. I felt the wet sheets and thought maybe I had peed in the bed. Sweat poured out of my skin. It took me about ten minutes or so to move my body, even a little, in an attempt to get up. I finally wandered into the bathroom and splashed cold water on my face.

I tried to recall as much of the dream as I could because it was so powerfully real. Later that morning, I called David. I didn't go into all the details of the dream, but I asked him to write down the word "Kundera".

"What's Kundera?" he asked.

"I'm not sure, just that it was the name of the Eastern European woman in my dream. Anyway, the word "Kundera" is spelled K-U-N-D-E-R-A. I don't know what it is or what it means. I thought maybe you might have heard the word before," I asked.

"No, I never heard that before," he said.

"Ask around in your office. Maybe someone knows what it means. Ask Tom. Maybe he has heard the word "Kundera" before," I suggested.

"I don't know--it doesn't sound like any word I know of, but I'll ask around," David replied.

"I know it sounds silly, but this dream was intense, and that word was so prominent in my mind while I was having the dream. I remembered it so clearly when I woke up," I explained.

"And you where were in the dream? Milan? David asked.

"Yes, Milan."

"Okay, I'll ask around and see if there is such a word," he agreed.

All day I kept going over the dream in my mind: Why was I in Milan? And in a basement apartment? I mused. Yet, it was the older woman's presence and the way she greeted me that left the strongest impression on me. "My name is "Kundera' and you are an actress." She spoke it as if to inform me of *who I am*. But why did the word "Kundera" seem so significant, and what did it mean? Why did terrorists suddenly take over the city of Milan, killing and dismembering everyone just as she said this? Why was Justin throwing hand grenades as he stood at the edge of the city with miles of brown desert behind him? Why was he standing there with a big, black dog? Why did I survive?

I walked around for weeks wondering what "Kundera" meant. I went to the bookstores and to the library looking for anything that might give me a clue, but I could not find anything.

I put it out of my mind, thinking that maybe it meant nothing at all. There were only occasional moments when the word "Kundera" haunted me. For the most part, I gave up on the idea of being able to find out what it meant.

Back at The Audition Lab, I gave an amazing performance for a major casting director; a monologue from the screenplay and film, directed by Wim Wenders' *Paris, Texas*. My monologue was natural and quiet, yet pensive, with rich subtext and pauses. One could hear a pin drop in the room. The audience was at the edge of their seat, a silent gasping for air. When it was over, the energy in the room had been transformed.

The casting director looked at me for a moment. "I have no criticism for you. It was brilliant. You pulled it off really well. Excellent. Thank you," he stated.

Edgar, who videotaped all the performances on the TV screen hanging above the front stage, zoomed in and magnified the camera in on my teeth.

"Yeah, but she's got bad teeth!" Edgar scoffed.

It was true. My teeth were straight from wearing braces, but they had a light gray stripe, not from smoking cigarettes, but because I had taken a lot of tetracycline as a kid. My parent's apartment was always cold when I was young, because we rarely had heat, and I often got sick with colds and sore throats. The doctor gave me tetracycline which permanently stained my teeth. They were not bad at the time, but they looked much worse when Edgar zoomed the camera in and magnified their image. The casting director gave Edgar an odd look as if to say to him, "What the hell is your problem?"

I could not afford cosmetic dentistry, and probably never would unless I made enough money as an actress. The only thing I had control over was being a good performer, and Edgar still tried to mess me up, simply because he could.

During the ten-minute break, David, Darcey, and I stood outside the building a few feet away from where the crowd of students were milling around.

"You see what I mean?!!" I screamed in a raspy whisper to David and Darcey as I paced around. "He's a creep. A sleaze-ball," I protested.

"Yeah, that was messed up. Why did he do that, zooming in on your teeth like that? Hell, my teeth would look that bad if you magnified this chip and this crack I have here. He's nasty. I can't believe he did that," Darcey clamored.

"I keep telling you that guy Edgar is a jerk. He shouldn't have done that," I fumed.

"You were amazing. Your monologue was awesome. You floored everyone," Darcey agreed enthusiastically.

"You don't understand. I'm not going to get anywhere staying here. I feel like he's going to sabotage me somehow," I cried.

"You're exaggerating. I'm telling you, this casting agent is too smart for his bullshit," David insisted. "Come on, let's take a walk down the block and get a cup a coffee before we go back in," David suggested.

Darcey and I followed David down the street.

On our way, we passed by a fellow actor standing suavely in a doorway sporting a Fedora hat and thoughtfully sucking on his cigarette. He gave me an endorsing smile. "Great work," he replied.

"Thanks," I smiled.

"You see? Everyone liked what you did. Don't worry about Edgar Wolf. He's an idiot. Everyone knows he's a scumbag," David said.

When I returned home, the apartment was empty. My mother was at work and my father was at the club playing cards in the middle of the day. I made myself a ham and Swiss cheese sandwich on rye bread with mayonnaise and poured myself a hot cup of coffee. I looked out the kitchen window the way I had as a kid and watched the planes flying out from JFK airport.

When I was only seven years old, I used to imagine that one day I would be on one of those planes flying to a fantastic, beautiful, and exotic place where rock musicians hung out and models like Twiggy wore mod high-fashion clothes, while posing for photographers wearing black sunglasses. Donovan would sit next to me on the steps of an elaborate European water fountain and serenade me on his guitar with songs like "Catch the Wind" and "Epistle to Dippy." Some of my favorite words in the song "Epistle to Dippy" were "elevator in the brain hotel." I didn't know what the words meant but they made me laugh. I could envision Donovan in his royal blue velvet Nehru-collar jacket; peacock feathers floating in the breeze behind him. I had thought that one day, when I grew up, I would marry Donovan, because he was so gentle, whimsical, romantic, and poetic or maybe I would marry the lead singer of the Herman Hermits. I loved Peter Noone's big warm smile and his charming English accent when he sang "There's a Kind of Hush". With Donovan, I could never quite tell where he came from with his unusual but mesmerizing, lyrical and musical dialect. Was he English or Irish or both? I learned years later that he was actually Scottish.

That day, as I ate my sandwich at the kitchen table, I hummed Donovan's tune "Catch the Wind" to myself and then quietly sang some of its lyrics. I looked at the planes flying past my window facing the back alley. I realized for the first time that the planes were not flying out of JFK airport, they were flying in.

CHAPTER TWENTY

ANGEL HEART

THE PHONE RANG, it was Central Casting offering me one day of extra work on a film called *Angel Heart* with Mickey Rourke. It was a period piece, and I would have to go in for a wardrobe fitting a week or so before shooting began. The costume fitting was in a factory-loft located in the garment district.

It did not look like a very attractive costume; a chiffon blouse, a long gray wool skirt, and white and black saddle shoes with white bobby socks. After they fitted me, tagged my costume, and placed it on the metal rack with all the other costumes, the woman at the door gave me a sheet of paper stating the place, time, and date of the shoot. I looked at the location sheet. Ironically, I would end up in Hoboken, New Jersey. As I waited for the freight elevator, I thought, "Gee, I hope I don't run into Justin on the day of the shoot."

A gregarious, donut-shaped woman jolted me out of my thoughts. "You have a white thread on your shoe!!" She shouted with enthusiastic joy.

I looked down at my shoe to see a small piece of thick white thread dangling over the side of my left sandal.

"Do you know what that means?" she asked, still smiling broadly as she waited for her fitting and I waited for the elevator.

Before I could answer anything, she continued, "It means you are going to get a big part, a lead role as an actress."

I looked at her puzzled. "Are you kidding me? I never heard anything like that before."

"Yes, that's what it means. It's an old superstition in the theater. You're going to be up for a big acting job, maybe the lead in a movie or a Broadway show. Finding a white thread on your shoe is good luck in show business," she explained.

I looked at her surprised and puzzled. "I never heard that before," I said again. The elevator came.

"You never heard that before?" she laughed heartily and with great enthusiasm.

I stepped into the elevator, looking at her with surprise and intrigue. "No, I never heard that before," I said once more.

She laughed heartily again, "Break a leg!" she shouted. And the elevator doors closed.

I looked down at the white, three-inch-long piece of string on my shoe. Am I supposed to try to leave it there, or is it okay if it falls off? I didn't know. I should have asked her. I walked down the street, trying to balance the string on my shoe so it wouldn't fall off, but the traffic and the hustle and bustle of pedestrians made it difficult. It kept slipping off, so I put it in the breast pocket of my shirt. I hoped that what she said was true and would remain true even though the thread was now in my pocket.

That evening, a young woman in her late twenties named Heather came to The Audition Lab. She was an Assistant to a major casting agent at the Alexis Cyrus office. Heather wore a tailored suit, was soft spoken and often pushed her long black hair behind her shoulders as she spoke. Her dark eyes darted around the room like she was a deer in the woods keeping an eye out for predators. She was there looking for an unknown for a leading part in a major film project. No one knew what the film was about. Agents never went into any detail about projects. They just came to watch us audition, give feedback, and hope they discovered the right actor to fill a role.

Heather almost gasped when she saw me. I wasn't sure what to make of her reaction. I knew my presence had made a strong impression on her, but it was questionable if it was positive or not. She had a self-conscious expression and even a frightened look on her face when she saw me. When I finally got up to audition, my performance was so-so. I knew I was not on top of it that night. I was not in the moment the way I had wanted to be, but it happens.

Heather nervously spoke to me. "We're casting a film based on a book, and you are definitely the right type to audition for this part."

My eyes widened.

"I don't know if you can act well enough for this part we're looking to cast."

"Sorry, my audition piece was a bit off tonight. I guess I was nervous."

"I see, well, that's okay. It happens. I want you to talk with me after the workshop," she requested.

At the end of the session, she walked toward me apprehensively. I couldn't understand why she was so tentative and yet so intrigued with me. I wasn't sure if she liked me or not. Her attitude lightened up a little as we spoke privately, but she was also very serious and intense.

"I want you to come in to be interviewed by my boss, Alexis Cyrus, for this part. It's one of the lead roles. We are looking for an unknown actress. The film is based on a book so you have to read it before the meeting. After you read the book, I want you to call me at Alexis's office and set up an appointment. If money is a problem, and you can't afford to buy the book, I'll lend the book to you. It is available in paperback, but it costs about seven dollars. You can come by the office tomorrow and pick it up," Heather offered.

"Thanks for the offer, but I think I can afford to buy the book. I'd like to have my own copy anyway so I can make notes," I replied.

"Okay, but don't be embarrassed or ashamed if you can't afford it. I'll be more than happy to lend you my copy. Here's my card, and I'll write the name of the book on the back of the card. You can purchase it at any major bookstore. I don't want you to discuss it with anyone, okay? Don't talk about it with your peers. We're trying to make sure actors don't bombard us with phone calls. It's not an open call," she explained.

Heather gave me her card, and I concealed it in a safe compartment inside my large and bulky handbag, too nervous and excited to even look at it or stay much longer. Everyone had already filed out of the studio, and David and Darcey were waiting for me outside.

"Thank you, Heather."

"Call the office after you finish reading the book," she reminded me.

"Okay, I will," I agreed.

Outside, David, Darcey and I hustled down the street towards the train station.

"So, what happened?" David asked.

"Yeah, what did she say to you?" Darcey jumped in.

"She wants me to call her office and set up an appointment for an interview in a week or so," I said.

"You see?" David said in an 'I told you so' kind of manner.

"You're going to be a big movie star. I know it," Darcey chimed as she jumped in front of me walking backwards.

"It's just an interview. I don't even know what the movie is about," I said.

"Yeah, but it's an opportunity. They invited you to their office to consider you for a movie! That's great!" David encouraged me.

"Yeah, and she thought you were the right type for it!" Darcey added.

"I think she's concerned that I can't act. My audition was sort of sucky tonight," I replied.

"So you were a bit off. You've been off before and bounced back. You know you can act. If they like you, you'll get another shot," David insisted.

"I feel very pressured right now. I'm nervous. I'm going to head straight home tonight," I said.

"Don't you want to hang out at the diner, and get a bite to eat?" David asked.

"Yeah, this is an exciting night," Darcey agreed.

"Nah, I'm tired from that wardrobe fitting today. I'm also nervous about the interview. I think talking about it tonight might dissipate the energy," I said.

"You and David can come over to our house and have dinner with Joe and me. We can celebrate!" Darcey beamed.

"We can't celebrate yet. What if nothing happens? It's just an interview," I snapped.

"What's the matter?" Darcey asked.

"Nothing, it's just a lot of pressure and too early to assume too much," I wearied.

"Yeah, but this is a positive thing," Darcey insisted.

"I did a great audition for the last casting agent, remember, but he never called me. Neither did Michael. He ended up casting Betsy instead of me, and you thought for sure he was going to cast me as the angel," I retorted.

"Don't be so negative," Darcey whined.

"I'm not being negative. I just don't want to be hopeful, then disappointed, then hopeful, then disappointed. It's like a freakin' roller coaster. I just want to do whatever I do and then forget about it, rather than have endless conversations about it at the coffee shop. It's too depressing," I explained.

"Gee, I'm sorry," Darcey whimpered.

"No, I'm sorry. Thanks for being excited for me. I'm just afraid to get too excited for no reason, that's all. Actually, I had a string on my foot today, so you might be right. I might get a big part in a big movie," I agreed.

"What?" both Darcey and David asked at the same time.

"I had a string on my foot," I repeated.

Darcey and David looked at me and then at each other, and they both gestured with their palms up.

"You know a white piece of thread on the foot, on my shoe? I guess you never heard of it either. This actress at the costume fitting told me if there is a white thread on my shoe it means I'm going to get a big acting job, a big part," I explained.

"Really? I never heard that before," Darcey said with curious eyes.

"Neither did I," said David with a puzzled look on his face.

"Neither did I until today," I agreed. "But that's what she said."

David and Darcey both looked down at their feet and laughed.

Arriving at the subway station on 28th Street and Broadway, we all kissed goodnight, and I headed down into the fluorescently lit tunnel. I sat down in the nearly empty train car. I put my handbag on my lap, and took out the precious business card. On the back I read the name of the novel Heather was so secretive about. It read, *The Unbearable Lightness of Being*, by Milan Kundera. A chill shot through my body and the hairs on my arm stood up – "Kundera". Now I knew what "Kundera" meant. I also knew why I was in Milan with a suitcase. Now I knew why the Eastern European woman said to me with such conviction. "You are an actress." It was neither comforting, nor relieving to know what my dream finally meant. It spooked me. I decided that no one but David would know about this prophetic dream I had. It was just too unbelievable, and people might think I was a nut, making up lies and stories.

I got up early for my temp office job in Midtown on the West Side of Manhattan. At lunch time, I ran over to B. Dalton on Fifth Avenue and bought *The Unbearable Lightness of Being*. I sat in a nearby coffee shop and started reading. My mind was being blown. My heart raced. I could not fight back the tears. The coffee shop was crowded with nine-to-fivers. I was embarrassed. I closed the book and left. I ran back to the office. I locked myself in a public bathroom down the hall. I sat on the floor under a window near the sinks and I read some more. No one came into the bathroom. Besides, I had locked them out. I was alone for two hours, totally absorbed in the words on the page. I was in awe of each word, paragraph, and page I read. I wept with an overwhelming feeling of gratitude for the author's compassion and understanding. The book was about me. I was one of the main characters in the book. I was Tereza, and I knew who Tomas was. I was the physical, psychological, and emotional embodiment of Tereza. It was overwhelmingly shocking to see myself there on paper. I could not read anymore. I fell to the floor and wept uncontrollably. I couldn't remember ever having wept like that. All my barriers, all the defenses I had built to protect myself in order to keep it all together were being torn down by this author's words. I couldn't catch my breath. It felt like I was at my own funeral and I was dying, and yet, at the same time I was being born again.

I looked at the black and white photo on the back of the book cover and I believed that this man must know me. He knew me better than my own family and friends. But how could he? He was born in Czechoslovakia in 1929 and lived in France. How could he know what was in my soul? How could he know what I thought? What I felt, what I looked like?

The suitcase I carried in my dream when I entered the dark basement apartment where the actress named "Kundera" greeted me, I now read about in *The Unbearable Lightness of Being*.

I washed the mascara from under my eyes, but they were still red and my nose was flushed. I told the office manager I did not feel well, and I left for the rest of the day. I needed to find a place to be alone. I walked all over Manhattan looking for a quiet place to read. St. Patrick's Cathedral was swarming with tourists. The doors at the other churches and temples were locked. Where the hell is a quiet church when you need one? I walked up towards Central Park, which was packed with pedestrians, tourists, jugglers, street performers, roller skaters, bicyclists, vendors, screaming children and break dancers. I headed to the Upper West Side and sat on a park bench on Broadway and 72nd Street. A homeless man immediately moved in on me, so I jumped down into the subway and ended up heading back to Queens.

The only place I knew where no one would be around to notice me was on the steps under the shade of the gray concrete dome of the Kaufman Film Studio. So that's where I spent the rest of the day reading my book. All the walking and searching had exhausted me and it also calmed me down a bit, but I found myself weeping uncontrollably again as I read. I finished the novel before the sun went down, and sat on the steps. The book rested on my lap, and I stared at the cover's illustration, hands touching the rim of a floating bowler hat. I sat there a few more hours looking out onto the dark, deserted street glowing eerily under a few dimly lit street lamps. An occasional car zoomed by blasting rap music.

I suddenly felt that I was caught between not two worlds but three – my existence as I lived it in Queens, and the opposite reality which is

Hollywood as I could only imagine it to be, a world of privilege, power, creative expression, and financial independence. The third world was not yet known, not a place I could see, describe, or even envision because I have never been, but for the first time I felt it existed.

I wanted to achieve something through acting. I had studied it, loved it, and worked hard at it for so long. Even if I did succeed, I would have to keep succeeding in order to survive. My wheel would just be bigger and maybe it would go faster, but it would still be a wheel. Hollywood didn't guarantee happiness and could bring its own set of problems. There were too many Hollywood celebrities in divorce court, rehab, or jail. Yet, the only way I could make a living at what I loved to do was to be in that world.

A group of kids listening to a boom box strolled by and offered to sell me some crack. I smiled and waved, "No, I'm good." They turned up the volume and moved on. I could hear them bantering and yelling at each other playfully in the distance. I don't want to be stuck in this world, either.

Now in the dark night and the deserted silence, I realized after reading the novel, that like most young adults my age, I had not had the emotional maturity or foresight to see that my parents had experienced their own dramatic ordeals throughout their own lives, and they were carrying their own emotional baggage. The drama of human existence was not just my struggle, but a shared collective consciousness that swept across all of humanity.

Everyone in the world, including myself, was seeking some sort of approval from the world that said we were "A-okay", and we deserved to be loved and happy, except, the world was never going to give us that approval, at least not on a consistent basis. There would always be something or someone that claimed we fell short of being "A-okay". Our most available solutions to medicate this indefinable pain of falling short of reaching impossible goals is to work more, shop more, have more, do more, and be more. When that doesn't work, there is always chocolate, beer, zoning out in front of the television, sex, drugs or anti-depressants.

A pure white pigeon flew overhead and perched on top of the ledge of the Kaufman building under a metal light fixture, its silent presence, a celestial angel. My mind became quiet.

Is it possible that I have a soul that is already stable and perfect, but my human existence, which includes my thoughts, emotions, physical condition, and experiences are constantly changing with the seasons like the façade of the church outside my apartment window back in Gramercy Park. Yet, like the stable structure and foundation of the church, my spirit remains unchanged, unaltered by external influences, and continues to exist with a peaceful smile. What a mind blowing idea! But is it true?

Is there a place where perfect peace and unending love reside; where struggle, suffering, and death were impossible? Why was I suddenly so sure that there was such a place, and if there was, how could I know for certain that it existed? Where was it and how could I get there?

I felt like I was orbiting in a black void, floating, with no control over my direction, isolated, alone, and homeless. Was there a world beyond this world? I wondered and yet I kept thinking of the author's reference to Beethoven's Opus 135, Es Muss Sein! (It must be!). Which world would I choose or would it choose me?

The next day, I was too overwhelmed by what I had just read to call the casting agent. It was too soon. I couldn't even speak to anyone or look at anyone, because I feared I would burst into uncontrollable tears of gratitude. I was utterly speechless.

I stepped out early the next morning, and walked through Central Park, which was tranquil and quiet at that time of day. I occasionally stopped to sit under a tree to read the passages I had underlined, which included practically the whole book.

Something happened to me. This book changed me, or maybe it didn't change me at all, maybe it just uncovered the truth of who I really am. I was like an onion, peeled of its many layers, and left with a thin, luminous skin where my soul was starting to shine through, but I felt naked and extremely vulnerable. It frightened me to feel this raw, this exposed. Milan's words, sentences, paragraphs, and metaphors freed me from my own barriers, but I also felt ashamed of my naked truth. It felt as if everyone was looking at me, and they could actually see me, but they might disapprove of my nakedness. I was relieved and liberated, and ashamed and frightened, all at the same time. I was also anxious. The book had revealed what I was on the verge of discovering, understanding and articulating for myself, but I had not quite grasped it yet. It put me on the very edge of a cliff, and if I jumped I would find myself, and the mystery of my entire life would be solved.

A leaf floated gently down on the grass in front of me like a message. A lady bug crawled up my ankle. The clouds in the sky passed by and stopped for a moment as if to wonder over me. An invisible presence was all around me.

It was the reason I was an artist – it was the purpose of my craft as an actor – to find *The Truth*! Not my truth, but *The* Truth. I didn't know what The Truth was yet, but I was so close to it, so near, that I could feel it only a millimeter away. An inner voice, a quiet knowingness, told me to just observe. Don't grasp for anything. It's just all taking place right in front of you. All I needed to do was to be quiet, patient, feel the empty space, the void, the silence, the pause that lies between the dialogue in a play. Sshhhh . . . listen . . . sshhhh . . . listen . . .

I spent the next four days reading the book three more times from cover to cover. The author's character Tereza, "looking in the mirror to see past her body to her soul," made an intense impression on me. I remember looking in the mirror while shopping at Bloomingdales, and asking a similar question, "*Who am I?*" Her search for herself spoke to my own longing to look past my own body to see my own soul. I longed to be in touch with the purity and innocence of who I was beyond my body. I wanted others to see the truth about me too. This book came into my hands to remind me that my "beingness" is not an object. I am not my body. I am not flesh. *But what am I?*

Kundera's character, Tomas, sleeps with many different women as a way to get in touch with each part of them that was different when they reached orgasm. A light bulb went on in my brain. I realized that Kundera was onto something, but he was also a bit off. It was not that I disagreed with Kundera's ideas on this; I realized his perceptions were moving towards truth, but somehow he missed the mark. I realized from my own perceptions that Tomas slept with many different women not to reach what was different in each one of them, but rather he was searching vainly in the wrong place for where we were all the same, where we were all pure love, pure spirit.   That's it! That's it! We are all the same. No one is different from anyone else. Nobody is really separate from anyone else. We are all love. Was what I had just discovered true? Was it possible? Was it real?

I was sure it was, but I was also not sure all at the same time. The thought made me feel humbled, peaceful, and quiet. There was nothing to say about it to anyone; it was a feeling of being. God just *is*. There is nothing else, and we are all *it*. Behind our bodies, masks, personalities, and illusionary existence we were pure light and joy, and that was the place we were all trying to remember and get back to. Most people were searching and longing for God, but most people, like myself, could not figure out where or how to find Him, and we kept looking in the wrong places. But where is this place that God can be found?

A young man unleashed his dog and let it run onto the grassy field. He placed his arms around his lover's waist and pulled her close as he whispered something in her ear. She kissed him on the mouth.

Sometimes we caught a glimpse of heaven when we fell in love. Sometimes we felt a glimpse of it when we heard a beautiful song, or our eyes fell upon a rose.   It was only a glimpse, but it was something, something other than the darkness we usually experienced in our day-to-day lives with all its demands, goals, deadlines, responsibilities, problems, and limited perceptions.

I brushed off the earth from my jeans as I stood up to continue on with another short jaunt through the park. I stopped at a vendor and bought a toasted almond ice cream pop. I then proceeded up to the top of a hill to rest again under a willow tree. I lounged against a rock and watched the joggers and cyclists on the road below.

I wondered how the production company and its people were going to approach this book. I found myself anxious again because I felt a great responsibility to make sure that I would do the author's words justice.   I knew it would be an enormous undertaking to get it right, as it was the author's philosophical view point that needed to be portrayed more than the actual story line, and why it required an extra dose of humility. A philosophy can be extremely difficult to orchestrate in the visual medium of film.

       This book was not about sex; it was about God. It was about love. It was about longing for a state of being where there was only love and nothing else, where there is only joy and peace; an "unbearable lightness of being" is beyond form and revealed only content. The story and the characters were the flimsy covering for what lies underneath. Was it possible that there was another world where only the love and light of God existed? It must be! It must be! It's the only thing that could possibly make sense.

       I waited a few more days before I called Heather to set up an appointment with the casting director. I was uncertain how to express the depth of my feelings, and I didn't want that to get in the way of an interview or audition. I decided that I would not tell her or anyone about my prophetic dream, or my spiritual revelations regarding the book, because I did not know how to articulate them, and I didn't want to offend anyone. Also, I doubted myself, because I had no concrete proof that what I was now thinking was actually true. I was holding on to an "idea" that only felt true. I had no actual experience or proof that it was true, just a gut feeling that it might be so.

       I wrote a brief, but heartfelt note to Heather and Alexis Cyrus, letting them know that I had read the book, and that it would be an honor and a great privilege to be considered for this role. I waited almost a week until I was sure that they had received the letter, and then I called their office to set up a time and day to meet with them. They gave me an appointment for five days later.

       A few days before meeting with Heather and Alexis, I had a day of extra work on the film *Angel Heart*. It was a six a.m. call. I'm not a morning person, but I'm still an actor and a professional. I always show up on time. I got up at four in the morning to get ready, and headed down to Hoboken, New Jersey to the set of an historical train station. The hair and make-up people curled my hair to make it soft, long, and wavy. They placed only a dab of rouge on my cheeks, and applied a small amount of eye make-up.

Once in costume, with my frilly, yellow blouse, long skirt, saddle shoes, and white bobby socks, I looked like the sweetest little 15-year-old immigrant school girl anyone had laid eyes on. When I walked on the set, the crew members, cooed, "Oh, how sweet! She looks like a little angel." I curtsied and smiled angelically.

I whispered to one of the extras standing near me, a lady in her late sixties, "I don't feel like an angel. I just got my period today. I feel horrible. I wish someone would shoot me like a horse."

She laughed out loud. Then she saw how I was holding my back up with my arm in a lot of discomfort. "I'd give you a Midol, if I had one, but I don't get "the curse" anymore," she said.

"Oh is that what you call it, "the curse"? My mother calls it "my friend".

The woman just smiled and suggested I sit on the side bench for a while, as it might take hours before they actually started shooting the scene. The star, Mickey Rourke, was late. I heard people talking in the costume trailer that he was a dirty, foul mouthed idiot who never took a shower. People found it hard to work near him because he smelled so bad, plus he had such a bad temper. I wondered if it was true, or just a rumor created by jealous peers. Maybe it was true, maybe it wasn't. I didn't know, and I didn't care. All I knew was that he was the latest movie heartthrob among young women my age. I thought he was cute and interesting when I saw him in the film *Diner,* but my knees weren't wobbling. He wasn't my type. I was never one to idolize movie stars anyway. After studying my craft for so long, it was simply a skill that one could easily learn if that was where one's interests and passions lay.

As I listened to a group of young women on the set sigh and swoon over the idea of Mickey Rourke being in the film, I laughed to myself thinking, if he was an extra no one would look twice. I knew by now that artists are born, but stars are made by the Hollywood publicity factories that pump millions of dollars into a particular actor's career with branding and marketing as a way to make them stand out more.

A person who studied and practiced their craft with love and attention was an artist, but if they were backed by a top talent agent, they were sure to be a star. Did it really make that person a better actor or a better person? No. It just made them wealthy, more fortunate and more popular in the world.

How many hours am I going to have to stand here in the hot sun, with throbbing pains shooting through my lower back? "This really sucks," I thought to myself.

Before I thought to sit down again, one of the production assistants repositioned me and the elderly woman strategically among the many other extras scattered about the train platform near the antique train. She then placed a brown leather vintage suitcase next to me. It reminded me of the suitcase that Tereza carried with her to Prague to be with Tomas in *The Unbearable Lightness of Being*. Was it a prophetic coincidence, or just a coincidence?

I snapped out of my thoughts when I heard everyone getting excited on the set. Mickey Rourke had finally arrived, and was now rehearsing his scene of running through the old train car. A long, black raincoat trailed behind him, and his long, greasy hair hung over his eyes. I thought, "Maybe it's true. Maybe he doesn't take a shower."

"What is this movie about anyway," I asked the elderly woman.

"I have no idea," she said. "I just show up, leave, and collect my check in the mail. That's the way extra work is after awhile. You just don't care anymore."

"I don't care either," I agreed. "I just want to go home and lie down."

"Why don't you ask one of the production assistants for an aspirin or something?" she suggested.

"I don't think they are allowed to give them out, even if they had any," I said.

"Oh, yeah, right I didn't think about that. Well, there must be someone here that can slip you an aspirin," she insisted.

"How come you don't have any aspirin for me?" I asked jokingly.

"I never get sick," she replied.

"Never? Not even a headache?"

"No. I rarely get headaches," she replied.

"I'm impressed." I smiled.

"Don't worry, you'll get to that place one day."

"What do you mean?" I asked.

"After you turn forty, you won't give a shit what anyone thinks, and you'll say it like it is. And after you're sixty there's nothing you can say that can shock people, because people assume you're too old to know what the hell you're talking about anyway," she concluded.

"People think I don't know what the hell I'm talking about now."

"That's because you're so young. What are you sixteen, seventeen?" she asked.

"I'm twenty-five!"

"Well! God bless you, you look like a child. A child in a bulrush basket floating down a river," she replied.

"What did you say?"

"A child, a child. You look like a child. You look like a woman, but you look like a child," she explained.

One of the production assistants announced through her bullhorn: "All extra's exit the stage, please, and immediately file yourselves in a single line into the break room where you will be served lunch! All extra's please exit the set in an orderly fashion. Please follow the woman in the red t-shirt near the ticket booth in front of you. We have lunch waiting for you in the break room!"

"Yeah, but the rest of it. You said something else about a child in a basket down a river. I asked urgently.

"Yes, the story about Moses in the Bible. He was a child in a bulrush basket floating down a river," she replied confused.

"The child in the basket floating down the river is in the book, *The Unbearable Lightness of Being*. Did you read *The Unbearable Lightness of Being*?" I asked.

"The unbearable what?"

"*The Unbearable Lightness of Being*," I asked again as we filed in a line with the other extras.

"I never heard of that. What's that?"

"A novel. It's a book."

"I don't read anymore. I haven't read a book or even a magazine since 1978," she scoffed.

The production assistant tapped me on the shoulder. "Don't forget your suitcase. We need to clear the set."

I grabbed the little brown handle, and tarried along with the woman into the break room.

"You never read *The Unbearable Lightness of Being*?" I asked again.

"No, I told you. The only thing I've read in the past ten years is the TV guide. I'm not even an actress. I was a photographer when I was a very young woman. I moved to New York many moons ago, probably before you were even born. I do this work for extra pocket change and to get out of the house," she explained.

"What kind of photographs?"

"Journalism, newspapers, magazines. I even got a few assignments for *Time* Magazine. Then I met my husband, we fell in love, and got married. I was very talented, but I wasn't very ambitious like you young girls are today. Photography wasn't my life. It was a means to an end. My husband was my life."

"What did you say?"

"What are you deaf, girlie?" she snapped.

"No, I heard you. I just want to understand what you meant. Like the girl in the book?"

"What book?" she snapped. "I told you I don't read books. I'm really tired. I have to lie down over here a bit and take a catnap. I'll see you later," she said as she wobbled away from me.

CHAPTER TWENTY-ONE

THE AUDITION

SITTING ON THE R train on my way to the casting office in Mid-town Manhattan, I thought about the prophetic dream I had about the novel *The Unbearable Lightness of Being* a few weeks before, followed by the synchronistic events related to it at my wardrobe fitting and on the film set of *Angel Heart*. Then I thought of Beethoven's Opus 135, Es Muss Sein! (It must be!).

I arrived at Alexis Cyrus' Casting office at 10:30 a.m., a half hour earlier than my appointed time. I milled around the corner on Park Avenue looking in the shop windows. At 10:45 I climbed the long, narrow staircase to the second floor for my interview.

Already sitting in the reception room on a leather couch were three women in their early twenties. They were similar in type - young, pretty, and slender with Eastern European-features, perhaps Polish, Russian or Czechoslovakian actresses. I assumed that they were there to be interviewed for the part of Tereza also. As soon as I entered all the women's eyes widened. They looked at me with surprise, turned and looked at each other, and then back to me. Was my dress caught up in my panty hose or something? I looked down to check.

I signed in at the front desk, and sat on the couch. I noticed a woman in her late thirties standing on the opposite side of the room waiting as well. She was an Eastern European-looking woman with a very feminine and shapely figure. We looked at each other, and I immediately felt like I knew her, and in a split second realized I did and I gasped. She was the woman in my dream. The woman who stated to me in my dream: "I am 'Kundera' and you are an actress." It was the same woman, and I realized that she must have been called in for the part of Sabina, Tomas's mistress in the book *The Unbearable Lightness of Being*. I was a bit shaken by the realization, but I also felt it was a good omen.

As I sat on the couch, the woman walked over to me, put out her hand and introduced herself in a soft Russian accent.

"Allo, my name is Sasha. I am here for the part, Sabina."

"Yes, I know. I can see that," I replied.

"Ve vere all talking about you, vhen you valked in," Sasha said. The other women nodded in agreement. She continued, "You are the girl in the book. You *are* Tereza."

One girl, who sat on the other end of the couch pointed to herself and the other two girls. "Yes, we were saying that we all might as well leave now because we think you have the part," she said. They all nodded in agreement.

"Wow, that's very nice of you to say. Thank you so much. I am so nervous," I said.

"Oh, you vill be fine," Sasha said.

I was pleasantly surprised that my competition was so openly supportive, and I was taken aback that they were surrendering their hopes of getting the part to me. How strange everything is, yet how delightful. Perhaps my ship had finally come in and things were finally turning around for me. Maybe Darcey and David were right; maybe I was going to be a movie star. Maybe the woman at the costume fitting was right about the lucky white thread on my foot. Even my experience working as an extra on the film *Angel Heart* seemed to verify this possibility as well. Maybe when something is so right, everyone else involved notices it too, and they want to be supportive.

Since I was a child I always felt a burning need to consecrate the desires of my heart which is what fueled me with a passion to develop the talents God has given me and pursue them courageously in faith regardless of the obstacles in order to reach the fulfillment of some unknown divine assignment. I am in such a state of wonder and awe in seeing this process accelerating now to its fruitfulness and completeness. I am speechless.

The women all chatted enthusiastically about how lovely the novel was. I nodded along, dumbfounded and amazed at my good fortune. Sasha then told me about her wonderful husband and her five-year-old son, and how they all came here from their home in Russia to be in New York City for the first time just for this occasion.

Suddenly, an aggressive, businesswoman in her late forties burst out of an adjacent office. She was exceptionally tall, with curly, black hair accented by thick streaks of gray. Her leathery face exuded a bitter existence. She stopped for a second and looked at me with a most hostile and contemptuous look on her face. I had never seen anyone give such a hateful look, especially to a perfect stranger. Then she marched like a soldier in her riding boots down the hall to another room and slammed the door behind her. I was hoping it was a figment of my imagination.

A moment later she marched out of the back room, but before disappearing into her office again, she turned and gave me another admittedly dirty look.

"Oh, my God, did you see that?" I said to Sasha. "I hope that wasn't the woman who runs this place. She looks mean. I hope that wasn't Alexis Cyrus," I said as I laughed nervously.

"I don't know," Sasha replied.

"Did you see the way she looked at me? You did see it, didn't you?" I asked.

"Don't be nervous. It is porheps a stressful day in the office," Sasha said flippantly.

"I've never been up for a lead part in a big film like this. I don't know what to expect. I don't know what I should do or say. What are they going to ask me?" I asked Sasha.

"Relax and be yourself. I don't think you have to worry. Believe me. It is like you valked out of that book. It is remarkable. You have absolutely nothing to vorry about," Sasha promised.

The other girls nodded in agreement.

Before I had been nervous and apprehensive, now I felt a streak of terror shooting through my body. What if that was Alexis, the casting agent, and why did she look at me like that? I couldn't help thinking that this might not be good day for me. A moment later, the fierce woman opened her office door again, stuck her head out, and motioned to me with her finger to come into her office while she continued to gab on the phone.

I briskly rose up, hurried into her room and sat on a chair in front of her. She continued to banter on the phone in a heavy Russian accent, never taking her eyes off me. The look on her face was that of a hungry fat cat eyeing me, a tiny canary, its helplessly trapped prey.

Heather, the assistant, who originally found me in Edgar's workshop, was sitting at a desk in the corner. I waved hello to her enthusiastically, feeling like here might be a familiar and friendly face to help calm my nerves. She said hello to me quietly from her desk, but quickly looked away, her glance disappearing into the papers on her desk.

I noticed Heather had a scared look on her face. Why was she avoiding eye contact with me? I kept looking at her, trying to figure it out. I then turned my head back again in front of me to the evil face of the woman on the phone who continued to stare me down with intense malice. It was difficult to hide my discomfort.

I didn't know what she was talking about, or to whom she might have been talking to, because my brain fell into a bubble. To avoid her stare, my eyes wandered around the room again, and again landed on Heather. I was hoping to find solace or warm validation and acceptance from Heather, but she kept her head down, and continued to avoid eye contact with me.

Finally, the woman slammed the phone down on her desk.

"Allo, I'm Alexis Cyrus. Vot can vi do for you?" she demanded, looking me up and down like I had just walked in off the street, an unsolicited door-to door-sales man who had barged in uninvited.

I looked over at Heather for reassurance and rescue. Heather never looked up, but kept her eyes locked down on her desk.

"Uuum, Heather, here, your assistant. We met in an auditioning workshop I was in..."

"Yeah, yeah, I know all that, but Vot can I do for you?" she demanded again.

I thought Alexis's head was going to start spinning around and green stuff was going to pour out of her mouth like Linda Blair in the *Exorcist*. I thought I was looking into the eyes of Satan himself.

The phone rang. Alexis picked it up. She chatted again on the phone, staring at me down some more with a smile of sweet judgment and hostility. I kept looking at Heather again, hoping she could see the look in my eyes that said, "Help me. Please." But she still refused to make any eye contact with me. She continued to look away but was unable to hide the guilt and fear in her face.

As Alexis talked on the phone, I looked around the room at pictures of actors and celebrities hanging on her office walls. I was sweating profusely, but not from the possibility of landing a lead role in a film, but from feeling so unwelcome. I wanted to flee, run, get out of there, but that didn't seem like a feasible option. My sweat became like mucilage sucking me to the chair as I waited for Alexis to hang up the phone. It felt like forever.

Finally, Alexis ended her phone conversation. Still looking at me, she said, "So vot do you have to tell me?"

"Oh, gee", I thought to myself. "Is there something I have to tell her? Is there something specific that she wants to hear?"

"Heather, made me the offer to read the book *The Unbearable Lightness of Being*, and asked me to make an appointment with you to be considered for the part of Tereza. I read the book, I loved it, and I feel absolutely sure that I would be right for the part. I wrote a letter to you and Heather about it. I mentioned in the letter that it would be an honor and a privilege to be part of this film," I explained.

I looked over at Heather, who still kept her head and eyes down.

"Ve don't even know if you can act," Alexis snapped as she leaned forward and then sat back in her chair with a self-satisfied gloat on her face.

A thought dashed through my mind that maybe this was a weird practical joke; was I on some kind of *Candid Camera* TV show? At any moment are camera crew and my friends going to pop out of nowhere, assuring me that the extreme hostility was nothing but a prank, and of course I was there for the part of Tereza?

Keeping my composure, and getting a boost of encouragement at that thought, I said, "Uum, that's true. You don't know if I can act. I can audition for you. I can do a monologue or reading here if you like."

"No, Ve don't vand to see any monologue or reading," she snapped.

The phone rang again. Alexis yapped some more, and stared me down again. Heather avoided eye contact with me. Sweat poured down my armpits, but I had on a black dress, so luckily no one would know unless they looked at the floor and saw a puddle. My sinuses and tear ducks swelled from the tears waiting to burst forth. This time it was a shorter phone call. I managed to pull away from the tears caused by the confusion, humiliation, and embarrassment.

"I feel I'm right for the part, and would like a chance," I stated.

"Ve are looking for an unknown for this part, but someone who can act," she said smugly.

"I can assure you, I am extremely unknown. You couldn't find anyone more unknown than me. In fact, I am *The Great Unknown* of all the unknowns!" I said trying to lighten things up.

Alexis smirked with contempt rather than amusement.

"And I can act. Let me do a monologue for you," I offered.

"No, Ve don't vand to see a monologue," she growled.

"Okay," I said perplexed.

"Besides, you vould need to learn a Czechoslovakian accent," she insisted.

"I can do that. I can learn the accent," I said confidently, thinking that communication might open up if I stayed confident despite her venom.

Alexis looked me up and down in disgust. "You don't even have the body for it," she barked. The way she said it was clearly another intentional insult.

I had no hang-ups about my body. I was 5'7," slender and shapely. I was often described by photographers as a child/woman whom they thought was sexy. I knew I was physically right in both facial and body features for the part, a perfect physical match for the character Tereza. If Alexis wanted to insult me and try to make me feel insecure or bad about my body, she was wasting her time. I wondered why she was being so harsh and cruel in the way she received me, but I was too scared to ask. *If I throw water on her, will she melt?* I thought.

The phone rang again. I sat there waiting and hoping to regain my composure while fighting back tears, and found myself getting angry. I got very direct with her when she hung up the phone.

"Why did you call me into your office?"

I turned to look at Heather again, but still got no eye contact. I looked back at Alexis, my eyebrows frowning with anger.

Alexis picked up a Polaroid camera and snapped a picture of me unexpectedly.

'Oh, great,' I thought. 'Now she has a photo of me looking pissed off after she antagonized the hell out of me for reasons I can't even fathom. I don't even know this person. What was going on here? I don't understand.' "Why did you call me in?" I asked again agitated.

"Oh, I don't know. Ve thought you vere a very interesting person. Thank you for your time, but ve are very busy right now az you can see," she grinned, turning away to the papers on her desk. I turned to look at Heather again, and still, her eyes were glued to the desk with the same fear on her face.

"Ve're done here, ve're pretty busy and behind schedule," Alexis snapped. As I was getting up from my seat to leave, she threatened, "Oh, and don't ever tell anyone you vere called in for a part in this film, because if you do I vill tell them you are a liar," she quaked.

I hurried out of her office, tears flowing down my face, as I headed out the door toward the staircase. Sasha ran after me, grabbing me gently by the arm.

"What happened, vhat's wrong?"

I stood at the top of the staircase, my head down, wiping the tears from my cheeks.

"I don't know. I don't understand. I don't know." I wept.

Sasha wrapped her arms around me. "I go next. Vait for me, okay? Vait downstairs, okay?"

I ran out to the street and spent the next twenty minutes wandering aimlessly around the block and then back and forth in front of the building. My head felt like it was going to crack open from a sudden migraine headache. Sasha finally came down stairs onto the street.

"Come, let's drink cafe. Are you alright? Come," she consoled.

She whisked her arm around my shoulder, and briskly led us down the street towards Lexington Avenue.

Tell me vhat happened?" Sasha asked.

"How did your interview go?" I asked.

"I don't know," Sasha, said with a disappointed look on her face.

"What did she say to you?"

"Not much. I vasn't there long," Sasha replied.

"Was she mean to you? Was she nasty to you?" I inquired.

"She vas not very nice, but she was not very bad. It vas just nothing. Really. I think something is going on there. It may have nothing to do vith us," Sasha mused.

Sasha and I slid into a booth at a nearby diner and ordered coffee. I told her what had happened, how Alexis Cyrus had treated me like I had killed her first born son, and how Heather, who invited me to be considered for this project, refused to make eye contact with me, and had a guilty, fearful look on her face.

"There is some kind of misunderstanding or lack of communication. Porheps she vas having a bad day -- business problems or personal problems. I think you may vant to vait let some time pass, and then try talking to her again," Sasha suggested.

"I don't know, Sasha, that woman hated me. I mean she really hated me, and we had never met. I don't even know her. I had never met her before in my life, and she just hated me. I don't think she is going to want to talk to me again," I shuddered.

"You feel this vay now, but tomorrow is another day. Maybe you both vill get a better perspective," Sasha consoled.

"A better perspective on what? I don't know what the problem is! That's just it. She hated me before I even walked in the door. She had it in for me before I even showed up today, and I don't know the woman, so how am I going to approach her? I don't know why she's so angry at me. I don't have a clue, and she doesn't want to tell me why she hates me."

"Listen," Sasha put her hand on mine. "You are the best person to play this role. I feel this. I can see this. I know this. As soon as you valked into the reception room today everyone can see this. Alexis must know this. It is her job. You take some time and regroup, okay?"

"I don't know if I could go back there again. She scared the hell out of me," I wept.

"Go home. Take bath. Relax. Call me tomorrow. Here, take my number," Sasha offered.

"Thank you Sasha, I don't know what I would have done if you weren't here. I do hope you get the part of Sabina, regardless of what happens with me."

"I don't vant to talk about this. It is neither here nor there. This acting thing, very frustrating. I vould rather not think about this," Sasha said annoyed.

"Alexis was at least civil to you, so you have a good chance."

"She vas not necessarily nice or not nice. She vas…uumm, flat. I don't know. I feel much tension in this office. For me, if it does not vork, I go back to Russia vith my husband and my son," Sasha sighed.

"I'm so confused. My head hurts," I groaned.

"Ve talk tomorrow. I have errands to run, and then I pick up my son from school. Call me tomorrow, and don't vorry," Sasha smiled consolingly.

When Sasha left, I finished what was left of my coffee and walked around the city for a few hours. I had no one else to talk to. I figured that David would judge me for giving a bad interview, and my parents would judge me as well. I felt so alone after Sasha left me, and I didn't know what to do with myself. My headache was so bad now that I felt like my skull was going to split open.

During my walk, I stopped in another coffee shop for a grilled cheese sandwich and a cup of coffee. I thought food in my stomach would help my headache. Shortly after, while walking through Central Park, I vomited behind some bushes and trees. I sat on a park bench wondering how I was going to fix all this.

By four thirty p.m. I decided it was time to confront my demons. It was time someone explained to me why things were happening this way. If people were going to invite me into their world, and then suddenly cut me off or get mad at me, they should at least give me the reason. If people were going to abandon me or attack me, maybe they could let me in on the reason. I needed to know. This was crazy.

I decided to return to the casting office and ask Alexis what I did or said to make her so angry. Whatever it was, maybe I could apologize and make it right. For the love of God, I just wanted to know what it was. How could I fix something that I didn't know anything about?

I arrived back at her office building at around five p.m. and rang the bell downstairs. I was buzzed in, and I walked up the stairs quietly.

Alexis rushed out of her office. When she saw me at the top of the stairs, she screamed, "Vot are you doing here!"

"I came back to find out why you might be so angry at me. I don't understand what happened today, and . . . ," I stumbled.

"Get out now! Get out now. Before I call the cops!" she growled.

'Call the cops? Oh, my God! Why would she call the cops? I better get out of here,' I thought. "Okay, I'm leaving, I'm sorry," I promised. I ran down the stairs and out into the street again.

I got on the "R" train to Queens during rush hour. I was panicked now. 'The cops? Who does this woman thing I am, and what does she think I've done? What in God's name is going on?' I kept asking myself. My headache came back.

I scrambled back home and ate dinner with my parents, trying to tune out the hostile conversation that they volleyed back and forth. They kept trying to drag me in. I darted into the bathroom, threw up again, and then rolled into the bedroom and fell asleep. I woke up at about midnight and sat in the kitchen while everyone was asleep. I drank coffee, smoked cigarettes, and watched the planes come in until about three in the morning. I was numb. A few hours later I drifted back to bed.

The next day I got up at ten a.m. in a zombie-like state. I showered and shuffled slowly into the kitchen to have toast and coffee. As I bit into another piece of rye bread smeared with butter and jelly, the phone rang. I picked it up. It was Edgar Wolf from The Audition Lab.

"Whitney, this is Edgar Wolf from The Audition Lab. I'm calling to let you know that you are not invited back to the workshop anymore."

"What? Why?"

"I got a call from Alexis Cyrus's office. You handled yourself very unprofessionally yesterday at her office. We can't have that here."

"What! I never handled myself unprofessionally. What are you talking about?"

"I'm just going by what I heard from her office," Edgar said.

"What did she say? What did I do? Tell me, what did I do?" I demanded.

"Well, you went back to her office late in the evening and threatened her."

"I never did any such thing! First of all, it was not late in the evening. It was five o'clock. I only went back to find out why *she* was angry with *me* when I showed up the first time. I don't even know her. The real question is why did she threaten me? I never threatened her! If anyone was threatened it was me! I left her office in tears; she was so mean to me. Why was she so mean to me? She hurt me; why did she want to hurt me? Why was she so angry? What did I do wrong? That's all I wanted to know! This is crazy!"

"I'm just telling you what I heard from them. I have to honor their requests. The people I bring into this workshop to see your work are very influential and experienced people in the business. She's a very powerful casting agent. She casts major films with major directors and actors. I can't have my actors threatening or harassing major casting people that I invite to The Audition Lab," Edgar reprimanded.

"I never did any such thing. That's a lie. Who told you that?" I demanded.

"Their office."

"Who in their office? Who? Was it Alexis Cyrus? Was it Heather? Who?" I asked again.

"I can't say," Edgar insisted.

"You can't say! You're making these accusations, and you can't say?"

"You can't come back here, you're not welcome."

"Fine, Edgar, fine, but you should tell me what I did. How did I threaten anyone? What did I do?"

There was silence on the other end of the phone.

"Tell me what did I do? How did I threaten her or anybody?" I demanded.

There was still an awkward silence on the other end.

"Tell me what did I do? If I don't know what I did wrong, how can I fix it? Edgar, you can at least give me that much," I demanded again.

"Uummm, she says, you spooked her."

"I spooked her? Yeah, I'm a real spooky person. How did I spook her?" What did I do? What did I say or do? How did I spook her?" I pleaded.

"I don't know. I can only go by what I was told. I'm sorry, you can't come here anymore."

"Edgar, you're the one who is unprofessional, not me. She was the one that was unprofessional, not me. I did nothing wrong," I yelled.

"Don't come back here." Click.

As I hung up the phone, my mother clambered into the house carrying groceries. I tried to help her with the bags.

"Get the hell out of my way, will yah!" She growled.

"Just trying to help you," I said.

"I don't need any help. Just get a fuckin' job, will ya," she said, gnashing her teeth.

"Stop telling me to get a job," I snapped.

"You fuckin' son of a bitch! Who the fuck are you, anyway? I tell you what the fuck I want to tell you!" She slammed her fist on the wall. "Get a fuckin job! Where the fuck were you yesterday? Looking for a job I hope!" she screamed.

"I had an interview yesterday. I was up for a part in a movie. And I didn't get it. Alright? I didn't get it!" I yelled.

"You didn't get it, because you've got no fuckin' talent! That's why you didn't get it!" she screamed, gnashing her teeth some more.

I got dizzy for a minute. I said nothing. I looked at her and thought to myself, she's never even seen me perform. Why does she say things like that?

The phone rang. I ran into the kitchen to pick it up. It was David.

"What the hell happened yesterday? I just got a call from Edgar Wolf," David said.

"Nothing happened. It's not true," I said.

"Well, something must have happened. He kicked you out of the workshop. What did you say to this woman? Whitney, what are you crazy? This was a major casting agent, with a big role – she was interviewing you for a big part. She's a casting agent for feature films. What happened?" David asked.

"I didn't do anything! God, I swear. I didn't do anything!! Why are you siding with Edgar Wolf? Do you believe him? I didn't do anything!" I insisted.

"Alright, calm down. Tell me what happened."

"Not now. I need to come over your house. I need to get out of here," I said.

"I won't be home from work until six, but you have the key. Let yourself in, hang out, and I'll see you when I get home," David suggested.

When I arrived at David's, I called Sasha, and told her about everything that had transpired since she left me.

Sasha replied, "Vhitney, I am sorry this has happened to you. There is much tension in her office. I don't know what vas going on, but I vas very uncomfortable for me. I tell you, I don't like dis business. I come all the vay from Russia for the part, and now I vant to go home. I am returning to my country vith my son and my husband tomorrow. I'm thirty-eight years old. I don't need this kind of thing in my life no more. I have good family. I have good friends. I have no problem. This business -- too difficult. They can't kill your dreams so they assassinate your character. It is too difficult I am so sorry for you."

I sat in David's living room the rest of the day, smoking cigarettes and drinking a few cups a coffee I had bought at the corner deli. When he came home, I told him everything I had experienced.

"I'm telling you, David, this woman was furious at me before she even met me or talked to me. She gave me a look of such contempt and disgust as she passed by me while I was waiting in the reception area. I don't understand it."

"This is messed up. You know that. She casts a lot of feature films. Your name is dirt now," David said.

"My name was dirt before I even showed up and met the woman. This is what I mean! This is why I told you I didn't want to be at The Audition Lab. I told you why I didn't want to be around Edgar Wolf. He must have something to do with this, because I didn't do anything! I swear! Oh God, I didn't do anything," I pleaded.

"Alright, I believe you. I believe you."

"Edgar must have said something to her to make her act that way towards me," I insisted.

"What did Edgar say happened?" David asked.

"At first he said that I had threatened her, and that made me furious. I challenged his accusations by asking him how. What did I do? But he could only come up with saying that I had spooked her. I asked him how I had spooked her. He couldn't answer me. I don't even look spooky. There's nothing spooky about me. Sasha didn't think I was spooky. None of the other girls auditioning thought I was spooky. They thought I was fine. I'm just fine. They thought I was *more* than just fine, that I was perfect, just perfect. They were rooting for me. I don't understand this."

"Did you tell her about the dream you had about being in Milan, and the actress named Kundera?"

"No, of course not. I never told anyone about that dream, ever. No one. You're the only one I told about the dream, and I told you about the dream before I even knew about the novel or the film. Do you think I would share that with an absolute stranger? I never had any intention or desire to tell her or anyone about that dream. All I did was show up, and she was hostile as she walked by me while I sat on the couch in the reception room waiting to see her," I explained.

"But the woman, Sasha, the woman you had coffee with?" he asked.

"Yeah, she was the woman in my dream, the Russian woman, who said her name was "Kundera". She was there. She was up for the part of Sabina."

"Did you tell Sasha about the dream?" David asked.

"No, I didn't tell anyone. I swear, I never mentioned it," I said again.

"Are you going to go back to Edgar's class without me?" I asked David.

"No, I can't go back there either. If what you say is true, then something is wrong. I'm going to back you up. I won't go back there," David replied.

I slept at David's that night, and hung out at his apartment the next day while he was at work. In the afternoon, I took his dog for a walk around the block. As I turned the corner on Twenty-third Street and Third Avenue, a street performer wearing colorful, pointy shoes with bells on the toes, and a matching harlequin hat, jumped in front of me, choosing me as his only audience. While juggling and balancing five, brightly colored balls in the air, he smiled broadly and told some silly jokes.

He caught all the balls in both hands, and kicked his heels into the air, saying to me, "Aaah, you must be an actress! A Czechoslovakian actress, I might add! Are you from Czechoslovakia?" he eagerly asked.

I stood there with my mouth open. How did he know about the book, the dream, and the film? Why would a total stranger on the street dressed in a court jester's outfit, no less, refer to me as Czechoslovakian? People have said that I look Italian, Greek, French, even Polish, but specifically Czechoslovakian? Why was he so specific? Why did he say actress? Why did he say Czechoslovakia? I quickly walked away.

"What's the matter? You don't speak English? I don't speak Checzoslavakian? Sorry. Have a nice day," he yelled out cheerfully.

I kept walking. I couldn't handle the synchronicity anymore. It was disturbing. I wasn't sure if I was being validated or mocked. I felt mocked.

As I walked a few blocks, I consoled myself with the idea that he was a happy, friendly, cheerful court jester just the same, and maybe it was a good omen. Maybe whatever misunderstanding had happened with

Alexis and Heather would miraculously clear up, and she would welcome me with open arms, and I would get the part in the film after all.

I decided to contact the man who was going to direct the film. I didn't want to go over Alexis' head and create more trouble, but I felt that I needed to do more. She was not approachable.

I wrote to the director through his agency, never mentioning Alexis nor my interview with her, only that I had read the book, and I believed that I would be right for the part. He probably never got the letter; it most likely got dumped in the wastebasket at the agency's mailroom.

I thought that perhaps I should try to contact the author, Milan Kundera, but he lived in France. I had a momentary thought of flying to France and trying to find him, but I barely had enough money for subway fare, let alone a plane ticket. Perhaps I could write to him. The publisher in New York refused to release his contact information in France. After a few more calls, I was directed to the English translator of the book in California.

I eventually wrote a heartfelt letter to the translator thanking him for his work on the book, and asked him to relay my gratitude for such an incredibly beautiful book to Milan Kundera as well.

I receive a very warm and gracious letter back from the translator, and it made me feel much better. At least I had had an opportunity to express my gratitude to both of them. The response gave me some peace of mind and some feeling of closure, but the haunting injustice of the film experience still weighed in my heart.

CHAPTER TWENTY-TWO

THE MELTDOWN

AFTER SPENDING THE night at David's, I traveled back to my parents' house, hoping to get a call for a job interview or at least more temporary office work. I needed some money even if only pocket change. Nothing was available yet. I kept thinking about the film, the book, and the dreams I had. I felt a tremendous amount of loss and disappointment. The catastrophic interview kept haunting me. A few days later, I got a call at my parents' house from a casting director I had never met or heard of before. She said they were casting a film, and they needed a Czechoslovakian actress for the lead. She asked if I could I come in the following Thursday to meet her for the film entitled *Anna*.

I took down the address and information, but the thought ran through my mind that this was a sick joke. I was no longer in Edgar's class and I didn't have an agent, so the appointment was questionable to me. How likely was it for me to be called in for another lead in another major film looking for another Czechoslovakian actress? I was an "unknown" and without an agent. How often does that happen? It felt suspicious, but I needed to stop being paranoid and get a grip. I would go, and it would just be a normal interview, I kept telling myself. I wished that I had an agent to represent me. I was being called in for major film parts with no representation, which is not the norm, and obviously a bit risky.

When I arrived at the casting office, I was greeted by a short, overweight woman in her early fifties. She had stringy, gray hair, and tiny, wire-rimmed glasses sat on her round face. She motioned with her hand for me to come into her office as she sat at her desk chatting on the phone. I stood at her desk while she continued on with her phone conversation. She kept looking at me. It was not an angry or hostile look, but it wasn't friendly or inviting either, just expressionless. Twenty minutes crawled by as I stood there waiting for her to end her conversation. Was she ever going to get off the phone?

Alexis Cyrus's words kept blaring in my head, "And don't you ever tell anyone you were up for the part of Tereza for this film, because if you do – I'll them you're a liar! " Then my mother's words reverberated in my head, "You didn't get the part, because you have no fuckin' talent! That's why!" Alexis smirking, "You don't even have the body for it!!! I don't even know if you can act. What can we do for you? Why are you here? What do you want!!! Want!!! Want!!! Liar!!! Liar!!! Liar!! When are you going to get a job! You got no talent!!! You're a fuckin' Liar!! Liar!!! Liar!! Who the hell do you think you are!!! We don't even know if you can act!!! What can we do for you? What do you want!! Why are you here!!! Can't you see we're busy!!! Busy!!! Busy!!! I'll tell them you were a liar!!! Liar!!! Edgar's ugly face screaming at me, "You're not welcome back here anymore! Yeah, but look at her teeth!! She spooked me, you're a spook!!! Spook! Spook!!!"

I became dizzy and hot with sweat. Where did these thoughts come from? None of these thoughts made any sense, and yet there they were. My heart was racing, and I couldn't breathe. I started sobbing. I ran out of the woman's office, out of the building, and into the street. I don't think she ever got off the phone. I never went back, never contacted her again, and I never heard from her again about the film *Anna* or any other part.

I never told anyone about the audition. There was no one to tell. Who would be interested, except perhaps David and Darcey. David would have been furious with me for freaking out and running away. He knew that I could be successful. I had been given another chance, and he would have accused me of blowing it, again.

I wasn't strong enough anymore to handle more irrational and unpredictable behavior from people. Leonardi threw me for a loop by disappearing on me, and so did Sidney and the guy with the knife she brought into the apartment. Then there was Justin, with his unpredictable drunken verbal and physical abuse. Now Heather and Alexis called me into their office, treated me like dirt, and made false accusations to get me kicked out of a workshop I never wanted to be at in the first place. There were my parents wearing me down day-to-day, moment-to-moment, along with the constant fear of my brother coming home from jail again. I couldn't take one more episode of insanity or false hope, and had very little experience to make me believe that I could trust any situation, anyone, or anything. I was in a constant state of terror, but I didn't have a clue how to heal it or where to go for help.

I got a call from one of the temp agencies to do some office work down on Wall Street. I always hated going to Wall Street. Downtown was the ugliest, most depressing part of the city, with its narrow streets, and old buildings that blocked the sun from view. The people in New York City may be impatient and rude compared to other parts of the country, but on Wall Street, it was populated with lots of stockbrokers and bankers, who embodied the words *crude*, *rude*, and *obnoxious* along with the term *pompous ass*. I always turned down jobs that were available in the World Trade Center because in the 1970's when the towers were completed, and I stood across the river viewing them from the Borough of Queens, God told me to never take a job in those buildings because they would fall. He did not tell me how or when they would fall but just that they would fall. So I never had a desire to work in those buildings, and I never had any desire to go to the top. I hated the way the towers blocked the sky. I hated the idea that they swayed in the wind. The one time I did visit them, I hated the eerie swoosh sound one heard in their elevators. I always got a foreboding feeling just seeing the buildings from a distance.

The temp job assignment was located in one of the buildings adjacent to the World Trade Center. I went this time, only because I needed the money, and it was only for a few days. Also, it was something to get me out of my parents' house and help keep my mind occupied during the day.

I did a full day of work at an accounting office in the financial district. I was feeling quite depressed. It was the kind of depression that can swallow a person up and make them drown in a sea of black muck. When the day was over at five-thirty, I slumped out of the office through a pedestrian bridge tunnel packed with hurried and anxious strap hangers racing for the subway.

As I schlepped along the pavement, my legs turned into 300 pound lead weights, and I couldn't keep myself standing up right. I fell to my knees. People rushed by me. No one tried to help me up or assist me in anyway. They kept brushing by me and knocking me to and fro.

I felt like the boy warrior, Atreyo, in the 1984 film, *The Never Ending Story*. Atreyo's beloved horse Artax dies in the Swamp of Sadness during their quest to save Fantasia from "The Nothingness". Atreya begs his beloved horse to hold on a little longer, to try a little harder, but to no avail. The beautiful, gentle white horse sinks in the murky, muddy quicksand of dark despair. In order to save the beautiful fairy princess, Moonchild, and her magical kingdom, Atreyo must now fight "The Nothingness" alone. "Stand your ground Fantasia, stand your ground!"

To get out of the flow of traffic, I crawled over to a side railing and lifted myself up. I held onto the railing and paced slowly down the end of the tunnel bridge. Every now and then I stopped to rest. I looked out the clear glass window of the enclosed bridge to witness a swarm of commuters, like ants, racing below to the buses and subways. "Anxious, unconscious, robot-like, emotionless figures all in a hurry to get *nowhere*," I thought to myself.

I couldn't understand what was wrong with my legs, and why my whole body was so heavy under me and why I was collapsing. Was I dying? Was this it? Was it over? I was surprised. Is that how it is? One day it just happens? Your body just stops functioning for whatever reason, and in whatever way, and then poof, you're just gone? "Stand your ground Fantasia. Stand your ground!"

I finally made it to the end of the bridge and found a bench to sit on for a while. I sat there for a few hours. By eight p.m., the rush hour crowd had thinned out. I was able to walk to the train, still feeling like I had the world on my shoulders, but at least my legs were not buckling below me anymore..

Back home, I reclined on the bottom bunk bed in the dark, thinking that I might die. I didn't want to die, but I didn't want to live either. It was a very strange place to be, not wanting to live, but not wanting to die. Justin's voice reciting Franz Kafka's words loomed through my head, "A first sign of the beginning of understanding is the wish to die." That made no sense to me. I wanted to live, but I did not want to live like this anymore. I had tried everything I could to be a person worthy of success, worthy of a better life, and worthy of love and joy, but I had failed at it every time. The worst of it was that I hadn't done anything bad or wrong, yet that's how people were treating me and behaving towards me.

I'd work hard and see my goal in front of me. However, just as I was about to reach it, not only was it snatched away, but I got slapped around and beaten up for getting too close to achieving my dreams. I realized that nothing I thought, did, or said, was going to change my life. I had run out of moves. I was powerless to solve my own problem. Who could help me?

I wondered if I should go to the doctor or the emergency room. I was drained of all my energy, and my body felt so achy and heavy that I was sure something was seriously wrong. I thought if I checked myself into the emergency room, I wouldn't be able to pay for it because I had no health insurance.

I thought maybe I should go to my family doctor, but what if he did tests, an endless amount of tests, and found a fatal illness. What if he found nothing wrong with me, but I still felt this way? What if he found something really wrong with me, and I had to fight for my life, when I really didn't have any incentive to live now?

Maybe I should see a therapist. If I go to a therapist, I would have to tell them this horrid story and experience it all over again. I was barely getting through it as I lived it now. Should I talk to a priest? Maybe I should go to the local church, and talk to a priest.

I sat in the confessional box and tried to remember what I needed to say before the window slid open. 'Ummm, forgive me, Father, for I have sinned. It's been, umm, let's see four, five, eight, ten. Thirteen years since my last confession! Thirteen years! Oh, boy! This priest was going to give me 8,000 Hail Marys and 10,000 Our Fathers to say just for that!' The wooden door slid open.

"Forgive me Father, for I have sinned. It was been a very, very long time since my last confession, and these are my sins . . ."

The priest's voice was that of gruff and surly old man. "Go ahead," he said.

"I don't know where to begin. I'm so confused. I'm living with my parents. I haven't lived with them in five years, and I was called in for the lead in a movie, an acting role, and I didn't get it, but that's not what's bothering me. The casting agent discredited me and had me thrown out of acting class. I had an office job, but when they saw my modeling photo in the paper, I got laid-off. So I've been out of work for a long time. I think the problem started when I cheated on my boyfriend, because I fell in love with my hairdresser. But the hairdresser refused to talk with me for no reason at all, and we didn't even have a fight. And one of his friends, a friend of one of his friends, threatened me with a knife. I got away, but . . . I don't feel well. I think I'm dying . . ."

There was a long silence. "You live with your parents?" he asked.

"Yes, and they hate me. I mean they don't really hate me. I feel like everyone hates me, and I don't have enough money to move out."

"Get a job."

"What?"

"I said, 'get a job'," he snapped while slamming the window shut.

I knocked on the window. The priest slid it open. "That's it? My parents say that to me all the time. That's all you have to say to me? Get a job?"

"Oh, yeah, sorry I forgot. Say eight Hail Marys and ten Our Fathers, and then get a job." And the window slammed shut.

I knocked on the window again. It slid open. "That's part of my problem. I can't find a job and I can't keep a job."

"Alright, then say twelve Hail Marys and twelve Our Fathers." He slammed the window shut for the last time.

I sat in the confessional box for a moment in the dark confusion. I knelt down at the altar, and prayed my twelve Hail Marys and twelve Our

Fathers, thinking to myself, "This is ridiculous", but I did it anyway. I left the empty church thinking, *No one knows anything.*

On my way home, I stopped for a time to sit on the brick stoop of a cornflower blue house. I pulled out *The Unbearable Lightness of Being* from my shoulder bag, and read over the words I had underlined, trying to grasp their meaning. I was lost. I had no will to live, and I had no will to die.

A few days later, I went to a therapist on the Upper Eastside in Manhattan. She was a chubby woman in her late fifties. She wore a conservative, raspberry-colored tweed suit adorned with a large silver pin on her lapel. She was frumpy and matronly with a pale face, thin gray hair and tiny wire-rimmed glasses. She appeared professional and pleasant. I began with my experience of the film and what had happened with Alexis Cyrus.

The therapist looked at me sternly and said, "You are delusional."

"Uh? I asked confused.

"Just what I said. You are being delusional. You need to get your head out of the clouds," she snapped.

I was shocked at her response, but I tried to explain it to her again.

"No, you don't understand. I've been studying acting for almost six years now, and I was called in for one of the lead parts--for a film based on a book called *The Unbearable Lightness of Being.* Because of the way things turned out, I feel like I have lost my will. I even wrote to the psychologist Rollo May who wrote a book called *Love and Will,* because I thought that maybe he could help me,' I explained.

"You wrote to Rollo May?" Her eyes sternly peeked out from the wire frame glasses she had pulled down to the tip of her nose.

"Yes, I mean, when I read his book back in the late 1970's, I wanted to understand more about what he wrote because with all that's happened to me recently, I feel like I've lost my will. And he wrote that book called *Love and Will,*" I explained again.

"Yes, I'm very familiar with the book, but Rollo May is a very famous and well-respected psychologist," she snapped.

"Yes, exactly, that is why I wrote to him, because I trusted he might be able to help me."

"You can't write to Rollo May!" she gasped.

"Why? I don't understand," I asked.

"Did he respond?" she queried with wide eyes.

"No, he didn't, but why shouldn't I . . . ," I stumbled.

"Who do you think you are, writing to someone as famous and well-respected as him? He's Rollo May. He's not going to converse with someone like you. He's a well-educated, intelligent, professional therapist, and writer," she scoffed.

"Oh, well, to tell you the truth, I wasn't thinking about that. I was just thinking about the fact that maybe he could help me."

"He's famous; you're nobody. Why would he want to help you?"

"So, if things had turned out differently, and the casting agent had liked me, I would have gotten the part in the film, and I would have been rich and famous, and then Rollo May would have responded to me? But then, if you think about it, whether I got the film part or not, if the casting agent had treated me like the decent human being that I am, I wouldn't have this problem to begin with, and I would not need to talk to Rollo May. I wouldn't even be here right now, right?" I inquired, trying to make my point.

"You were never up for the part in any film. What I am trying to tell you honey, is that you are delusional. You think you are somebody. You are nobody.

I can prescribe anti-depressant medication for you, and you can try to arrange it with your parents to pay me for my services, which, as I told you over the phone, after the initial free consultation today, is $120 an hour. If you don't have a job, I strongly recommend that you talk with your parents about helping you pay for your treatment. I'm sure your parents love you and care about you and would want to help," she explained.

"No, uumm. I can't get my parents involved, and I really don't think you can help me anyway, but thank you for your time."

"You need treatment. Writing to people like Rollo May is--"

I got up from the chair and collected my jacket and handbag to leave. "Yeah, I know. It's a serious offense, and the sign of a serious mental illness. Who am I to write to Rollo May? I'm nobody. I know. This seems to be my problem. I obviously think too much of myself," I said sarcastically.

"Then you should consider treatment. I really recommend that you talk to your parents to help you pay for your treatment," she implored again.

"No, I'll be going now. Thank you," I said.

As I left her office and headed down the street towards the subway, I got chills up my spine. Was that woman labeling me a liar and a narcissist? How did she manage to get a license to practice therapy, and get paid $120 an hour for it? She needed therapy. She actually saw people as more important and less important than one another based on their credentials, notoriety, and fame within society. "The woman is nuts!" I thought.

My father says, "You're problem is that you think you are somebody, when you are nobody." My friends and peers say, "You're problem is that you think you are nobody, when you are somebody." Neither concept felt true.

I marched down the subway steps in anger and defiance. I paced back and forth on the platform while waiting for a train. Ugh, the frustration of it all.

We live in a society where ivy league degrees, celebrity status and wealth determine whether someone is valuable or not! She thinks I'm not worthy enough to receive a response from the almighty Rollo May, the great Oz himself. "Stupid bitch," I muttered to myself. Finally, I relaxed my back against a rusty subway beam. An inner thought came, "*The world and its establishments are set up to deny you access to the lofty truth of what you are.*"

I'm an artist. What I do is neither valuable nor valueless. It just *is*. I am not trying to be important nor unimportant. I just want to be myself.

My eyes rested on one of Keith Haring's graffiti chalk drawings, simple lines of faceless people and open hearts. I thought to myself, "Art is not as important as the *love* that inspires it. Nothing is as important as the *love* that inspires it. Where is this *love* coming from and why is this *love* so threatening to people?"

The train pulled in with a loud screech. The doors stayed closed. I felt impatient. They finally opened. I hurried in and plopped down at a window seat. As the train moved on into the dark tunnel, there was nothing to view through the glass but trailing black walls, the occasional bright light bulb imprisoned by a wire encasement, and my own reflection.

The train abruptly kicked back and stalled, then moved again at a snail's pace. The deafening screeching sound of its wheels echoed in my chest. The train would occasionally pick up a hopeful pace, only to stop, stall, and screech again through the black underpass. All I could think was, "Dear God, please get me out of hell."

When the train finally picked up a steady speed and moved out of the tunnel into the blue skies and bright sunlight my breath deepened, my chest expanded, and I closed my eyes for a moment with a sigh of relief. Here it dawned on me that even though I don't know who I am, neither does the therapist, the priest, my parents, Tony Scott, Edgar Wolf, Alexis Cyrus, nor David or Leonardi, or anyone else, for that matter, can know who or what I am. Nothing out there can tell me who or what I am. Nothing out there can possibly know, but what does know? 'What is true?' I asked myself. No answer came.

And what would have happened if I had ever agreed with all these people that I was, in fact, a guilty, worthless, and incomplete "nobody" who deserved nothing but struggle, lack and punishment. Where would I be? The thought came, "*You would be dead.*" Why would anyone want me dead? No answer came.

The next day I slept until noon, and I had no will to get out of bed. I had no strength in my body, no energy, and no will to live. It was a hot, muggy Indian summer's day in September, and my parents' house had no air conditioning. I sat up on the bottom bunk in my brother's room that late morning wondering what I was supposed to do. I admitted to myself that I didn't know anymore, and even if I knew, I didn't have the strength or the will power to pick myself back up again. I couldn't see any way out but to die, yet I didn't want to die, and even if I did want to die, I wouldn't be able to kill myself. I had no stomach or mind for that kind of thing.

Therein lay my confusion. I didn't hate myself, yet my life looked like it was filled with self-hatred, but the hatred was coming from other people, not me, and I had no control over other people's attitudes and behaviors, only my own. Being conscious of my own behavior and attitudes did not solve my problem. I was unable to find any solution to my problem, and I was too tired from trying. I was exhausted. Not from the joy, and the music and the art, but from the judgment. I was so tired of spending my life trying to find a solution. Although I didn't think I hated myself, I realized that something must hate me. I thought maybe it was God that hated me.

For some reason, Professor Yogi Shand popped into my head. Maybe I should go back and visit him at his office. I hadn't seen him in over three years. I don't know why or how the idea leaped into my head to visit him again, but it did. Professor Yogi Shand seemed to be the last resort and my only hope.

CHAPTER TWENTY-THREE

THE REVELATION

SOME PHILOSOPHERS OFTEN say, "There is not much to life. One is sitting, standing, or lying down. Life is that simple and only we make it seem so complicated." *What about dancing?* I thought. Maybe people didn't want to stand, sit, or lie down so much. Maybe they want to dance.

As always, the small waiting room was crowded with women. They sat in their chairs quietly. Some read books, some magazines, some read the Bible quietly, and some knitted. The women occasionally acknowledged each other with a gentle smile, but no one started up any kind of conversation with one another. We just sat and waited and waited for hours until someone came out of the adjacent room and invited the next person in.

There was the soothing sound of a portable fan near the window. It made that occasional rhythmic clicking noise as it swirled from right to left and back again from left to right. The aroma of Candela incense in the air wrapped around my senses like a new born baby's blanket. The blinds on all the windows were drawn low, and the light from outside only hinted of a bright, sunny day.

Scanning the room, I noticed it looked pretty much the same since the last time I had been here three years ago. The walls were a gray-yellow, and the moldings and panels painted in a fading, pink and mint green. Old metal folding chairs made with black vinyl covers, some with holes and white stuffing sticking out, lined the room. The same dusty artificial plant sat in a corner. A few rainbow-colored posters of the Indian

Bhagwad Gita Gods and Goddesses hung here and there. Wrinkled and crumpled up magazines sat in untidy piles on an old, beat-up wooden coffee table in the middle of the room.

I looked around the room at the people. The clientele had not changed either. They were all female, all middle aged or older, all poor, and all black with a few Hispanics. I was always the only young white girl in the room, and it never bothered me, I just wondered why.

The door to the adjacent room opened and everyone sat up eagerly and expectantly. An Indian woman with a long braid in her hair, wearing a colorful sari, surveyed the area.

"RK?" Everyone looked around the room at each other.

The Indian woman called out the initials again, "RK? Is there anyone here with the initials RK?"..

One eggplant-plump West Indian woman snapped out of the concentration of a book, and jumped up with an excited smile. "That's me. That's me," as she quickly gathered her belongings and with a spring in her step disappeared into the next room.

Even though I had been waiting for two hours, I expected to wait another three or four hours to meet Professor Shand. Patience is a virtue here, because you had no other choice. I sipped down the last drops of my coffee from a white Styrofoam cup, which was now mostly syrupy sugar.

The first time I had ever heard of Professor Shand I was eighteen years old. I had decided to have braces put on my teeth so I could pursue my modeling and acting career. At the orthodontist's office, I met his nurse, an African American woman named Doris. Doris was tall and robust with a jolly laugh, and a joyful spirit. After my first few visits with the orthodontist, Doris gave me the business card of an Indian man named Professor Yogi Shand who had an office in Manhattan on the Upper West side. Professor Yogi Shand was a Fortune Teller.

I visited Professor Shand every six months or so for a few years, and he read my fortune with Tarot cards and a regular deck of playing cards. He told me about the future, which was fun, but he also assigned me homework of reading certain Psalms in the Bible. I never did read them.

After a few years, I stopped seeing him. My life had gotten better and I was too busy growing, exploring, and learning. Also, I questioned whether there was any real value in seeing him. Most of his clientele were poor black women, and I wondered if I, like these women, was just vulnerable to believing or trusting in superstitious nonsense because of our low station in life. Did we come here for hope, even if it might be false hope? Therefore, I had not returned to Professor Shand for over three years.

Now in September of 1985, at twenty-five, my life had taken a serious turn for the worse. Professor Shand seemed to be the last resort and only hope. While waiting in the reception room I kept going over in my mind what I was going to say to him. Where I was going to start? How I was going to make sense of all this? What was I going to ask him? I thought about all the events that had transpired over the past year that had brought me to this place of fear, confusion, loss, and anger. The betrayal, judgment, and abandonment I had experienced, as well as the deep, deep sadness and helplessness. My heart was shattered in such a way that I did not know how to go on.

I had tried explaining it to a priest, then a therapist, and I had tried to explain it all to myself. The words just got in the way, and nothing made any sense.

An hour later my turn came. The woman in the sari came out again and called me into the back office, which was the size of a small bathroom. Professor Shand looked the same as he did three years ago, a petite, slender man in a dark paisley print Nero suit. I sat at the cloth draped table in front of him. His hands, long and graceful with well-manicured finger nails, shuffled a deck of cards. He stirred his tea in a white porcelain tea cup with a pretty red, green, and gold floral design on it. The spoon clinked on the saucer as he placed it down. His accent was pronounced, and his voice a soft whisper.

"I have not seen you in a long time?" he said, as he shuffled the deck of playing cards. "Where have you been?" he asked.

I had no answer.

"Cut the deck twice from right to left," he instructed.

I cut the deck.

He placed the cards back in one pile from left to right. He smoothly spread out the deck across the small portable table. "Pick a card while thinking of your question."

I picked a card, and tears rolled down my cheeks as he turned over an Ace of Hearts. "What was the question?" he asked.

"Am I going to die?"

He smiled softly and handed me a tissue. "No, you are not going to die."

In that moment, when we looked into each other's eyes, everything changed. I felt an incredible peace and serenity. I felt a lightness and calm that I couldn't even describe. We both chuckled quietly. He shuffled out more cards for me to pick from.

As we continued on with my card reading, I asked him about the casting agent, Alexis Cyrus. He replied, "She had the devil in her. She was possessed by the devil." My mouth flew open and my eyes widened in fear. "It's nothing really. Nothing to worry about," he calmly assured me.

I immediately relaxed but was a bit perplexed. I thought to myself, 'The devil? There's no such thing as a devil. Why did he say she was possessed by the devil? I'm not even going to ask. "What about Leonardi? What was that all about? I asked.

"You were bitten by the snake," he stated flatly while turning over more cards.

"I was bitten by the snake?" I repeated confused.

"Yes, you were bitten by the snake. Don't worry about it. It happens to the best of us," he replied in a matter-of-fact manner. I felt consoled, yet still perplexed. Professor Shand moved onto other matters concerning the cards.

After he finished my reading, he suggested once again, as he always did, that I read some Psalms in the Bible. This time I knew that I would read them.

After I left his office on the Upper West Side, I sat on a bench near Central Park, enjoying the clear, cool autumn day. The world around me looked lively, but mostly serene, and hopeful. I lost track of time until I noticed a small pack of commuters dispersing from the buildings and disappearing into the nearby underground subway station. It must have been five o'clock.

I strolled down into the subway heading back to my parent's house for dinner thinking about the recent past as the train rattled on. Only a few months ago, I was living with my boyfriend of six years in Manhattan. Together, we pursued our acting careers, traveled, ate out with friends at trendy restaurants, went to movies, and rock concerts. My life with David was upbeat, creative, and adventurous, but mostly peaceful compared to the life in Queens I had left behind as a teenager.

Now, I was back in Astoria with my dysfunctional family where everything was dark and emotionally toxic. I had no money, and I still had no job. But, for some strange reason, after meeting with Professor Shand, all those bad feelings suddenly disappeared as if they had never existed at all. That lasted a week.

My father's hostility and my mother's unhappiness and frustration wore on me. The Psalms were not giving me much comfort or answers, and I was falling back into a dark depression. Whatever positive change had occurred in my state of being, was quickly wearing off. By evening, I fell back into a state of paralyzed helplessness until I fell asleep.

A car alarm wailed. I opened my eyes from a sound sleep, leaving behind a dream more spacious and serene than the low-wooden planks of the bunk bed I now stared at directly above me. I was back in my nightmare. Humiliation, devastation, confusion, and anger washed over me like toxic morning dew. I slowly sat up in my brother's old bunk bed and wandered into the kitchen for my morning coffee. The house was empty. I was relieved to be alone. I returned to my brother's room, settled back on the bed, opened up the Bible and made another attempt at healing my tattered soul by reading a few more Psalms. I decided to investigate other books in The Holy Bible, other scriptures and passages in the hopes that it would contain the resolution to all my pain. I could not make heads or tails of any of it.

I did not understand anything I was reading. It made absolutely no sense to me. Was I a sinner? Did I hate myself? I did not think I hated myself. I thought maybe it was God that hated me. Not that I believed in God at the time or practiced any kind of religion. I had given up on the idea that God existed in my early teens and pretty much never thought much about it since then.

Still, I was in pursuit of "The Truth" – and not "my truth" but "The Truth". Maybe they were the same thing, but I did not call it "God". I called it "The Truth". I followed my dream and aspirations in search of "The Truth." But what is *The Truth*? I still did not know, and these Psalms didn't seem to know either.

I never understood the Bible, and it always gave me a headache trying to understand or interpret it, ever since my Catholic grammar school days and that had not changed. If there is a God, I always felt that he would be simple, and his message would be clear and direct, and available to anyone at any time. The Bible, and its many interpretations and interpreters, never came across to me as clear or direct, nor was it coming across that way to me now.

I read through some passages, and my frustration and fury exploded as I came across a line that read: *Are we not gods?* I sprang from the bed, and screamed up at the ceiling. "Are we? Are we gods! Are we not gods!!!"

I was not only furious and enraged in asking God, I demanded that he tell me because I really, really wanted to know.

"Do you, in fact exist, and if you do, what the hell do you mean by all this? I want to know specifically, clearly and simply what all these words in the Bible mean, and what in particular does *Are we not gods?* actually mean? Is it a metaphor, and if so, what does it mean, or are you stating a fact! I demand to know. Are we gods!" I screamed in rage at the ceiling. *"Tell me! I want to know!! Are we gods!!!"*

Suddenly, a light broke through the top of the right side of the ceiling above and before me, and instantly, I was pushed to the ground by an invisible force from above. It was a powerful energy with great strength, but at the same time, very gentle and loving. I was abruptly on the floor, my body totally paralyzed. I lay motionless, surrounded by nothing but a beautiful golden white light. Nothing but light was visible. I couldn't see my body, and the room around me disappeared. Light filled my vision and only light, and I was in that light, and that light was in me. There was nothing else.

1 John Chapter 1:5 – This then is the message which we have heard of him, and declare unto you, that God is light, and in him is no darkness at all. (KJV)

I was out of time, out of events, out of space, and experiencing myself as an immaculate being immersed in this pure light. The world disappeared, and there was nothing but God and me, and we one and the same. But the "nothing" was not "nothing"—it was everything. I did not feel anything but deep waves of indescribable love exploding through me and around me; an incredible sensation of peace and total bliss. It felt like a warm, yet soft electrical current pulsating in and out of me with such intense power perhaps that of a zillion suns, and it was continuous and ongoing. Tears welled up in my eyes and ran down my face, but they were tears of utter joy and absolute peace. I was in a state of absolute awe. I was home. God existed and he loved me.

1 John Chapter 4:18 - There is no fear in love; but perfect love casteth out fear: because fear hath torment. He that feareth is not made perfect in love. (KJV)

The world appeared to hate me, but God loved me, and I was finally home where I belonged. At home in God, a place I had never left except within my own mind. I was free of the molestation of the world's judgments, free of my own judgments, free of *all* worldly beliefs, concepts, and identification with a carnal "I". I could now see my own self clearly with the eyes of God. In God's eyes I was stainless, immaculate, and pure as He had created me. No loss, no judgment or rejection from the world had any effect on me at all. I am as I have always been, God's Daughter.

Romans Chapter 8:35-39

[35] Who shall separate us from the love of Christ? Shall tribulation, or distress, or persecution, or famine, or nakedness, or peril or sword?

[36] As it is written, for thy sake we are killed all the day long; we are accounted as sheep for the slaughter. [37] Nay, in all these things we are more than conquerors through him that loved us. [38] For I am persuaded, that neither death, nor life, nor angels, nor principalities, nor powers, nor things present, nor things to come, [39] Nor height, nor depth, nor any other creature shall be able to separate us from the love of God, which is in Christ Jesus our Lord. (KJV)

I don't remember exactly how long this experience lasted, perhaps a moment, perhaps two. It was impossible to say. Time does not exist in such a place. But it was so clear, so real, and so incredible that I walked around the rest of the day speechless. I never told anyone about it. There was no way such an experience of *The Great Unknown* could be shared. It can't. It can only be experienced by the self through "the grace" of God. I just contemplated the experience by myself.

John Chapter 15:19 - If ye were of the world, the world would love his own: but because ye are not of the world, but I have chosen you out of the world, therefore the world hateth you. (KJV)

Romans 10:13 – For whosoever shall call on the name of the Lord shall be saved. (KJV)

When I stood up coming out the experience, my heart and mind felt clean, whole, and brand new. My body felt free and light. I felt like all the filth in my heart and mind which I had accumulated from all these negative experiences throughout my life to date was completely washed away.

Now, after walking around in speechless awe for days, I began to realize that this third world that I had been contemplating actually does exist. The world in Queens of poverty, lack, struggle, abuse, violence and oppression I had categorized as one world, and the world of Hollywood filled with privilege, power, creative expression and financial independence to be the second world,.   But now I know there is a third world where perfect peace and unending love reside; where struggle, suffering, sorrow, and death does not exist. Aaah, of course, now I understand; the third world is heaven! There is such a place and it is called heaven! And heaven has chosen me!!!   Jesus Christ who sits at the right hand of the Father in heaven came for me!!!

The Holy Son of God, King of kings, the Lord of lords, died on the cross for my sins so that I may spend eternity with him in heaven. When I went to church that day and confessed my sins to that surly, grumpy priest in the confessional, and then days later cried out in anguish with all my heart for God to come and save me, he did. He came and he touched me with his perfect love that casts out all fear. God loved me so much that he sent his only begotten Son to die on the cross so that I may have life and have it more abundantly. Jesus, who is alive and sitting at the right hand of the Father in Heaven, came to restore me and set me free. God loves me!!! He is the God of everlasting kindness and his mercy endures forever.   Praise the Lord!!!

Timothy 2:5 KJV - For there is one God and one mediator between God and men, the man Christ Jesus.

Acts: 4:12 Neither is there salvation in any other: For there is none other name under heaven which is given among men whereby we must be saved.

Psalm 91:15 He shall call upon Me, and I will answer him; I will be with him in trouble; I will deliver him and honor him.

I still did not know what I was going to do about my life or how to fix it, or what to do next, but somehow I felt that perhaps the answer would come. The ultimate answer had arrived so I figured this was the beginning of figuring out the rest. And I was sure that God would tell me what to do next.

THE END

Acknowledgements

I would like to thank the following:

To my grandfather Steve Kalin for surprising me as a little girl with the most beautiful gift for my birthday -- four large hard cover books of classic literature.

Fred Gilmore for his warm friendship, encouragement, and believe in me.

Maureen Jones my editor for her support and encouragement in completing the final draft.

Jennifer Marden for being an avid reader and checking my manuscript over for typos.

George Patsouras for assisting me in placing the book cover design in Photoshop.

If you are ready to accept Christ Jesus as your personal Savior, please read through the prayer below and then recite the following prayer with sincere humility.

PRAYER OF SALVATION

"Lord Jesus, I know I am a sinner. I believe in my heart you are the Son of God who died on the cross for my sins and that you were raised from the dead.

Thank you for paying the price for my sins. Forgive me and make me a new person. Cleanse me of my sins with your blood, wash me in the water of your Word, and come into my heart. I commit my life to you today and I receive you as my Lord, as my Savior, and as my High Priest. I pray this prayer to God, The Father Almighty, in the name of Christ Jesus. Amen."

If you just said this prayer and you meant it with all your heart, we believe that you just got saved and are born again. You may ask, "Now that I am saved, what's next?" Purchase a King James Bible, read it, study it, and ask the Holy Spirit to help you interpret the scriptures. Be patient with yourself and allow yourself to learn the character of God and the character of Jesus Christ overtime. Attend a faith based church that actually teaches the GOOD NEWS that we are reconciled unto God through Jesus Christ and saved by GRACE. Get baptized, pray daily, and study your Bible.

Resource information on abuse

Work Place Bully Institute
www.workplacebullying.org

Spartan Life Coach
www.spartanlifecoach.org

Verbal Abuse
www.Verbalabuse.com

For survivors of narcissist. Sociopaths and psychopaths
http://narcissistsupport.com/

National Coalition Against Domestic Violence
www.ncadv.org

A 12 step program for family and friends of addicts
www.nar-anon.org

Resource information on healthy eating to assist in the healing of trauma

Heal Mind and Body through Healthy Eating
www.chrisbeatcancer.com

Dr. Axe
www.draxe.com

Drew Canole
www.mindbodygreen.com

Dan McDonald – Regenerate Your Life
www.regenerateyourlife.org

BIBLE RESOURCE

King James Bible
www.kingjamesbibleonline.org

Pastor Joseph Prince
www.Josephprince.org

When life gets too hard to stand, kneel

Author

Whitney DeLise is a native New Yorker, and has been an actor/improv comedy performer and a member of Screen Actors Guild since 1982. Her screenplay, a romantic-comedy *On My Way to Now/Here* received outstanding reviews from UCLA Film and Television Dept. and other industry professionals. She wrote and performed her own theatrical solo play; a comedy entitled *Scottish Fever* in New York City. She is also a self-taught painter and a musician.

WHITNEYDELISE.COM

Wdelise777@gmail.com

Chandelier Classic

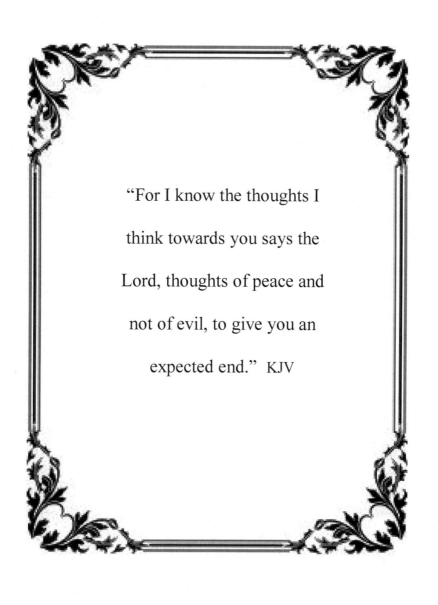

"For I know the thoughts I think towards you says the Lord, thoughts of peace and not of evil, to give you an expected end." KJV